Never Say Goodbye

A true story.

By Robert Gerard Anstey

This book is dedicated to my Mom, the most courageous woman I've ever known.

"Never, never, never, give up." – Winston Churchill.

I would like to thank my two sons,
Bobby and Colton.
Proudly carry your past into your future.
I love you both very much.

Thank you to my sister, Peggy, for all that you do.
You are amazing, and I love you very much.

Special thanks to Melanie Phillips, for final
formatting and copy editing.

Special thanks to Lori at
clear.voice.editors@gmail.com.

Special thanks to Shelly Brown, you have the keys
to my heart.

And to our veterans, we can never thank you enough.

.

This book is a true story, one of many millions of stories of those who served and lived through World War II.

This book is based on hundreds of letters sent home by the characters in the book, hundreds of documents and photographs, interviews, and the historical record.

While many names have been changed, unknown dialog has been added, and some events have been condensed for the sake of pacing, the stories within the story are true. The truth is that I could have never created a story better than the one they lived.

The goal of this book was to honor the people that lived those stories — sometimes tragic, sometimes triumphant — but seeks to also honor all those millions of stories that were never told and are now lost to history.

My only regret is that I can't tell all of them.

Chapter One

It was 1929 England, in an abandoned house just outside London. The family moved into this dirty, dusty house that was too small for so many of them. Seven children meant a lot of mouths to feed.

"Why don't you just die, you bastard? You stinking bastard."

The resentment showed in the lines carved into her face from the permanent scowl. She was angry that she was stuck here in this God-forsaken place, living a life she hated with kids she never wanted.

"Just die, you bloody bastard," she again yelled into the doorway.

The covered windows blocked out the light except for a few cracks around the edges that stabbed like knives, betraying the otherwise invisible sparkling swirls of dust that filled the air and settled on everything. Roaches skittered across the ceiling while spiders spun webs in the corners. Telltale rodent droppings were everywhere.

The room stank of sweat and urine, and a single piece of furniture occupied the room — a bed, upon which lay what once was a mountain of a man, now reduced to a moaning hulk, covered in a gray sheet.

Before he became sick he was raising his family in an apartment in London, where he worked as a house painter. He was well known for his ability to work hard, drink hard, and fight hard. At 6'- 6" tall with a bad attitude, people moved out of the way when George Bradley walked down the street.

Even the London "Bobbies" preferred to look the other way when George was out drinking and telling stories.

Anyone foolish enough to get into it with George was on their own.

Drinking didn't help his temper. He often brought his drunken rage home with him and used his wife and kids as punching bags. That also showed on her face.

But now he rotted away on a stinking bed with his body covered in sores, lungs gurgling with fluid, and eyes that could no longer see. George Bradley was dying a miserable death and few people even cared.

It had taken over a dozen years but the gas was finally killing him — the gas used in World War I. As a British soldier in the war commonly referred to as "The war to end all wars," nothing would have made him happier than to go out there and fight it out like the scrapper he was. But the trench warfare that led to a stalemate had both sides stuck in their muddy holes.

If their heads raised above the trenches, they would get shot off. If they charged the other side, they got mowed down, and vice versa. So then came the gas. Both sides used it and both sides died from it. As it rolled across the battlefield like a fog and settled into the low places, it killed whatever it found there.

He was one of the so-called "lucky ones." His wounds were invisible when he came home to his wife and three sons, but four daughters later he started spitting up blood and soon wound up in this stinking room waiting for death.

Without George, the family couldn't stay in London. All seven children were "Cockneys," or born within the sound of the bells of St. Mary-le Bow, a romantic sounding place that was actually a slum full of beggars and thieves. The family would be easy prey for every kind of criminal that skulked in the dark alleys and every con artist who walked the streets.

The broken down old house had once been in her family but now was abandoned. She went there hoping to appeal to some distant cousin or in-law for shelter and help, but upon finding the place nailed shut, she claimed it as her own.

2

They managed to scrape out a few potatoes and onions from the garden from time to time, and when the boys weren't fishing, they were out stealing chickens or doing odd jobs, and, of course, fighting.

"I like living in the country," five-year-old Lillian Rose said to her two little sisters. Molly was four and Mary was three.

All three were dirty and wearing ragged clothes, but they were cute, nonetheless, with their blonde hair and blue eyes. They looked so much alike they could almost pass for triplets.

The oldest girl was Alice, at eleven. She smiled while washing the dishes, looking out the window at the younger girls playing on the broken down old porch. There was little play time for Alice, as she was always working along with the boys or cleaning up after them.

"It's so much nicer here," Lillian continued, while the other girls nodded in agreement.

Mary was about to say something when their mother bellowed again, this time at the boys, making them all jump. It seemed the pickings were slim today and the boys came home with just a fraction of what they would need to eat today. The great depression was just getting started and things were only getting harder.

"Do you think we will get some food tonight?" asked Mary.

"Maybe a little bit," said Lillian. "Don't worry, it will be alright."

Lillian felt protective of her baby sisters, but the three of them were last on the food chain — just extra mouths to feed. The boys always came first, they had to work. The girls knew better than to complain. They'd rather go hungry.

Mother resented the three little girls. As far as she was concerned, her days of making babies were over after Alice, but when George came home drunk there was no saying no.

Then one day the stranger's car came chugging down the road, kicking up a cloud of dust behind it. The girls jumped

3

up and darted into the house. Within a moment, their three dirty faces appeared in the window.

"Go close that goddamned door," Mother barked at Alice, nodding towards George's room so his moaning couldn't be heard. "And get me that goddamned broom."

Alice moved to the window with the girls as their mother walked out onto the front porch with her usual scowl, prepared to meet the bad news that strangers usually bring. The man pulled up and smiled at her while he wrestled something out of his car.

He carried the strange looking machine to the bottom of the sagging, creaky old porch and smiled again as he took off his hat. His clothes were dusty and his bow tie was crooked. His narrow face was pale and his long hooked nose contrasted his sunken eyes and thin lips.

"What is that thing?" asked Mary.

"Shush!" hissed Alice.

"What are they talking about?" asked Lillian.

"I said 'Quiet!', you buggers, or I can't hear them," barked Alice, and the girls fell silent as they looked up at her.

"It's a fine model, Madame, perhaps the best on the market," the man said. "And you won't be needing that anymore."

The broom in her hand was to be used as a weapon, but he didn't need to know that. As he talked she looked back and forth from him to the vacuum cleaner. It was a fascinating-looking contraption, the likes of which she had never seen before.

"Afraid you wasted your time stopping here," she said. "I can't even afford a decent cup of tea."

He nodded and tipped his hat. He was used to hearing "no" as he traveled house to house trying to sell his expensive machines in this day and age. Not wanting to leave empty handed, he looked around for something to barter. Seeing the girls in the window, he froze in his tracks.

She looked over her shoulder and saw what caught his eye. She looked back at him and caught a glimpse of something sinister on his face. She grinned and he nervously looked at the ground as if he had been caught cheating. When he looked back up and saw she was still smiling, the grin once again curled his lips.

Lillian saw the grin, like the grin of a hawk with its prey. She was unnerved by it and slunk down to the floor away from the window. Mary and Molly did the same, as they all stayed there underneath Alice on the dirty kitchen floor.

"It's a hard job I've had," she said, "since my husband fell ill."

"'Tis a lovely family you have, madam," he said, barely hearing her as he licked his lips. He watched the little girls until they dropped out of sight.

"I've worried so much about the little ones," she said. "It's been harder and harder to feed them, and we only have so much."

She was playing him and he was playing her and they both knew it, but neither one cared. She knew what he wanted but wasn't sure what was in it for her. She would take the vacuum cleaner if she could get it, even though electricity to run it must be stolen from the pole outside. George Jr. almost killed himself trying to hook it up. She could always sell it. Alice did most of the cleaning and she didn't care about making her life easier.

"You need one of these more than you know, madam. It will make cleaning so much easier and give you time to attend to more urgent matters."

"I told you I can't afford the bloody thing," she barked. "No matter if it saves me all the time in the bloody world. Time I have, money I don't."

"Perhaps we could come to some sort of arrangement," he said nervously. He shuffled his feet as his eyes darted about. He seemed to be having trouble saying what he really wanted to say. She had been around enough con artists and gutter

5

trash long enough to pick up on ill intentions, especially from an amateur like this. Now she was in control.

"What sort of arrangement?" she asked, with hands on hips, looking him straight in the eyes.

"Well," he mumbled and kicked at the dirt with his shoe. "The missus and me have been wanting a little one for a long time. We could take good care of her, we could."

"I'm listening," she said, as she glanced down and saw no wedding ring on his finger.

"Let's just say I could take one of your little angels to care for, and you could take care of my machine. If you change your mind you can take her back. I will give you my address."

She smiled an evil smile at him, and knowing the deal was done, he smiled back.

"Alice," she yelled, "bring those girls out here."

Alice froze as her mother's voice boomed from the porch. There was no place to run and no place to hide. She was being forced to be complicit in whatever action was about to unfold.

"Now, Alice, goddamn it," she bellowed.

With tears forming in her eyes, Alice pulled the girls to their feet and pushed them towards the door. They tried to get behind her and hide as they went outside but their mother jerked them by their little arms and pushed Alice away leaving them standing there huddled together.

They stood there on display with dirty faces and ragged clothes and wearing no shoes. They were skinny and pale and now they were crying.

Looking at the stranger was enough to make them try to hide behind their mother as a last resort, but again she shoved them forward and lined them up.

"Choose," she said. "Choose the one you like."

The stranger's eyes narrowed and he licked his thin lips again, starting up the porch towards the terrified girls.

"Wait," Mother yelled, making everyone jump. The salesman's eyes widened as he took a step back down the creaky front porch boards and looked at her with guilt all over his face.

Mother's scowl slid from her face and her lip curled up into an evil grin.

"That first," she said, as she nodded toward the machine.

He nodded, and with trembling hands he pulled it up on the porch and looked over at her. Seeing her still smiling, he once again looked down at the girls.

He scribbled his address on a piece of paper and handed it to her, and without another word he reached down and snatched up three-year old Mary, carrying the screaming girl to his car.

Molly and Lillian screamed for her, but were slapped and ordered back inside where they once again pulled themselves up to the window next to the now crying Alice.

Tears made tracks down their dirty faces as they watched the car pull down the dusty road, around the corner and disappear out of sight. Mother didn't even watch it go, she was so focused on her shiny new toy.

"Alice, goddammit," Mother yelled. "Take those bloody girls out back so I don't have to listen to them."

Mother looked down with pride at her new machine, the sound of their wailing drifting further away as Alice dragged them through the house to the backyard.

She looked at the address on the scribbled note and smiled, then ripped it to pieces and scattered it to the wind. Probably fake anyway.

"One down, two to go," she whispered. "Two to go."

The word went out to churches and neighbors and workhouses and everybody else that might spread the right rumor to the right person. A sick hero soldier with too many children in need of help would hopefully tug at some heartstrings.

She got lucky with Mary and actually got something in return, but just getting rid of these other two would be good enough for her.

Some concerned neighbors got word to the church and the church spread that word around. Contacts were made and favors were called in. There was a growing concern that the children might be left on the side of the road or worse, but times were tough and choices were few.

The two girls were being neglected more and more every day. They had less food to eat than ever and slept on a hard floor, sharing a blanket. Alice would smuggle them an extra morsel when she could, but she feared her brother Jake, who now was in charge of punishment — a chore he seemed to enjoy.

The girls would ask Alice about Mary every day, and every day Alice would shush them and tell them not to ask anymore or they would get in trouble. Alice heard some of the rumors being spread by her mother, but she, of course, said nothing to the girls.

A few weeks after Mary was taken away, Lillian and Molly were sitting on a dirt pile in the backyard, imagining they were princesses sitting in a castle, when Lillian suddenly became aware of someone standing over her and leapt to her feet.

She saw her mother pulling Molly up roughly by her arm. Molly started to scream and reached towards Lillian, but before Lillian could reach out to her, a woman grabbed her from behind and held her there.

Mother passed Molly to a man and another woman standing close by and they quickly whisked the screaming child away towards a car that was just pulling around back.

Lillian tried to break free but could not, and was instead spun around to face the woman that was holding her, hearing Molly's screams fading as the distance between them grew.

She glanced towards the house only to see her mother climbing up the porch stairs and going in the back door, never turning around.

As the woman who held Lillian turned her around and bent down to face her, she said in a gentle voice, "Don't be afraid, child, nothing bad will happen to you or your sister."

Lillian was struck by her kind face and gentle smile, and she liked the way she smelled. But she still struggled for Molly, even as the car took off with her sister, just like what happened with Mary.

"Have you ever been on a train ride?" the woman with the kind face asked, but Lillian only craned her neck to see the dust cloud that swallowed her sister.

"Wouldn't you like to go on a nice train ride? And buy a pretty new dress?"

Lillian wiped at her eyes and nodded. "Will I see my sisters there?"

"Of course, my dear. And when you see them they will have pretty new dresses, too."

"I want to go with Molly."

"You will see Molly again soon, my child. I promise. Take my hand and let's go buy that dress and get you cleaned up. What is your name, my child? My name is Mrs. Sharpe."

"Lillian. Lillian Rose Bradley."

"Well, Miss Bradley, it looks like we have a lot of dirt to clean off of you. We will go to town and make you look like a princess. Get in my car and let's get started on our adventure."

As the car pulled away, Lillian looked at the old house out the window and saw Alice looking back with tears streaming down her face, and then she was gone.

By that evening she was sitting on the train with her new shoes dangling off the seat. As she looked down at them they seemed to sparkle.

"You look so pretty in your new dress, Miss Bradley. And you are actually a lovely young lady under all that dirt."

"I never felt so clean," she said. "And my hair looks so shiny."

Lillian asked about her sisters a few more times, and asked where they were going, but between the excitement of the day and the gentle rocking of the train she soon feel asleep, leaning against Mrs. Sharpe.

When the train stopped at the busy station they were ushered off by car and pulled up in front of a big fortress-like building, like a castle but gray and dark and cold. Lillian shuddered when she looked up at the old building.

She was hesitant, but Mrs. Sharpe nudged her along and nodded when Lillian asked if this is where they brought her sisters.

The big creaky door swung open and a nun, possibly the biggest woman Lillian had ever seen, greeted them. Lillian tried not to laugh at her big face poking through the black and white covered head.

They were escorted into a room with only two wooden chairs and a cross on the wall with a man hanging on it, which made Lillian shudder at the look of pain on the poor man's face. Lillian had never been to church so she had no idea who the man was.

Mrs. Sharpe and the nun spoke softly for a few moments, then, walking over to Lillian, she said, "Wait here, my child, I will be right back."

She kissed the little girl's cheek and stepped out with the nun.

A few minutes later, two nuns came into the room without Mrs. Sharpe and without the big nun, and one of them said, "This way."

Lillian, now alarmed, jumped out of the chair and said, "Where is Mrs. Sharpe?"

"I said, 'This way'," and turned her back to Lillian. The other nun stepped in behind her.

"Where are you taking me?"

The nun suddenly snapped around and bent down face to face with Lillian, the scowl on her face so frightening it made her take a step backward.

"This is the first rule, young lady, the first rule you will learn: You will never, ever speak unless you are spoken to. Unless you are asked to speak you will remain silent, is that clear?"

Lillian nodded her head and the tears once again started to flow.

"I didn't hear you."

"Yes."

"It's yes, *Sister.*"

"Yes Sister."

She was escorted down a long dark hallway with stone walls dripping with condensate and smelling like mildew. Only small shafts of light peeked through some narrow atrium windows along the top, filthy with fifty years of grime on them.

They passed through two squeaky wrought iron gates that were again locked behind them, and into a cold and damp, barracks-like room with a few dozen other girls. As one nun gave her one of the blue uniforms — ugly dresses like the other girls wore — and a wool blanket, she said, "Give me your dress and shoes."

When she sat on her bunk and looked around she saw the pale faces and sunken eyes of the desperate, broken children that filled the room with her, and realized she was now one of them.

Mrs. Sharpe had lied to her. She lied to her and stole her from her sisters, and she never even got to say goodbye to them. She lay down and started to cry.

Chapter Two

July, 1935. Brooklyn, New York.

Bob went down the half flight of steps and into the alleyway that separated the two apartment buildings. The alley smelled like old garbage and cat pee; it was strewn with broken glass with a checkerboard shadow created by the maze of fire escapes overhead.

To twelve-year old Bob and his thirteen-year old cousin Dicky, this was their playground. Boys growing up in the country climbed trees, but boys growing up in Brooklyn climbed fire escapes.

Bob's heart was pounding and his hands were sweating. *I can't believe I'm doing this.* He turned back and looked at Dicky and by the look in his eyes he couldn't believe it, either.

"Go, go," Dicky prodded him from behind. They were crouched down and slowly approaching the square courtyard that opened between the buildings where all the laundry lines were stretched across.

Bob was terrified and could feel himself trembling. He would love to abandon this "mission" but Dicky would never let him live it down. He would not let Dicky one-up him.

Dicky was the king of practical jokes and would not relinquish that title easily. Bob had a lot of friends, but his cousin was by far the most fun, and the most likely to get him in trouble.

"C'mon, Bobby," Dicky said, with his thick Brooklyn accent. "What are you waiting for?"

The slingshot handle was wet in his hand from sweat and the leather pouch holding the pea size rock was shaking. *Oh, what the hell.*

Taking a big gulp, he steadied himself and peered around the corner until he found his target. He started pulling back the bands and bought the "Y" up to sight her in.

Mrs. Maguire. Every kid in the neighborhood hated Mrs. Maguire and so did half the adults. The kids hated her because she would tell their parents everything she could get her business into and make big deals about everything she could.

If she got ahold of the ball when kids were playing in front of her building they could forget about ever seeing it again. She would blame the first kid who came along for every scrap of paper in the streets and chased off the hot dog vendors and even the ice cream man.

This was payback. This act of heroism would make them legends around the neighborhood. Anonymous legends, but legends just the same.

"We will be the dragon slayers of Brooklyn," Dicky liked to say.

"This is the perfect shot," Bob whispered. She was hanging clothes on the line one floor up and was turned away from him, standing on her tiptoes displaying her ample rump as a bull's eye.

"This is fate, Bobby," said Dicky, grinning. "Destiny. Do it now."

When he released the missile he could actually hear it whistle, which surprised him. The two boys took off running at the sound of the snapping band, not even waiting to see it hit home, which it did.

Bob knew Mrs. Maguire was going to have a hard time sitting for a while and he couldn't help but start laughing as he ran. Hearing Bob laughing while running behind him got Dicky going, too. By this time Mrs. Maguire was screaming and it was echoing through the alley.

They did it, they pulled it off. Now the plan was to lay low for a while and pretend to know nothing about the whole thing. It would soon be all over the neighborhood. It was a perfect plan and it was perfectly executed. Perfect except for one thing. Perfect except for Mr. Maguire.

When they burst out of the alley laughing with Mrs. Maguire shrieking in the distance they ran right into him, and he gave them a puzzled look, not sure what to make of it.

"Oh crap," said Bob, and saw his short life flashing before his eyes. He knew how much trouble he was in and it was going to hit the fan soon.

They kept running for another two blocks when Dicky said, "He's not going to take long to figure out who shot his wife in the ass. She's probably screaming at him right now."

"Two plus two equals us," said Bob, shaking and breathing hard.

He and Dicky separated at the corner and Bob headed home to his house on Fifty-Sixth Street, skulking in fear, knowing Mrs. Maguire now had a welt on her ass with his name on it.

Bob lived on the second floor of a three-story brownstone. It was a row house with railroad rooms and an alley out back with a sidewalk for a front lawn. It was Bob's responsibility to keep the sidewalk swept in summer and shoveled in the winter, though never to Archie's satisfaction.

It was only a matter of time before the news reached Archie. Bob was beginning to understand how a condemned man felt.

Archie was a hard old man who had lived a life in which nothing came easy. He had immigrated to New York in 1920 with his wife, Anne, and Bob's older sister June. They came from St. Johns, Newfoundland, from generations of fisherman. He worked hard for everything he had, and had no tolerance for anyone who didn't do the same.

By the time he was twelve, he was hauling nets of codfish into his uncle's fishing boat. He had hands like leather, and though he was soft spoken and wiry, he was strong as an ox.

A sixteen-year old Archibald Stanley Anstey met a fifteen-year old Anne Churchill and they married a few years

15

later. Ten years after that they were making their way to New York with their infant daughter.

Archie landed a job as a carpenter's helper and was recruited into the union. He worked like a slave, but compared to fishing it was easy, so he never complained. He climbed the ladder and wound up as a rough carpenter at the Brooklyn Navy Yards, earning the respect of his peers and the fear of his helpers.

They would never be wealthy, but a steady paycheck from a good paying job kept a roof over their heads and a few rainy day dollars in the bank. Archie was also as cheap as they come so that helped stretch the money out a little, too.

Archie would often grumble about the vagabonds and hobos passing through, most looking for a handout. The church insisted that those who could help, must, so he reluctantly did so. Times were getting tough for most, but ship building was starting to boom as contracts came in for big transport vessels and for some military ships.

Bob eased up the squeaky stairs into the kitchen. In the kitchen was a small round table with four cheap, squeaky chairs around it, each with a dingy old cushion atop. Sitting at the table facing the stairs like a gatekeeper to the kingdom, was Archie.

Archie was sitting in "his chair," with his Bible on the table next to him and the newspaper folded and in his lap. He was looking over the top of his reading glasses and frowned at Bob as he came in.

The kitchen had a fishy smell from the dried fish in the pantry. That, along with the hard tack bread, were staples of any "Newfoundlander."

Bob knew exactly where he didn't want to look. He knew the seat the old man always sat in, and getting past him without being seen was pretty much impossible. It was just a matter of avoiding eye contact and not doing anything to make him angry, and that was when he behaved. God only knows what was in store for him today.

Walking through the kitchen, Bob had to go through the living/dining room to get to the first bedroom, the one he shared with his sister, and which had to be walked through to reach the second bedroom, hence the term "railroad rooms". Thankfully, his sister was not there, for if she were, she would surely make things worse.

In all fairness to her, she was about to be a senior in high school and had to share a room with her twelve-year old brother, not to mention their parents going back and forth through it.

Suddenly, Bob heard a commotion outside as the door buzzer began buzzing almost non-stop. He heard his mother click-clacking down the stairs, knowing the shoe was about to drop.

A few moments later he could hear the muffled but angry sounding voices coming from downstairs; and to his horror now charging up the stairs, the sound of them like a herd of angry beasts, shaking the house as they headed up.

Once he heard them enter the kitchen, the shouting and whining and threats could clearly be heard two rooms away, maybe even two blocks. Mrs. Maguire was in rare form. By the sound of the conversation she was doing most of the talking, or yelling, rather.

Archie was sitting in his chair taking it in, never saying a word, while the frantic Anne was beside herself. Bob also knew that the less Archie talked, the angrier he was.

After a few minutes of this, the Maguires were once again on the stairs, this time going down, with Anne apologizing again and again all the way. Before they even made it out the front door, the old man appeared in the bedroom doorway and ordered Bob to stand in front of him.

"Give it to me," he said, hand outstretched and never raising his voice. Bob handed him the slingshot and Archie held it in front of Bob's face, snapped it like a wishbone, and let it fall to the floor.

"I'm sorry," Bob said, a tear forming in the corner of his eye.

Archie saw the tear and his eyes flashed red with anger. As fast as lightning his hands came up on either side of Bob's head as he boxed his ears and slapped his face. Archie walked out shaking his head in disgust.

Anne came running in to find Bob on his knees with two red handprints on his face and his ears popped, hurting him badly. His face hurt for days, but his ears really hurt. The next morning he even had a trickle of dried blood on his pillow.

Eventually the swelling went down and the ear stopped hurting and life started to get back to normal, but something was not right.

"Deaf in that ear," said the doctor. "Permanent, I'm afraid."

Archie never apologized and never changed the scowl on his face, but he never hit him again.

Bob struggled in school for the next few years and even had to go to summer school to keep up. It didn't get any easier in high school, and he even tried to drop out a couple of times but his mother begged him not to.

Archie had expressed what a waste of time school was for Bob. He resented that he was hard at work while Bob was barely making it in school.

"The school of hard knocks is what that boy needs," he would say. "The school of life."

Archie had no room for weakness and Bob was weak. "He will never amount to anything," he would say, sitting in his chair.

Bob's last year of high school had him convinced that he could never do well enough to please his father. He would never earn his respect no matter how hard he worked, so he did it for his mother.

He worked as hard as he could, studied every chance he got, and never missed a day of class. When he came home from school with his diploma, he also came home on the honor role.

"Look, Archie," said Anne. "Look at this."

Archie looked at the papers in front of him for a few seconds, then looked up and said, "It's about time. Tomorrow you can go out and find a job."

"Sure, Pop," he said, and shrugged his shoulders, walking away. That's about how he expected his dad to react. It was his way.

Yeah, Pop. I love you, too, you old bastard.

One thing that Archie had said that was ringing true — work was a lot harder than school. He would rather be back in school or just about anywhere else than to be working this crappy job. This crappy job that Archie got for him.

"Oh, shit," he gasped, as a cold wind blasted him right in the face.

There was a misty, light rain coming in off the harbor, making him wet and compounding the cold. Bob's heavy wool coat smelled like mildew when it got wet and his feet were cold all the time.

He was now a security guard at the Navy Yard where his dad worked as a carpenter. He could have gotten Bob into the union, maybe even as a helper in his crew. He could learn a trade with a job like that, a career even. He could have, but he didn't.

Archie had a reputation. A reputation he wasn't about to put on the line for his good-for-nothing son. "Let him make his own way, just like I had to do," was his mantra.

This crappy go-nowhere job is bad enough in nice weather. Now I have to do it on this cold and wet crappy ass day. Thanks a lot, Pop.

The war overseas was good for the ship building business, and they were hiring new people all the time, but nobody was going to hire Bob without Archie's blessing, and that wasn't coming anytime soon.

I guess I should be thankful for any job. He tried hard to convince himself. *Even this crappy one on this crappy day.*

But it was an even crappier day than Bob could ever imagine. It was December 7, 1941.

Bob noticed a lot more activity down in the yards and could hear police sirens in the distance that seemed to be everywhere. Walter Carnes was his supervisor, and he seemed pale and shaken as he approached.

Bob had never seen this big, boisterous man so out of sorts, and the first thought he had was that something happened to his dad, and he braced himself for bad news. Nothing prepared him for what Walter told him.

"Pearl Harbor, where the hell is that, Walter?"

"Some damn place in Hawaii. Apparently half the fleet was in port when the Japs caught them with their pants down. It's bad, Bob, really bad. Now go home, Bob. Just go home."

Bob was speechless when Walter turned and walked away. He finally turned and put his hands in his pockets and headed home.

Since he worked the night shift he was able to go down to the army induction center first thing in the morning and found he wasn't the only one. It seemed half the neighborhood was here. His whole senior class from Ft. Hamilton High School seemed to be lined up there, as far as he could tell.

The center was small and ill-equipped, with only two doctors and a handful of clerks to push the papers. It was Bob's turn to step up on the small platform for the physical exam.

"You could drive a truck through that eardrum, do you know that?"

"As long as you can't see all the way through, doc, because then I'd be worried."

"No need to worry about that, son. But you can't get in with only one good ear. Sorry kid, but you are 4F."

"Please, doc," Bob said, stumbling for words. "Just give me a shot. I'm used to it. I can hear just fine."

"Sorry, kid."

And so that was that, case closed. Many of his friends and classmates would go on to fight the Japanese, but not him. He walked past the line of guys at the induction center with his head down, almost in shame. He didn't want them feeling sorry for him, even though he was feeling sorry for himself.

He was even hoping to make his father proud, of earning something on his own, but could only bring home more news of his disappointing son.

"4F," Bob said. "They won't take me."

Archie had been sitting at his usual place at the table and turned down the radio just long enough for Bob to say those few words, then shaking his head in apparent disgust, turned it up again.

Bob didn't elaborate why he was 4F, it didn't matter. The old man would just see it as another excuse anyway, so why bother. Oddly enough, he had forgiven his father a long time ago, so he felt no need to bring it up.

Over the next year as Bob walked the docks in winter and summer, in rain and even snow, the country was growing into a giant war machine. The United States was building a massive army and everything an army could ever need.

Young men disappeared off the streets and women started taking on their jobs. Now and then a black army sedan would be seen going through the neighborhood, bringing with it bad news and a star to hang in the window.

"You have a letter," Archie growled, as he nodded towards the far end of the table. "From the government."

"This is a mistake," Bob said as he read. "It's a draft notice. I'll take care of it tomorrow."

"No record of it, pal," the clerk said on the other end of the line. "You need to come down and take it again."

"Shit," Bob sighed. "Another day of standing in line waiting to be humiliated."

Bob hardly recognized the place. It had grown to be a huge processing facility churning out thousands of soldiers for Uncle Sam. It was like going through an assembly line.

Each of them had to strip down naked and walk through a gauntlet of doctors — one checked their feet, one listened to the heart, one checked for hernias, etc., etc. The inductees

21

were each given a folder to carry with papers in it to be checked off at each station.

When he got to the doctor who was checking his ears he presented his right one, then as he turned, the papers slipped from the folder and scattered, so he bent down and picked them up. When he stood he showed his right ear again, got his check mark, and was pointed towards the next station.

Holy shit. Am I actually going to get away with this? His heart was pounding.

When he made it all the way through, the clerk took the papers, and though all out of order, they were all stamped, and he was officially drafted into the United States Army.

When he got home he had a big smile on his face and as he dropped the papers in front of his dad he said, "Looks like I'm going in after all, Pop."

Archie just looked down at the papers and shrugged, but Anne brought her hands up to her face and gasped.

"First thing tomorrow I'm going down and quitting that crappy job," Bob said, as he walked out with more spring in his step than he'd had in a long time.

Anne was beside herself with worry, wringing her hands as she shuffled around the kitchen. Archie just sat there shaking his head.

"Walking away from a perfectly good job. I told you he'd never amount to anything. I told you."

Chapter Three

South Wales, 1932. Fall was passing into winter and eight-year-old Lillian Rose shivered at the thought of another cold season in the Convent of St. John.

Growing up in this dark place where sunshine was fleeting and the cold and dampness of the stone was constant made her think of the old dirt pile in the backyard, and how she used to play with her sisters, building castles of magic kingdoms while the sun shone down warm on them. *I miss the light and the sun.*

Lillian was the youngest girl there, and the youngest girl ever taken in by the convent, but that didn't matter to the other girls. It just meant she was smaller and weaker than them, therefore not a threat, and so she went mostly ignored.

There were no friends here, but there were enemies among the rivals. It was hard to be social, good or bad, when everyone was required to remain silent. If one of the girls got caught whispering back and forth, they paid for it. They paid for every rule violation, even the slightest.

The standard punishment was a stick across the back of the legs, leaving red stripes that would bruise and often become welts — purple and red blotches across the pale skin of the sun-starved girls.

Lillian wore the stripes more than once and more than once she saw smiles on the nun's face as the punishment was doled out on her. Sometimes half the girls in the barracks would be walking around with the stripes.

"I want to go home," Lillian would whimper in her bed some nights.

"Shut up about your bloody home," the girls around her would say. This crybaby was not worth getting in trouble over if she attracted the attention of the sisters.

"I miss my family. I miss my sisters."

"Shut up about your bloody family," one of the girls snapped.

"I'm bloody sick of hearing about them. If they cared about you then you wouldn't be here, now would you?"

She closed her eyes tight and cried as she realized that it was true. That made it even worse and even more hopeless.

But she still thought about them every day. She didn't want to forget them, even though it seemed they forgot about her. She repeated their names every night in her head as she lay there.

Mary and then Molly. Me and then Alice and then Sam, George Jr. and then Jake, the oldest.

The girl next to her looked over to see Lillian sobbing again and staring at the ceiling with tears on her cheeks as she rolled over in disgust, making her bed squeak until she settled in. Every bed in the room squeaked and every sound was magnified, making it a dark and scary place at night.

"She's never going to make it," the other girl said. "Too weak and pathetic."

"From the oldest there is Jake and then George Jr. Then there is Sam, then Alice, me, Molly and Mary. Molly and Mary, I miss you so much."

She tried to keep the good memories of them alive in her head and to remember their faces, but the last time she saw them they were being pulled away screaming from her and she could never stop thinking of that.

Lillian turned nine that January with little fanfare or notice. Certainly no cake or presents. She didn't even realize it was her birthday until one of the sisters mentioned it, but it was more in the context of letting her know how much longer she would have to be here.

The Sisters of Charity decided they wanted the stone floors of the great hall cleaned so they put a group of the girls, including Lillian, to work on hands and knees scrubbing with brushes and soapy water.

Wearing only their blue prison-like uniform dresses, they worked until their hands were blistered and their knees were bleeding, and then they worked some more. It was that or the stick so they worked while the sisters sat there reading or dozing off.

"To hell with your knees, clean my damn floor," one of the less reverent nuns would bark at them.

The overworked and undernourished girls looked smaller and less developed that their actual ages. They were fed a mixture of gruel and watered down soups, usually made up of boiled potatoes and pieces of stale bread. Never any milk or good proteins, not that she ate well before coming to the convent.

The sisters had no such shortage in their diet; most were overweight except for the ones that were grossly overweight. They took the cream of the crop off the food supply, which came to the convent mostly by donations.

They also did little or no physical activities as they sat on their rumps barking orders to the girls, and used them as slave labor to do everything from washing their clothes to clipping their toenails off their fat, smelly feet.

It's all this time on the stone floor. If I could just get off them for a little while, maybe this pain would go away.

It was getting harder and harder to work through it and even hard to get out of bed in the morning, but she tried not to show weakness to the other girls. She was too stubborn for that.

"Please, Sister," Lillian asked. "May I do a different chore for a little while until my legs are better? Just for a little while?"

"Growing pains," the sister said. "Get back to work."

She winced in pain as she got back on the floor and one of her legs started to cramp up. "Please, Sister, just for a few days."

The sister looked over the top of the book she was reading with a look of shock and then anger on her face.

"Get up," she said to Lillian and all the other girls dropped their heads in fear and seemed to scrub even harder. They wanted no part of this act of rebellion.

She pulled Lillian to the window and said, "Do you see that tree out there?"

"Yes, Sister." She was standing on her tiptoes as the sister held her up by her collar.

"That tree is growing and that tree is in terrible pain. Every day that tree grows just a little bit and every day it hurts to push out new branches and leaves. Do you hear that tree crying in pain?"

"No, Sister," she whimpered. It was almost unbearable just standing there at the window — her legs felt like they were on fire.

"No, of course not. All of God's creatures grow but they don't cry out in pity for themselves, now do they?"

"No, Sister." She stared at the tree and felt a light-headed nausea start to come over her.

"Back to work then. And no more crying."

Lillian was blinking her eyes trying to focus on the tree but it wasn't there anymore. She could make out what seemed like wooden beams of a ceiling above her, but that couldn't be right.

Was I dreaming about the tree? Or am I dreaming now?

She struggled to break out of her haze but everything was so foggy and she was so groggy that she was terribly confused.

I must have been so tired that I can't even remember going to bed. She was beginning to become more aware. *The fire smells so good.*

None of this made any sense. She was covered in a wonderful soft, warm blanket, in a room with a roaring fire that she had never been in before. She decided she was either dreaming or she had finally gone to heaven.

"Where am I?" she asked aloud. She tried to sit up but fell back into that soft bed as though she weighed a thousand pounds. Suddenly a pang of hunger went through her, along with a wave of nausea, making her feel like she may pass out again.

"Just lie there, my child, you are very sick."

Lillian blinked her eyes and tried to focus on the nun standing over her with a frown. It seemed to be a frown of concern rather than one of anger, which she wasn't accustomed to, so that only added to her confusion.

"I'm sorry, Sister," she said. "I'm sorry if I couldn't finish my work yesterday."

"Yesterday!" The nun had a surprised look on her face. "My dear, you have been in this bed for two weeks. You had a very high fever and we had to keep you warm. That's why you are here."

Lillian looked around and saw the rock walls so common in the convent. But the wooden beam ceilings were not, neither were the hardwood floors. And the fireplace was wonderful, with the big crackling fire and the smell of burning oak in the room.

The bed was so soft and warm with the thick, furry blanket, and there were a pair of nice oak chairs in front of the fireplace along with a rocking chair in the corner, still rocking slightly as the nun had just left it.

"I'll be alright in a few minutes, Sister. I will get my work done, I promise." The dreaded stick crossed her mind.

"You just rest for now," said the nun. She propped her head up and spooned a little cold potato soup into her mouth and insisted she drink some water.

"Just a day or two, Sister. Just a day or two and I will be alright."

But it wasn't a day or two and it wasn't a week. For three more weeks she lay in that bed sleeping most of the time and eating what she could. She shivered with cold even with the fire.

Eventually she was moved to another room. Not the cellblock-like barracks with the two dozen other girls, but a small room with two other girls. They were also sickly but Lillian was the only one who couldn't walk.

The room was not as nice as the one she had just spent more than a month in, but it was quiet and warm and hopefully a good enough place to heal her uncooperative body.

Within a few weeks the sisters had her back to work. "Work is the best medicine," they would say.

While she couldn't walk, she could certainly work. She was given jobs such as polishing the tarnished silver and sewing the torn dresses. The nuns would have other girls stack things on the table in front of her that had not been cleaned in years just to give her something to do.

Her hands cramped up from peeling so many potatoes, and every shoe of every nun in the building was brought to her to shine. If this was good medicine she should be all better by now.

And every day and every night she repeated the names: "Mary and then Molly and then me. Alice, Sam, George Jr. and Jake, the oldest."

As she polished the silver crucifix, she prayed to that poor man to help her find them again. She wanted her sisters back and she wanted to go home and she wanted her legs to work and she wanted to be the pretty little girl in the pretty little dress again. She prayed and she prayed but nobody answered.

In May a visitor came to the convent, a little earlier than expected. Her name was Margaret Digby. More than half the food donated to the convent came as a result of Margaret's work. Margaret had a passion for feeding the hungry and was able to form co-ops around the country to help farmers get the most efficient yields and profits for their crops.

As part of the plan the farmers had to donate a portion of their now more bountiful harvest to charity. With Margaret's help, much of this made it into the hands of orphanages, convents, group homes and soup kitchens. In doing so, she established a large network of contacts, including Mrs. Sharpe.

"Where is she?" Margaret asked sternly.

The Mother Superior was clearly nervous about Margaret's visit and understandably so. Mrs. Sharpe had called Margaret to enlist her help in her desperation to place the two girls. Margaret did a lot for this convent and was not happy with them when they refused the younger girl.

The nuns didn't want to deal with younger girls, and sisters posed an even more difficult situation. Difficulties were not something they wanted.

"Would you like a cup of tea first, Margaret?"

"It's Miss Digby. And I want to see her now. I am told she is ill, is that correct?"

"Yes, Miss Digby. She has Infantile Paralysis, I'm afraid."

This affliction that was ravaging little Lillian was also to strike the next President of the United States.

"Do you mean Polio?"

"Yes, Margaret—I'm sorry, Miss Digby—she has polio."

"I want to see her. I want to talk to her."

"But she doesn't even know who you are. She doesn't know how she got here. She only knows Mrs. Sharpe."

"When she is older, I will tell her everything. For now I must try to help her. Take me to her now."

"Please, Margaret."

Margaret stared at her and never broke eye contact.

"I'm sorry, I meant Miss Digby," the nun said, clearly getting broken by Margaret's resolve.

"Now, Mother Superior, right now."

The nun led Margaret through the maze that was the old convent, past many young girls that had the same vacant look on their pale faces that Margaret had seen so many times in so many places.

The place was still dingy and damp but Margaret was surprised to see the sparkle of the stones in the floor of the great hall. Glistening silver crucifix and candlesticks sparkled against the mossy walls.

"She's over there." The Mother Superior nodded toward the little blonde girl sitting at the table with needle and thread and a pile of blue dresses in front of her.

Margaret went over and sat down next to her and said, "Hello young lady, my name is Margaret. Margaret Digby."

"It's nice to meet you, Miss Digby," Lillian said with a smile. "My name is Lillian. Lillian Rose Bradley."

"Well, Lillian Rose Bradley," Margaret chuckled. "It's nice to meet you, too."

Lillian kept working the entire time, aware of the Mother Superior lurking in the background. She knew Margaret would not be there for long but the sisters would always be a threat.

Margaret told Lillian about her job to help feed the hungry and Lillian was surprised that anyone had such a job.

Lillian told Margaret about her family, and named off their names for her, and with Margaret choking back tears she relayed how she was ripped away from her sisters.

"Lillian," Margaret asked, "would you mind if I have a doctor come and look at your legs?"

Lillian darted her eyes about, catching the Mother Superior looking at her and looked back at Margaret, petrified that she might cause trouble.

"It's alright, Lillian. You don't have to be afraid. Your Aunt Margaret is here to protect you now."

"Can I call you Aunt Margaret?" Lillian's face beamed. "I would like that very much."

"I would like it, too, child. I will write to you and you can write to me."

Lillian just smiled.

"And I will have a doctor come and look at your legs. Will that be alright?"

"Yes, Aunt Margaret," Lillian said with a big smile.

Margaret leaned down and cupped the little girl's cheek and kissed her forehead and with a smile she turned to leave.

"Aunt Margaret!"

She turned around.

"Thank you."

Margaret nodded and smiled and walked out with the Mother Superior.

"I'm not happy with the condition of these girls," Margaret said.

"We try, Miss Digby. We do our best to educate them and shelter them and nurture them," the nun lied.

"I want that girl to have the medical attention she needs right away, do you understand?"

"Of course, Miss Digby."

"I want a doctor here right away to treat her and I want progress reports, even if I must pay for it myself."

"I will start looking for a doctor in the morning, Miss Digby."

"I lead the committee that will assess your needs for the next year and I would like to put in a good word for you, even though you don't deserve it. Do you understand me, Sister?"

"Perfectly, Miss Digby. Perfectly."

"Do not disappoint me, Sister." She held eye contact with the nun for a few more moments and then stood up and walked out of her office. She left the convent, leaving the Mother Superior sitting there, never even saying goodbye.

The sister stood in the doorway as the little girl winced in pain while the doctor pushed and pulled on her legs. The whole time he was frowning and shaking his head as if Lillian wasn't even there.

"Impossible," he said to the Mother Superior. "She is too advanced and too weak and far too old to treat successfully."

"Please, Doctor," the nun said out of desperation. "We need a miracle here at Saint John's and we need it to be her."

The doctor looked up at the Mother Superior, who seemed to be pleading with her eyes, and then back at the little girl who smiled at him, even though she still hurt.

He shrugged and nodded his head and said he would be back next week, but warned not to expect much because this would truly take a miracle.

It took three weeks, but he finally returned with Lillian's new leg braces. He also gave her a pair of crutches.

"It's very important that you put them on correctly and keep the straps tight. This is how you tighten the straps and this is how you adjust them as you grow," he explained, as he showed her what to do.

Lillian nodded and took it all in. He also gave her a lesson in using the crutches.

"Ten minutes a day," he said. "No more at first. Ten minutes a day. Do you understand?"

Lillian nodded while looking down at her "leg irons."

"This will take a long time so you must be patient. Ten minutes a day until I return or you may hurt yourself. Don't push too hard. Ten minutes, no more."

From the moment she put them on for the first time, they hurt. When she tried to stand for the first time the pain was excruciating and she fell back on the bed. She was shocked as the pain shot up her legs and her back.

She tried to pull herself up with the crutches but just didn't have the upper body strength, and she dropped back down with lightning bolts once again shooting up her legs.

I can do this. It will get easier. She knew the rest of her life depended on it.

This time, in an effort to just stand, she set one crutch aside and planted the other one directly in front of her as she grabbed it with both hands. Leaning forward and pulling as hard as she could, she couldn't quite straighten her legs and once again fell back on the bed in pain.

So it's better with one. I almost stood that time.

Undaunted, she once again planted the crutch in front of her and grabbed it with both hands. Throwing herself up and pulling as hard as she could, her knees locked in place but the momentum carried her forward, sending her crashing to the floor on her face, her leg braces tangling and the crutch bouncing across the room.

The Mother Superior had been secretly watching from the door and now slipped away shaking her head as Lillian lay there crying and bleeding from her nose. She knew the little girl had to do this herself, so it was now entirely up to her.

Lillian lay there sobbing and bleeding. "Mary and Molly," she whispered. "Then me, Alice and then Sam. George Jr. and Jake, the oldest."

She repeated their names again and again and let the pain soak into her body. Then she rolled over, reached down and tightened the strap on her brace, took the crutch in her hand and slid towards the bed to try again.

And try again, and again, and again. Not for ten minutes a day, but for all day, every day, every moment she could spare between work, studies, and more work, she spent trying to walk.

It took almost a year before she could pull herself to her feet with the crutches and stay there. She had no upper body strength, and her legs were like noodles, so getting to the point where she could stand up and then walk was a huge milestone.

My world just got bigger. Before this, it was only as far as I could crawl.

She fell down again and again and again, so much so that the other girls got tired of making fun of her. They would call her names like "Tin man," and "Robot," but now they just stepped over her or ignored her.

It went on for years, what seemed like a lifetime to Lillian. She was now thirteen years old and was beginning to lose hope. She had to get off these crutches; she would never walk unless she did, which meant she could never walk out of this place. That prospect was unthinkable.

Getting up on those crutches was a huge milestone in her life, getting off them would be an even greater one.

Her leg muscles had to be strong enough to hold herself up, but no matter how hard she tried, they seemed to get no stronger than they were three years ago. She worked her muscles every day and tried to stretch them at night when the braces were off.

She would sometimes get a cramp so bad that it left her with curled up toes, whimpering in the bed. She always had cuts and bruises from the straps, and even more from falling down. Under her arms was badly bruised from balancing on the crutches, but as bad as she hurt she was like the tree, and she wouldn't complain. The doctor would come by a couple times a year.

"I'm fine," she would always say with a smile when the doctor would inquire.

"Yes, I can see that," he said as he looked up and down her badly bruised and still under developed legs.

"Well, Lillian, your progress has been slow," he said, shaking his head and frowning. "But it is progress. If nothing else you have kept yourself out of a wheelchair, and I must admit, I thought you would be in one by now."

Lillian wasn't sure if he was telling her good news or bad news, so she decided it was a little of both.

"And Lillian," he said. "How many times must I tell you not to push so hard? You need to rest, as well."

"I will, doctor. I promise."

He sat next to her and, looking at her with a smile, said, "No you won't."

"No, I suppose I won't," she smiled back at him.

"I just don't want you to hurt yourself, love. After all the hard work you have done, we don't need a setback right now, do we?"

"I won't hurt myself, I promise."

"I will check with you in about six months. Keep up the good work."

"Thank you, Doctor, for everything," she said as he left the room.

He gave her a little wave on the way out, and then he was gone.

"The doctor said I'm making progress, Aunt Margaret," she wrote in her letter, putting a positive spin on it.

She didn't want to let her down and she had no plans of doing so. She had written her six times so far this year and had not gotten back a single letter. She was worried that Margaret was disappointed in her.

I wonder if she has been talking to the Mother Superior. I wonder if she told her that I'm not walking yet.

The Mother Superior had not spoken to Margaret because she didn't have any good news for her. She couldn't tell her how well her little charge was doing, because it seemed like Miss Bradley had gone as far as she could go.

Sometimes she would spy on the little girl as she practiced, as she fell. Eventually she stopped watching, choosing to not know, so it was not in her best interest to write to Margaret.

Lillian finished up her letter and set it down on the bed next to her. She wanted to get in a few hours walking up and down the hall as she did every night. But tonight was different, she felt different.

They really hurt tonight. She looked down at her legs. While they were not functional, she could feel every bit of pain a leg could have.

As she rubbed her tired legs and tried to stretch her arms and shoulders, she turned and looked at the pile of scrap metal that was her braces on the floor, and the crutches leaning against the wall.

Not tonight. I can't do this tonight.

She pulled her legs up on the bed and rolled on her side, facing away from the crutches as the waves of guilt went through her. She had made a promise to herself to try every night every minute she could, so this walk was something she had done every single night.

The doctor said I should rest, so tonight I rest.

She lay there for a few minutes, disappointed in herself for breaking a promise, a promise to herself. She felt like every hour she didn't try to walk was one more hour before she ever would. Her mind kept trying to talk her out of lying in bed, but her body wanted her to stay right there.

Tomorrow. I will try again tomorrow.

Then she closed her eyes and, wishing tomorrow wouldn't come, she drifted off to sleep.

Another year ticked by with very little changes in the Convent of Saint John. Lillian was now fourteen, was still in braces, and still on crutches. The doctor hadn't called in over a year, and there was still no word from Margaret.

With these people drifting out of her life she was again feeling alone and abandoned. She had certainly had these feelings before, but this time it was breaking her spirit. It was getting harder and harder to get on those crutches and easier and easier to stay in bed.

One night she was laying there, her back to the crutches, she argued with herself as she had come to do a lot of lately. She had to push the doubts out of her mind, she had to find the hope she'd lost.

She didn't need that Doctor, she didn't need Margaret, and she didn't need her family. What she needed was to believe in her imminent success, and never give up hope. Nobody was going to do this for her.

"Time to go to work," she said as she swung her legs around and reached for the braces.

"Time to go to work."

A few months later the Mother Superior stepped out into the great hall to find Lillian sitting on the floor tightening the ragged leather strap on her battered old braces. Lillian looked up and smiled at her.

The old nun slowly sat down on a chair across the room. Her hip was hurting, her feet were swollen, and she had a terrible toothache on one of the few teeth she had left. She didn't need any more problems right now, but more problems were coming.

Lillian watched her and saw the grimace as she sat down with the weary look on her face. She also noticed she had a letter in her hand, and by the look on the nun's face, it must have been bad news.

"Is everything alright, Sister?"

"I have a letter here from your Aunt Margaret," the sister said with dread in her voice.

Lillian, startled at the news, just sat there blinking with her mouth open.

"She is coming here to check on your progress," the nun continued. "To check on all of the girls, actually, but she specifically asked about you."

"I'm glad she is coming. I haven't seen her in years, or even heard from her in over a year. She'll be proud of my progress."

The nun lifted up her head and looked across the room at the bruised up, banged up, pale little child with the worn out and undersized leg braces, sitting on the floor like a broken toy, and then dropped her head back down and slowly shook it.

Then she heard the familiar sound of metal scrapping on stone, and the creaking of the wooden crutches, and she knew that Lillian had just pulled herself to her feet.

"Sister," Lillian said.

The sister ignored her.

"Sister," she said again."

The nun ignored her again, and now was staring down at the letter and shaking her head.

"You don't spy on me anymore, Sister."

The nun snapped her head up and looked at Lillian, and this time it was her that could only blink in shock.

"Did you give up on me, Sister?"

The nun once again dropped her head down but this time slowly nodded. She had indeed given up. There simply were no miracles at the Convent of St. John, she should have known better.

"Sister," Lillian said again, and the nun looked up.

Lillian had been sitting right in front of the window where five years before she had learned of the terrible pain a tree is in as it grows, so she was now standing in front of it. One by one she propped her crutches against the window sill.

Though she was a little shaky, she was standing without the crutches. She then put her arms out like a tightrope walker, and took a tiny step towards the sister. Then another, and then another. One foot in front of the other, putting her arms down halfway across, she made it all the way to the sister's chair.

When she reached the sister she had to flail her arms and regain her balance because she wasn't good at stopping yet. The frightened look on the sister's face because Lillian almost fell on her was funny.

Lillian proudly stood over the Mother Superior and outstretched her hand. "May I see the letter, Sister?"

"Of course you may," The nun said as she quickly wiped away a tear that was trying to form before Lillian saw it.

Lillian took the letter and read through it, and sure enough Margaret had asked about her. She had some concerns she needed to address with the Mother Superior. Lillian didn't know what they were but Margaret seemed disappointed somehow.

"Do you feel better now, Sister?" she asked.

"Yes dear," said the nun. "She will be pleased to see you walking. Now help me up, please."

She steadied herself holding the back of the chair and locked arms with the nun with her other hand, and she planted both her feet as firm as she could, and then she pulled. With a moan and a groan the nun managed to get to her feet, nearly pulling Lillian down in the process.

She then turned away with a hand on her painful hip, and started waddling down the hall, and she let out a chuckle as she left.

"Don't throw your crutches away, Miss Bradley. I may need them someday."

Lillian smiled at that as she watched the fat nun struggle out of sight.

Growing pains. I should have told her she has growing pains. Her buttocks have been growing for years."

Chapter Four

His orders came in to report to Camp Upton in Long Island on January 10, 1943, so he was able to spend Christmas and New Year's Day with his family, running around with Dicky.

It was a quiet Christmas with his mom full of worry and Pop walking around all sour-faced, as usual. Not much different than other holidays, but clearly there was some tension in the air.

The constant news of the war and pictures from the front lines would get Anne upset at every mention of it. Bob tried in vain to reassure her that he would be okay. He told her that by the time he got there, if he ever even did, there would be nothing going on, but she wasn't buying it.

He wasn't buying it himself but he couldn't tell her that. At night he would lie there staring at the ceiling, too restless to sleep. The night before he had to leave he couldn't sleep at all, his mind racing at the very thought of heading out.

What the hell am I doing?

He knew he would have an out if he were to tell them about the ear; a chance to back out that most other guys didn't have, but he wished he didn't. Not wanting to use that as an excuse, he decided he had to suck it up and just go. He had to. He couldn't stand another day of walking that dock or another day of walking past Archie at the kitchen table. He had to go, and he knew it.

He got up early and found his dad sitting there at the table reading his paper and drinking his tea. He sat down next to him as his mom brought him some toast and jam, clearly more upset than he'd ever seen her.

"Thanks, Mom," he said. "And don't worry so much, ok?"

She nodded her head yes and then shook her head no and then nodded yes again before gathering up a pile of clean laundry and heading towards the bedroom with it.

When she was out of earshot Archie finally lowered the paper and said, "Promise to write your mother every chance you get. She worries too much."

"Ok, Pop," Bob replied. "I will, I promise."

"And for God's sake, be careful. It would kill her if something happened to you."

"I'll be careful, Pop. I promise."

With that he lifted his paper back up in front of him and didn't speak again.

Bob grinned a little grin. His father just told him in the only way he knew how that he loved him. He loved him and he loved Anne. Spending his life hoping for even a morsel of love from his father had taught him to catch them when they came along, and this was a pretty big morsel.

I love you, too, Pop.

When it was time to go, Anne scurried around in a near state of panic. She ran upstairs and downstairs and upstairs and back down trying to make sure he had everything he needed and then some. She would have done it a dozen more times had he not stopped her.

Pop didn't come down to see him off; he had said everything he needed to say. His mom reminded him again to write and again he promised her he would. She stood there waving and crying until he turned the corner and headed towards his train to take him to Camp Upton.

Once he arrived he was sworn in and started going through the process of being made to look like a soldier. After having his head shaved, he had to give up every stitch of clothing as he was issued regulation everything. Within two days the men were organized into groups and shipped out to basic training.

He was assigned to a bus going to Camp Livingston, Louisiana with a bunch of other New Yorkers. The buses were old and green and terribly uncomfortable, smelling like feet; but then again, it wasn't like he was expecting the army to be fun.

"Herby Weinstein," the guy next to him said, while offering his hand. "From the Bronx."

"Bob Anstey," Bob grinned. "From Brooklyn."

"You're not a Dodger fan are you? Those guys are bums."

"Of course I'm a Dodger fan. You're not a Yankee fan, are you? Those guys are sissies."

Herby smiled broadly and said, "Nice to meet you, Brooklyn. Glad to have someone to talk baseball with, even though your pitcher throws like a girl."

"Nice to meet you, too, Bronx, even though your fielders couldn't catch a cold."

They talked and laughed all the way to Louisiana. They talked baseball and they talked about how good New York Pizza is. They talked about the best hot dogs and the best beer and the best cars and the prettiest pin-up girls, but somehow Herby always managed to swing it back around to baseball. Herby figured that as long as there was baseball, there was hope for the world.

The fun stopped when the bus stopped. Camp Livingston turned out to be hell on earth and basic training, in a word, sucked. They had to march, drill, and crawl through muck and climb over walls and do it all after waking up earlier than Bob even thought possible.

Bob was tired all the time and sore all the time and every muscle in his body ached. Through all of it he had to keep his boots shined and his uniform pressed and his bed made and all were subject to inspection at any given moment. He was being yelled at all the time and he hated every minute of it, but there was no place else he would rather be.

Bob and Herby befriended another New Yorker from a small town upstate whose name was Doug Hansen. Much to Bob's chagrin another Yankee fan, though not as rabid as Herby.

41

Doug's main interest was girls, a subject he never tired of, and he considered himself an authority on the matter. He liked girls and girls liked him. He would captivate the guys with stories of meeting girls, of where and how and the great opening lines he used. Doug was the king.

But Doug had an advantage — with his blonde hair and blue eyes, chiseled face and big toothy smile, he was by far the best looking guy in basic training, maybe even the whole damn army.

By the time they graduated from basic the three were the best of friends. They were once again loaded up on buses to head off to their new assignments, and anything had to be better than that God-forsaken hell hole they were leaving.

"Poor bastards," Bob said to Herby as he looked out the window of the bus at the next wave of trainees being dropped off. He wondered if some departing soldier had said that about him at his arrival.

"Thank God that's over," said Herby.

"So where are you going, Bobby boy?" Doug asked as he slid in next to him.

"Camp Edwards, Massachusetts," Bob answered. "I'm in the 32nd Provisional Battalion. How about you?"

"Same place. It must be a New York battalion because every New Yorker in our group seems to be going there."

" What are we going to be doing?"

"What's the matter, you worried, big boy?" Doug chided. "A provisional battalion is one that hasn't been assigned yet. It means they are still deciding what to do with us."

"Oh, well, that explains it," Bob said sarcastically.

"Well, Camp Edwards is an artillery training ground, so I'm sure it will have something to do with that. When they figure out where they need us then that's where they will put us."

"So we are sort of in limbo," Bob said.

"I guess you could say that," said Doug. "But probably not for long."

"How the hell do you know all this?" Bob asked. "You always know everything before anybody else does. They should make you a General because you already know everything."

Everybody laughed and Doug nodded his head, smiling. He was quite a character and everybody considered him their best friend. He had a way of making people feel that way when they were around him.

"Not a General, a movie star!" Herby said, looking over the seat in front of them. "Just ask him."

"Laugh now, laugh now," Doug said grinning. "Just remember this bus ride when you're standing in line to see one of my movies."

"You would have to pay me to go to one of your movies," said Herby, prompting hoots and laughter from the bus as the two tried to outdo one another.

"I bet your wife won't let you go see the Yankees unless you take her to see my movies," Doug shot back.

"Unlike you, I plan on marrying a girl with some class," said Herb, and the bus roared with laughter.

"Yeah, and how do you plan on doing that? Are you going to be a movie star, too?"

"Nah," Herby replied. "I think I'll be a General. They have an opening since they heard you didn't want it."

"I thought you were gonna play for the Yankees, Herb," said Bob. "It's not like they could be any worse."

"They don't need much to beat the Dodgers, Bob," he shot back.

They laughed and threw comebacks at each other the whole trip, with Herby winning just about every line. He was the undisputed funniest guy in the battalion. The battalion in limbo.

The convoy of buses made the trip to Camp Edwards in two days, stopping only for quick meals and bathroom breaks. They played a little poker and tried to catch a little sleep at night but the hard seats of the old bus kept them shifting from cheek to cheek, and always looking for something to use as padding.

"I didn't know it was possible for my ass to hurt this bad," Bob said.

"Sorry about that, Bobby," said Herb. "Does your face hurt, too?"

"No, why?' Bob said, looking rather perplexed.

"Because it's killing me," came the response with an elbow to his ribs.

"Shit, I walked right into that," Bob said, rolling his eyes.

"These seats are almost as bad as my dad's tractor," Doug said.

"Tractor!" said Herby. "You have a friggin' tractor? We don't have friggin' tractors in New York. What are you from, Nebraska or something?"

"They may not have tractors in the Bronx, you big dumb bastard, but they do have them in New York. There are mountains and lakes and trees and stuff, too," Doug chided.

"I don't like mountains and lakes and trees and stuff. I like skyscrapers and subways and Yankee stadium. Now that's New York. Well, I guess it could be worse, though," Herb said, winking at Doug. "At least you don't live in Brooklyn."

"Hey, I heard that," said Bob.

During the last few bumpy hours of the trip Bob pulled out a pencil and paper and shot off a quick letter to his mom. He figured if she knew he was in Massachusetts, which was a lot closer than Louisiana, it would ease her mind a little.

If I wind up going overseas she is going to be a basket case.

He told her how they hadn't even been designated an actual task yet so she had nothing to worry about, which was half true anyway.

The convoy finally rolled into Camp Edwards and they hobbled their sore behinds off the bus. While they didn't know what was in store for them next, they were glad to be

44

back on their feet again and really glad to get out of that hell they called Camp Livingston back in Louisiana.

As they piled out of the buses, another bus convoy pulled in and even more men started pouring out, also fresh out of basic, and also New Yorkers.

The sergeants of the battalion organized into groups and rows all eight hundred men, then mustered them up on the parade ground with amazing speed, all of them snapping to attention as the order was given. The 32nd Provisional Battalion was now in full force.

Within a minute of standing at full attention and in dead silence, hearing nothing but the breeze that whispered through the ranks making the flag flap and ripple, they saw their Commanding Officer for the first time.

He was a big colonel wearing a cavalry hat and cowboy boots, with a Colt 45 on his hip and a cigar in his mouth. He had two lieutenants walking a few steps behind him as he strutted up along the front of the column and turned to face them.

This Texas colonel was a last minute replacement for the New York colonel originally designated to lead this battalion, who had been forced to forego this command due to health reasons.

"My name is Colonel Robert Gibbs, and I am the Commanding Officer of the 32nd Provisional Battalion," his voice boomed out. He paused for what seemed like forever, but was probably just a few seconds. "So now you work for me."

"As of right now, this is no longer the 32nd Provisional Battalion," he continued, once again pausing for dramatic effect. This colonel really knew how to play to a crowd, and the men were utterly enthralled.

"This is now the 386th AAA and AW Battalion. That means Anti-Aircraft Artillery and Automatic Weapons Battalion. We are going to shoot down airplanes, gentlemen. Training begins in the morning. I suggest you pay attention."

With that, the Colonel turned and walked away the same way he came, with his two lieutenants trotting along behind. Doug poked his head out of the line a little, smiled and winked at Bob, then pulled back in again.

Artillery. Bastard was right. Bob cracked a smile.

The sergeants of the battalions walked up and down the rows barking orders, breaking them into smaller groups, assigning them a barracks, telling them where to eat, and all the other "where to's and what to do's and what not to do's" about the camp.

Herby and Bob and Doug stood close to each other and as they hoped, wound up in the same group. The building they were assigned had many small rooms with four bunks in each. It was there they met their new bunkmate — a guy from Fulton County, New York — named John Lemons.

After lights out, Herby whispered, "Hey John, you're not a Dodger fan are you?"

"Yankees," said John.

"Thank God for that," Herby replied. "I like this guy already, Bobby boy."

"This is gonna be a long war," Bob groaned, and rolled over and went to sleep.

Chapter Five

By the time Aunt Margaret arrived Lillian was hobbling and limping around the convent with only her leg braces. She was a little unsteady on her feet but was getting better every day.

"I'm very proud of you, my child," said Margaret with a smile.

"Thank you, Aunt Margaret, and thank you for helping me."

"You did this all by yourself. Don't ever let anyone take that away from you. You are stronger than you even know you are. After what you have gone through in your young life you must always remember there is nothing you can't do."

Lillian nodded and let the words sink in. She had always seen herself as weak, a crippled girl torn from her sisters without the ability to protect them, but Margaret saw strength in her and she was surprised at that.

"Has there been any word of my family?" she asked. "Any word of my sisters, anything at all?"

"We have been looking as hard as we can, Lillian. They moved from the house they were living in and seemed to have disappeared."

"They took my sisters away to other places. Maybe we could find out where."

"Your mother had agreed to tell us where the other girls were. We had hoped to get you all in one place, but it seems that for whatever reasons she had, she lied to us about their locations. She made one excuse after the other for about five years and when we really started to push her, she left."

Lillian's face dropped to the floor at the bad news even though she was expecting it. In her heart she knew that if Margaret had any news of them Lillian would not have to ask.

Margaret put her hand on Lillian's cheek and gently lifted her head back up while using her thumb to gently brush away the tear trying to form.

"I will keep looking, child. I promise," she said.

"Would you like to go for a walk, Aunt Margaret?" Lillian asked. She decided to show Margaret some more of that strength she didn't know she had.

"I would love to, and I have been long looking forward to the day when we could."

Lillian beamed with pride and said, "If you fall behind don't worry, I will wait for you."

Margaret chuckled and followed along with her. Lillian clanked and squeaked like the tin man when she walked.

"Next time you see me I will be walking without these," she said, nodding downward and grinning.

"Of that I have no doubt."

"Tell me about some of the exciting places you have been, Margaret. Tell me what you have been doing!"

"I have been spending a lot of time in America recently. The Americans have some wonderful ideas on more effective irrigation methods and we are trying to apply that here."

"I want to be like you someday, Margaret. Helping feed people and helping little girls," she smiled.

"I told you, you did that all by yourself," Margaret said as they walked into the Great Hall.

"I know but I wanted to hear you say it again," Lillian joked.

They came to the window and looked out at the green landscape and Margaret said, "It's a lovely world out there, child, you will like it."

Lillian saw the tree that was in great pain and shuddered a slight shudder, but it didn't go unnoticed by Margaret.

"Don't be afraid," she said. "You are stronger than anything out there. Now I must leave because I can't miss my train. Write to me, alright?"

Margaret had some business with the Mother Superior so Lillian walked with her to the nun's office and waited with her until they were done. At the big doors Margaret gave her a big hug and promised to write often.

"I look forward to it, Aunt Margaret, and I will pray for news of my sisters."

Margaret got into the back of the Taxi and was taken away, leaving Lillian with a certain sadness, but also a sense of pride and hope. Because of Margaret's words, she was no longer afraid.

Over the next year Lillian worked her way out of the now falling apart leg irons to walk completely by herself. Her legs were scarred and still weak but she was more determined than ever to walk out of this place under her own power and she had all but achieved that goal.

Outside the convent walls the world was becoming a dangerous place. The Nazis had come to power in Germany and Hitler was getting ready to flex his muscles.

The war that Winston Churchill had been warning of was nearly at the doorstep of England, and The Convent of Saint John would soon become a casualty of it.

Lillian was not quite sixteen when the Mother Superior called her to her office. Things around the convent had seemed less disciplined of late, and the nuns were a little more subdued. Though subtle, Lillian could feel something different but she couldn't put her finger on it.

Walking in with barely a limp she took a seat in front of the big desk and peered over it to see the big nun studying her with a pensive scowl on her face.

As she was taught to do, she sat up straight and, looking into the Mother Superior's eyes, waited with respect, feeling the twinge of fear she always felt at the thought of what punishment would come with any misstep.

The Mother Superior sat there and frowned, never breaking eye contact. Lillian stared back. The room was quiet except the ticking of the old clock on the wall, and it smelled slightly of the lavender scented soap the nun used.

Even though the office had a window, it was covered by a heavy curtain, making the room as dark and gloomy as the rest of Saint John's.

The nun continued to stare her down and Lillian continued to stare right back. She noticed the thick wrinkles that time had carved into her face, and the gray streaks that a life without joy had painted in her hair.

Time seemed to slow down and almost stop. She could feel her heart beating gently in the still quiet of the moment, and she stared at the sister's stone, grim face who was still looking at her for what now seemed like an eternity.

As hard as she tried to fight it off, Lillian had the urge to smile. The harder she fought the funnier it got until she could hold it no longer. The corner of her mouth started to curl up and when the bigger smile tried to break out she put her hand over it to try unsuccessfully to hide it.

She broke eye contact and, looking down, giggled slightly, then snapped back up with another effort to hide the smile, failed and looked back down again, unable to hold it back.

She was amazed at what she saw next. The nun reluctantly broke into a smile of her own. Lillian could tell she was trying to fight it off but was caught up in the moment along with her.

The smile was fleeting, but the once again pensive look was somehow softer. Lillian could see that a change had come over her.

"What is the matter, Sister?" Lillian asked. "What is wrong?"

"I'm afraid it's time for you to leave, my dear," the Mother Superior replied softly.

Lillian stared at her wide-eyed, shocked at the news that came years before she thought it would.

"The convent is closing, Lillian. There will be no more Convent of Saint John."

"But why? Where will we all go? Where will you go, Sister?"

The nun didn't answer the last part of her question but was surprised that Lillian so quickly showed concern about her, too.

"It's the war, my dear. It is a terrible thing and all resources must be dedicated to it. We can no longer survive on the meager rations and the resources it takes to maintain and sustain us."

"Then what are we to do? There must be someplace to go."

"The decision has been made, Miss Bradley. The convent will close and we all must leave. We have placed many of the girls but I'm afraid the older ones will be on their own."

"And what of me, Sister?"

"A rare opportunity, Miss Bradley. An opportunity I can give to but one girl. There is a family in Bath that is looking for a nanny. Have you ever heard of Bath, or perhaps Bristol?"

Lillian shook her head.

"No matter. The gentleman is a Commander in the Royal Navy and he and his wife and two children live there, along with several other domestics, I understand. They seek help looking after the children."

"Why me, Sister? I don't understand."

"I will tell you why, Miss Bradley," the nun said, leaning forward. "There is only one chance like this, and there is no coming back if you fail. If you fail you will have stolen this chance from one of the other girls that may have succeeded. Do you understand?"

Lillian nodded.

"When you leave here, the doors will close behind you. There will be no place to return to, there will be no one here to help you."

Lillian sat there trying to take it all in.

"Miss Bradley," the nun said softly. "I have watched you all these years. There are girls here that are stronger than you, there are girls that are smarter than you, but I have never seen

51

a girl with your resolve in all my life. You appear to have no fear of failure, because you know you won't."

"But I don't want to go, Sister. I'm not ready."

"After breakfast, Miss Bradley, you will be taken to the train station for your journey to Bristol. Be ready or someone else will take your place."

Lillian stood and the Mother Superior looked back down at her desk and started going through her papers. Lillian rushed around the desk and hugged her. The nun returned her hug and patted her on the back a few times.

"Go now, and don't be afraid."

After Lillian left the room the nun pulled a letter out and reread it. It described the position in Bath and the need for a special girl to fill it; of the rare opportunity for one girl, and one girl only. The nun nodded at her decision to send Lillian. The letter was signed, Mrs. Sharpe.

The next morning after breakfast Lillian watched out the window of the taxi as the Convent of Saint John disappeared from view. The Mother Superior didn't see her off and she never said goodbye.

Six weeks later the convent closed its doors forever, and the nuns and the girls were scattered across England, many lost to history in the shadow of the Great War that was changing the world.

Lillian with her one suitcase was dropped alone at the crowded train station with her ticket, quickly getting caught up in the crowd. She could smell the womens' perfumes, feel the brush of the coarse mens' coats, and hear the many sounds, all seeming to rise up into one great crushing noise.

She couldn't see where she was going and had no idea if it was the right way. She could feel the panic rise up in her as her heart pounded.

I have to get out of here. She began to panic and claw her way through the crowd. She was about to scream out in fear when she finally burst through the seemingly endless wall of people and onto the train platform where a train sat on either side.

After a few calming breaths and a few inquiries showing her ticket, she boarded her train and settled in by a window, feeling the adrenaline flow from her system.

As the train lurched free of the station any feelings of panic were now giving away to exhilaration. A feeling of realization that she was free. She didn't expect it to happen quite this way or quite this soon, but it was happening.

I walked out of there. I stood up on my own two feet and I walked out of the Convent of Saint John." She couldn't help but smile.

As the train click-clacked down the track, she opened the window next to her like many of the other passengers and took in the sights and smells of the countryside as it went by, daydreaming as she rode along.

Margaret will be so proud of me. I won't let her down after all she has done for me.

Thoughts of her sisters went through her mind from time to time but she was beginning to realize that she would probably never see them again, and she had shed so many tears already.

She thought about the Mother Superior, and about how strange it was to have feelings for a woman she feared and hated for so many years, and she hoped the other nuns and girls would be alright.

As she traveled along she could sometimes smell the sweet country air of the open fields, or the freshly plowed earth that the farmers were readying. Sometimes she would smell the oak burning in the locomotive that stoked the boiler.

She could hear the chugging of the steam as it drove the wheels forward and the grinding of the cars as they went around a bend in the track.

Hours later she was snapped out of her daydream by a loud blast on the steam whistle that startled her, nearly making her jump out of her seat. All the windows in the passenger car were slammed shut by the riders sitting next to them, which only further startled and bewildered her.

Suddenly the car went pitch black, and about thirty seconds later it lit up again. She looked down to see that her whole upper body was covered in filthy, grimy black soot. Her face was black except for her teeth and eyes.

A man on the other side of the aisle handed her handkerchief as she sat there stunned and blinking.

"A tunnel, love," he said. "When they blow the whistle it means they are going into a tunnel. Just remember to close up when you hear the whistle."

Lillian looked down at herself and saw that she was dirtier than she had ever been before, and then looked back up when the conductor announced they were pulling into Bristol.

The handkerchief did little more than push the dirt around her face. Still filthy, with head down and shoulders slumped, she stepped off the train. The station here was crowded, as well, and she wondered how she would ever find the person meeting her.

She looked down at the card with their names. "Commander and Mrs. William G. Grisham. They had two children: William Jr. was ten, and his sister, Victoria, was eight.

That was all the information she had. She had no address nor did she know who would pick her up or when. She had not a penny in her pocket, nor did she even have a purse to carry it in if she had one.

It seemed hopeless. There were so many people and they all ignored her and her dirty face. She didn't know who to look for or where to wait.

I should be upset. But I'm just too bloody tired.

"Miss Bradley?" a voice said from behind her.

"Yes!" she said, spinning around. She looked up into the pale thin face of a very tall man in a black suit looking down his nose at her grimy face and clothes.

"My name is Durham," he said. "William Durham, the Grisham's driver. My wife, Joyce, is the cook and she will have a meal waiting for you. You must be hungry."

"I'm very hungry," she said. "But I don't wish to be a bother."

"No bother, miss," he said as he took her suitcase. "You are one of us now, we must keep you fed."

She nodded but didn't quite understand what he meant.

He looked down at her again as he got ready to open the car door and smiled. "Didn't close the window, did you?"

She shook her head and a little tear made a trail down through the soot.

"Don't feel bad, love. My wife has done it three times now. You would think she would learn after the first."

Lillian cheered up with that as they talked along the drive to the Commander's house. He told her about his wife and about Ted, the groundskeeper, and of course, about the Grishams. It was getting late in the day as they skirted around Bristol and turned on the road leading up to Bath when Lillian saw it.

It was an enchanting small city on top of a hill made up of a mix of old ruins and lovely homes and buildings.

"Have you ever seen Roman ruins before, love?" asked William, while looking in the mirror at the wonder on her face. She could only shake her head as she marveled at the sprawling ancient structures and roads.

"It's a lovely place," said George. "It's lovely when the sun shines and lovely when it rains. Sometimes when the fog rolls in, it takes on an almost magical look and feel. Almost as though it were alive."

A few minutes later they pulled up in front of the Grisham's house. It was the most beautiful house she had ever seen or even imagined could exist. It seemed Commander Grisham had money, family money. He didn't get a place like this by serving in the Royal Navy, no matter the rank.

Lillian was ushered into the back door leading into the kitchen where Joyce was waiting for her. She laughed when she saw Lillian's face and Lillian loved her immediately.

They talked while she ate and Joyce said the family was settled in for the night.

"You'll meet Mrs. Grisham in the morning, but don't expect to hear two words out of that pompous bastard husband of hers," Joyce said. "He will stand there saying nothing because he is too bloody important to talk to you. He's got a bug up his arse or some such thing."

Lillian almost shot tea out of her nose she laughed so hard.

"After breakfast you will meet the little buggers. Better you than me, I'll give you that."

Lillian sat there nodding her head and taking it all in as she nibbled on the snacks Joyce had put in front of her.

"After our workdays are done, we usually meet here and eat and talk and listen to the little radio. The Grishams have the large radio they listen to out in the family room and usually don't want to be bothered by us after dinner."

Lillian never heard anyone talk so fast and so much in her life.

"Sometimes Ted will come up and take meals with us, but his mind always seems elsewhere. He is an odd duck, my dear, but we love him."

She was shown her little room and instantly fell in love with it, it was so beautiful. The light blue walls contrasted with the white eyelet bedspread, complete with a soft puffy pillow atop a soft bed that didn't squeak. Two of the walls in her room had windows, one of which overlooked the rolling hills. She opened the drapes in anticipation of waking up the next morning to be greeted by the sun, but she could only see pitch dark out of them now.

When she awoke she could smell the faint smell of the oil on the recently polished oak furniture, and the crisp scent of her fresh clean sheets from hanging to dry in the country breeze. A few days ago she could never have imagined the turn her life would take, literally overnight.

"Oh my God," she said aloud as she jumped from her bed. The dream was real and now as she stood at the window she said again softly, "Oh my God."

As far as her job, it was not bad compared to the convent. She had to cater to the children's every whim, be snapped at constantly by Mrs. Grisham, and be utterly ignored by the Commander.

She was expected to clean every free moment that she was not helping the other domestics or taking care of the children, but she never complained, and the truth is, she never had it so good.

She would sometimes play dress up with little Victoria and daydream of her own sisters and what may have become of them. She liked the little girl, even though she was very spoiled. Never having been around boys before, she struggled to understand little William, but she made a go of it regardless.

There are too many Williams in this house.

She always enjoyed her evening chats in the kitchen with Joyce. Sometimes Ted would join them but more often than not, he was off with William having a "Toddy."

She enjoyed something else that she never had before. She had Sunday off to do whatever she pleased.

"It's ironic," she said to Joyce. "Sunday was the worst day of the week living in the convent. The day of rest was only for the nuns. Now it's my favorite day in the whole world!"

Her least favorite part of the job was laundry. Hanging clothes to dry in the wind of the hills often had her chasing sheets down the road.

"I hate to see that," Ted said to her as they looked down the hill to see a convoy of British troops and tanks moving through, going God knows where. "I really hate to see it. Things will never be the same, mind you. They will never be the same."

In April of 1940, Germany attacked Norway and Denmark as the Nazis went on the offensive again. Prime Minister Chamberlain, who had tried to appease Hitler and the

Nazis, saw his government falling apart as the people lost confidence and began to realize the mounting threat.

King George VI asked Winston Churchill to form a new government on May 10th, the same day Germany invaded Luxembourg, The Netherlands and Belgium.

Lillian, Joyce, William, and Ted listened to their little kitchen radio while the Grishams listened to theirs as the Prime Minister addressed the House of Commons, on June 4, 1940:

> "I have, myself, full confidence that if all do their duty, if nothing is neglected, and if the best arrangements are made, as they are being made, we shall prove ourselves once again to defend our island home, to ride out the storm of war, and to outlive the menace of tyranny, if necessary for years, if necessary alone. At any rate, that is what we are going to try to do. That is the resolve of his Majesty's government, every man of them. That is the will of Parliament and the nation. The British Empire and the French Republic, linked together in their cause and in their need, will defend to the death their native soil, aiding each other like good comrades to the utmost of their strength. Even though large tracts of Europe and many old and famous states have fallen or may fall into the grip of the Gestapo and all the odious apparatus of Nazi rule, we shall not flag or falter. We shall go on to the end, we shall fight in France. We shall fight on the seas and oceans, we shall fight with growing confidence and growing strength in the air. We shall defend our island, whatever the cost may be. We shall fight on the beaches, we shall fight on the landing grounds, we shall fight in the fields and in the streets, we shall fight in the hills, we shall never surrender. And even if, which I do not for a moment believe, this island or a large part of it were

subjugated and starving, then our empire beyond the seas, armed and guarded by the British fleet, would carry on the struggle, until, in God's good time, the new world with all its power and might, steps forth to the rescue and the liberation of the old."

Joyce reached over and clicked off the radio as a tear rolled down her cheek. The words of their new Prime Minister were powerful and defiant, but the threat was so grave, and the cost was so high.

They all sat there in silence, digesting the words of the speech, and wondering what the future would hold.

"I would rather starve to death than surrender to those bastards," said Ted. "The new PM is right."

William put his arm around Joyce and said, "It's alright, love, everything will be alright."

Eighteen days later, on June 22, 1940, France surrendered to Germany. Great Britain now faced possibly the most powerful force in the history of mankind, and they faced it alone.

A few months later Lillian got a letter from Margaret. She had some news of her brother, but not her sisters.

The British had sent to France an expeditionary force to bolster the French defense and deter the German invasion but the French were swept aside by German armor and air power.

The British force abandoned their limited stock of heavy weapons and tried to retreat to the coast to avoid capture. They made it to Dunkirk, and found themselves with their backs to the Channel and nowhere to go.

The Germans, intent on destroying the broken force, bombed and shelled them, trying to starve them out.

The English patriots were not about to let "their lads" die on the beaches of France, so over eight hundred small boats, many mere fishing vessels and ferries, set sail for their rescue mission. Under heavy air attack and through days of fighting they managed to pull 335,000 men off the beaches of Dunkirk and bring them safely home to fight again.

"I'm sorry, my dear Lillian," Margaret wrote. "Your brother Jake was not among the rescued soldiers. He is listed as missing in action."

Lillian was numb. She really didn't know her brother and she really didn't remember him. He was little more than a name on her list that she would recite when she needed comfort and feared she may forget them.

Molly and then Mary, me and Alice and then Sam, George Jr. and then Jake, the oldest. She tried to picture his face and the sound of his voice, wondering if her mother knew. She wondered if her mother ever got to say goodbye to him.

"I'm sorry about your brother, love," Joyce said to Lillian as they had tea and muffins for breakfast. "It's an awful thing, it is."

"I can't imagine what it must have been like. It must have been awful for them, Joyce. So very frightening."

"It's going to get worse," said Joyce. "Hitler was dancing a jig in Paris — the bastards are not done yet."

After a long pause with neither one speaking, as Lillian gazed out the window looking at nothing in particular and nestling her teacup, she said, "I didn't know him, Joyce. I don't remember what he looked like."

Joyce turned her head and stared out the window with her. She didn't know what to say, so she didn't say anything.

William stuck his head in the door and seeing the two women sitting there with gloomy faces, he quietly slipped out and went down to have a drink with Ted.

Commander Grisham, despite his obvious wealth, was doing his part in the war effort in the intelligence community. They had broken the German code and discovered a plot to lure the British Royal Air Force into a trap.

The Germans were building a fake airbase in occupied France just across the English Channel. Fake buildings and fake airplanes, all made out of wood and quite realistic when viewed from above. They made fake wooden barracks, fake wooden fuel tanks, trucks and even fake wooden people.

The only thing real was the hidden ring of anti-aircraft guns and the wing of German fighters standing by nearby. They built the entire site in the dark and covered it up during the day, so as not to be discovered until they were ready.

The Brits found out about the project early on, but just stood by and let the Germans waste time and resources on their trap. When they were nearly done, the British sent one single bomber to the site and dropped a fake wooden bomb on it.

On July 10, 1940, sixty German aircraft screamed out of their new bases in occupied France. They had taken over the French air bases and built quite a few new ones, but no more wooded decoys.

They attacked shipping in the English Channel and conducted raids in the Dover area, testing the defensive capabilities of the RAF and probing for weaknesses to exploit. News of these raids quickly spread across England and the people were outraged at such bold attacks.

The Germans attacked northern England with 140 aircraft and sent 800 planes to southern England to conduct overwhelming raids on the RAF airbases.

After getting caught up on the news of the day, William made his way down to Ted's shack in which he lived and worked out of, just off the beach. He was carrying a bottle of Brandy, as it was his turn to buy.

"The ladies are up there glued to the radio, as usual," William said as he plopped down in his usual chair. Because Ted had no radio, he depended on William to bring the news as well as every other bottle of brandy, or scotch, or whatever was cheap that week.

"I don't think the bastards can cross over here," said a tipsy Ted. "What few boats make it past the RAF flying over the Channel and the mines on the beaches will have to climb over that bloody barbed wire while being shot at left and right."

"Serves the bastards right. I hope they try."

"As do I, bloody bastards."

"To the English Channel," said William as he held up his glass and clinked it with Ted's.

"To the Channel," Ted agreed. "And to the Royal Air Force."

"God save the King," came the reply with another clink.

As was so often the case, the two men found the bottom of that bottle and called it a night. The tall thin William stumbled his way upstairs and found Joyce already asleep, saving him from the usual lecture on spending too much time drinking with Ted.

Beginning the next day the RAF launched at least five major air battles with at least 974 attacks on the German marauders. This turned out to be a much more difficult task then the Germans expected, and were met with a greater resolve than they thought the British were capable of.

"They seem to have so many more planes," Lillian said, as she sat and shook her head just after Joyce clicked off the radio.

"More experienced pilots, as well, love," said William.

"Our lads won't let us down, mark my words," said Joyce.

In September the Luftwaffe stepped up its bombing campaign. A four hundred plane raid was launched at the London docks and airfields up and down the Themes River Valley. The Germans were shocked when fifty-three of them were shot down by anti-aircraft fire and British fighters.

On Sept 15th, a two-pronged attack was launched against the London docks involving some 1,300 bombers. There were so many bombers that they couldn't all be over the target area at the same time for fear of crashing into one another.

All day long the two sides battled each other all over southern England, many being chased out to sea by British Hurricanes as the horrified and helpless population could only watch.

The Germans lost another fifty-six planes that day while the RAF lost twenty-seven. The Luftwaffe of the Third Reich was still hopeful they were only seeing the last gasps of the Royal Air Force.

Near the end of September the Germans launched another eight hundred plane raid that met with similar losses. Along with numerous smaller and unsuccessful attacks, the German High Command became convinced that British air power had been underestimated and would not be so easily swept aside.

Since the Nazis came to power, Hitler finally found a line in the sand that he could not cross, at least not for now. With their elite but vastly outnumbered fleet of Hurricanes and Spitfires, and the brave overworked pilots that would often land to refuel and reload, then take off again, the RAF drew that line.

"Never in the field of human conflict was so much owed to so many, by so few," said Winston Churchill.

Lillian, Joyce and William were elated at the news as it reached them through their little radio in the kitchen.

"The bastards can't have our Island, and now they know it," said Joyce.

"They will leave us alone now," Lillian said, while William nodded his head and smiled. "The Prime Minister has shaken their resolve."

"Make no mistake," said Ted the next night with far less enthusiasm. "As long as those evil bastards are in power, we are all in grave danger. He wants all of Europe and he just may get it."

William could only nod his head and sip his drink while pondering the fate of a world ruled by Nazis.

Chapter Six

"Hey, Sleeping Beauty," Herby said while kicking Doug's bunk. "You're going to miss breakfast and we all know how bitchy you get when you're hungry."

"It's too damn early," he groaned. "And it's hard to be hungry when your face is the first thing I see."

"What the hell time is it?" asked Bob, trying to blink his eyes awake. "It feels like it's still about ten o'clock at night."

"You mean twenty-two hundred hours don't you, Bob?" John grinned. "It's 0430 right now. You're in the army now. There's no such thing as ten o'clock."

"I wish there was no such thing as 0430," said Doug.

"You big babies," said Herb. "I'm a morning guy and I'm used to getting up early. Rise and shine, ladies, we get to play with guns today."

"You're a morning guy because you have no life," chided Doug as he swung his legs off the bed. "What the hell do we get for breakfast here?"

"Oatmeal," said John. "A nice big bowl."

"Oh God," Doug said, as he bent over looking down at his feet while sitting on the edge of his bunk. "Oatmeal makes me gag and vomit. I'm in hell."

Herby laughed. "Oatmeal makes you gag? The movie star wants Eggs Benedict!"

"Just don't sit next to me," Bob smiled.

"If we don't get over there in a few minutes, we won't get anything," said John.

Fortunately for Doug, it was powdered eggs and biscuits for breakfast. The four of them were about thirty seconds late and wound up getting screamed at in front of everyone by the Sergeant, who was always trying to make an example of someone, so they were lucky to eat at all.

At dawn the newly named 386th AAA/AW Battalion was mustered up on the fairgrounds where it was announced that they would be broken up into four gun batteries and a headquarters battery.

"Each gun battery will consist of one hundred and sixty men, with eight of the 40mm Bofors and eight quad 50cal machine guns. You will now be assigned to Battery A, B, C or D and each battery will be taken to a range area for training."

The Battalion was divided into four batteries and because the four buddies were standing in muster together they all wound up in Battery C, and then were further divided to gun crews, and all went to Gun Six.

"Jesus Christ," said Bob, as he looked at the gun in awe. "That's the biggest friggin' gun I've ever seen."

"Look at those big ass bullets," said Herby, nodding at a stack of 40mm rounds each over a foot long and big around as a beer can.

"They call them shells, Herb, not bullets," said John. shaking his head.

"Dumb bastard," Doug whispered. "Glad you know so much about artillery, General."

"Go to hell, movie star," he shot back a little too loud.

"Do you ladies have something to share?" The big sergeant yelled in their faces as he pulled Doug and Herb out of line.

Sgt. Mike "Dutch" Van Holland was the crew chief on Gun Six. This was his gun and his crew and it was his job to keep them alive and make the enemy dead. Dutch was not going to let a couple of goof-offs set the pace on the first day of training, so Doug and Herby found out what it was like to run all the way down the range and all the way back, each carrying full ammo cans for the 50cal machine guns.

The first week of training they learned all about the guns. The 40mm Bofors is a magnificent weapon. The five thousand pound gun was trailer-mounted and pulled by a two and a half ton truck.

The tow bar doubled as a lever when the gun was off the truck and could be swung around into position while lifting the rear wheels off the ground. The rear wheels then swung out for stability as did two outriggers with crank handles that allowed the gun to be leveled.

A good gun crew could have the gun off the truck and set up ready to shoot in less than a minute. It took a tremendous amount of practice to get the choreography for this action and everything else about the gun.

It took two men to aim the gun. There was a seat on either side of the barrel with an aimer looking through his own sight. One was called the "Trainer," and the other was the "Layer."

They each had a crank handle in front of them and one would control the up and down movement of the gun while the other would control the left and right movement. They would each put their sights on the target and the barrel would be pointing to the right spot.

Standing behind the gun was a man with a mechanical computer, also known as a "Stiffkey stick." It was a pendulum-like device that he would hold up in the air and it would quickly calculate how far to lead the plane with the shot.

The idea was to aim the shell ahead of the aircraft so the shell and the aircraft would arrive at the same place at the same time. This was not a good thing for the pilot.

The gun was actually fired electrically, wired to a foot pedal to the side of the gun. The firer would step on the pedal as the shells got close to target and then hold it down once it was sighted in.

Holding that pedal down is what makes the 40mm the unique and very awesome weapon that it is. Holding it down made it a fully automatic weapon — a machine gun. To this day it was the largest machine gun ever built.

The Bofors could fire one hundred twenty rounds per minute, or two per second. That's two, two-pound projectiles per second up to twelve thousand feet in the air. The 386th had

32 of these fire-breathing dragons. They were indeed a force to be reckoned with.

The big guns also had a "baby brother," to protect their rear flank. The Bofors had a swing of 300 degrees, so there was a 60 degree blind spot that could not be defended. That's what the quad 50's were for.

The M-51 quad 50 machine gun was also trailer-mounted, and was made up of four 50cal machine guns mounted behind a thick steel plate with the barrels sticking through. This gun was sure to give a nasty little surprise to any aircraft that dared to try and sneak up on the Bofors.

Every man had to know every position on each gun, and had to practice those jobs endlessly. They each had to know the other men's jobs because the fact is that if one got killed, another had to take his place. A couple of men getting knocked off the gun could not render that gun ineffective on the battlefield.

Of course, some men were better at some jobs than at others, and the Sergeant was always keeping an eye out for talent.

The Quad 50's had their own shooters, and they had feeders to keep the string of ammo belts smooth so as not to jam. Each gun had men to make a "bucket brigade" type of line to pass ammo to the guns.

The big 40mm even had several men to constantly clear the area of empty shells as they fired because they were so big and accumulated so quickly.

But one of the most difficult jobs on the gun was being a loader. Two loaders stood up on the gun platform near the aimers. The big shells came on big and heavy four round clips that were pushed down into the gun from above.

Since the gun could shoot out this clip in two seconds there had to be a constant feed of uninterrupted ammo into the gun or it would run out and possibly miss the kill shot. The two would alternate feeding their clips in while being handed another in between. All this was being done while the gun was swinging about in a frenzied effort to site in its target.

This position had to be drilled and drilled and drilled and had to be the most precisely choreographed action on a successful gun crew. No matter how good the aimers and shooters were, they couldn't do much without bullets.

Nobody was better at that than Douglas Hanson. The movie star made it look easy as he spun with the gun and pushed down clip after clip, grinning like he was enjoying the ride. The only thing that ever slowed him down was when the other loader would slip up.

John became one of the aimers, and he was pretty good at it. As they trained he got very good and wound up as the number one "Layer" on the gun. He, of course, loved rubbing it in the other guy's faces that he was a better layer.

"Four out of five women would agree," he teased.

Bob was not as coordinated as Doug or John, and Herby was even lower than Bob on the graceful scale. Bob's job wound up as passing ammo to the 40's in the bucket brigade, and Herby was on the Quad 50 feeding ammo belts and trying hard to keep from pinching his finger.

He would come back to the barracks with little cuts and snags on his fingers, and once got his shirt caught on a belt, nearly ripping it from his body as it was sucked into the gun.

It was taking a while, and they were yelled at a lot by Dutch, but Gun Six was coming together and they were getting good, really good.

"God help the dirty bastards that come within sight of Gun Six," Dutch said proudly of his crew.

"I hate this part of the job," Bob complained as they cleaned and greased the gun.

Maintenance on the gun was a big part of the job and it was a dirty job after a day of practice. Other duties included carrying into the field truckloads of spare parts and grease, all the ammo, food and supplies needed to sustain them, including all the logistics that go along with it — a clear indication that this battalion would most likely see action.

"What kind of plane is that?" asked Herby, squinting his eyes at the horizon.

"P-38," said Bob glancing at it. "It's hard to tell because of the angle, but that's what it is."

"You sure?" asked John. "It doesn't look like a P-38. Looks way too small."

"Just watch," Bob replied confidently. "It will fly almost right past us. Wait about a minute, you'll see."

The four men stood there never taking their eyes off the plane as it got closer and closer. Bob sat there smugly knowing he was right.

"That's a damn P-38," said Herby. "What are you an eagle or something?"

"I told you. I should have bet you."

"Soldier," said Major Parker, after walking up behind them and hearing a little bit of what went on.

"Yes sir," Bob said as the four of them snapped to attention. Dutch started making his way towards them wondering what these misfits had gotten themselves into this time.

"How did you know, Private? How did you know that was a P-38?"

"I don't know, sir, I just did."

"How did you know the angle it was coming in on? Was that just a guess or could you really tell? You seemed pretty confident about it."

"I don't know how I can tell, sir, I just can."

Dutch saluted as he walked up. He nodded when the Major asked if this man was on his gun crew.

"If you don't mind, Sergeant, I'd like to borrow this man and see what kind of forward observer he would make. Have him report to the headquarters battalion at 0800," the Major said without waiting for an answer, and then walked away.

Major Parker was in the intelligence section of the battalion's headquarters battery. He was in charge of the men that plotted out the gun positions for maximum coverage and kept the communication up and running within the battalion.

The next day Bob was assessed for his ability to identify targets, and more importantly, to gauge their angle and speed.

"Congratulations, Private. You're going to radio school. When we are in situations that require forward observers, you will be one of them. Otherwise you will remain assigned to your gun."

"Radio school, sir?" Bob gulped.

"Of course, radio school. It wouldn't do much good having a forward observer if he can't report what he is observing, now would it?"

Bob walked back to his gun. *Crap, radio school. I'm probably the only guy in the army that's deaf in one ear and he picks me for radio school, for Christ's sake.*

"Radio operator," Herby laughed. "You're still gonna have to clean guns with the rest of us. What the hell they need a forward observer for? We observe them while we are shooting them down."

"Are you forgetting how bad you suck at shooting anything," Bob asked, momentarily shutting Herby up.

"Hey Bob," said John. "If they get close enough you can throw your radio at them."

"Don't listen to them, Bob," said Doug, and he put his arm over his shoulder. "Radio operators have dangerous jobs. You can fall while running with it and put your eye out."

"Very funny, very funny. You guys are just jealous."

Bob was putting on a happy face but inside he was almost in a panic. He had a secret that he kept from everyone, even these guys, and now he feared it would be exposed and he would be booted out.

Bob showed up the next morning as ordered for two weeks of radio school. Just like working on the gun crew, he had to know everything about the radios including field repairs, running cables, switchboard operation and even Morse code.

The radios were connected to each other with cables that were run between the various outposts and the switchboards. The radios themselves were like telephones that were held and connected to a box, which was connected to the cable. The

71

cables came on large spools and were often strung over long distances, so everything was basically hardwired together.

Ironically, Bob found that he had an advantage being deaf in one ear because the men with two good ears had to deal with ambient sound drowning out the communication. They often had to plug their other ear or hold one hand over that side if they were in a noisy environment.

"Were you a good boy in school today?" Herby would tease.

"Be nice," said John. "Bob's had a hard day."

The guys had been drilling hard on the art of shooting down planes and taking apart guns, so they picked on Bob for sitting in a nice clean room playing with radios.

"You guys keep up the good work," Bob grinned. "Maybe I'll even put in a good word about you to my friend the Major."

Doug said, "Don't do that Bob, or he will have us doing some weenie job like yours." All the guys burst out laughing.

"Morse code," Bob said. "Damn Morse code is the one thing I just can't seem to get. The one damn thing I will probably never have to use and it's what's holding me back. If I don't learn it, I'm back here passing bullets to you mutts."

"Well let me tell you, Bob," grinned Doug. "We feel so sorry for you up there in that awful, awful classroom working so, so hard to tackle those mean old dots and dashes."

'I'm with you, movie star," said Herby. "Poor guy must be working his little index finger to the bone."

After putting in his two weeks, Bob graduated radio school with his switchboard operator's certification and he rejoined the men of Battery "C", Gun Six.

Dutch made sure he was not falling behind on his training so he was worked extra hard each day, much to everyone's delight but his own.

"Damn, I'm sore," Bob complained the third morning back, as they made their way to breakfast.

"That's because you were getting soft up there in that little schoolhouse, you weenie," said Doug.

"I'm just glad you are so slow loading that gun that I don't have to work near as hard as the guys on Gun Two. Now that guy can load."

That stopped Doug in his tracks and his face flushed red and his nostrils actually flared. Doug was the undisputed champion loader of the Battalion, but there was a guy on Gun Two that was a close second. The movie star was competitive, that's for sure.

"That's not even funny, Bob," he said, shaking his finger at him. "I can kick his ass any day of the week and you know it."

The four of them stood there silently for a few moments outside the mess hall surprised at the normally good-natured Doug's outburst. Clearly Bob touched a nerve.

"See," said Herby. "I told you he is bitchy before breakfast."

The guys all chuckled and Doug snapped right back into being Doug.

"Come on, movie star," said Bob, and he put his arm on his shoulder. "I'll buy you breakfast."

Herby went in the front door first and then stopped and immediately came out laughing hysterically.

"Guess what's for breakfast! Just guess," he laughed.

"Oh no, don't tell me," said Doug.

"That's right, movie star. Oatmeal. Goddamn oatmeal. You poor dumb bastard."

Training was coming to an end and the Battalion received the deployment orders that would take them to England. Everyone got a one-week pass to say their goodbyes.

Bob spent his week at home with Anne and Archie and enjoyed sleeping in his own bed for the short stay, even though there were times he hated it growing up, and even after growing up.

He spent a little time hitting a couple of neighborhood bars that he frequented and got some free beers because he was in uniform and damn proud. He visited his sort of

73

girlfriend and she cried and promised to wait for him, but he knew she wouldn't, and she knew it, too.

Most of his friends had already gone over and some would never come back, so the neighborhood was a little quiet. He had gotten a late start because of his ear but late was better than never.

Pop liked his girl because her father was old school like him. He wanted grandsons to carry on his name and Bob was his only chance, and he just didn't trust him without a strong woman.

"Stay away from those women over there," he told Bob as they sat at the table. "They will be lined up like vultures looking for a meal ticket."

"Ok, Pop, I will."

"And stay out of the bars. Nothing good can come out of you going to those bars."

"I will, Pop."

"Write your mother."

"I will, Pop, I promise."

With that Archie went back to his paper. He probably read it already but it made him look busy so he used it to tell people he was done talking. He didn't say goodbye, he wouldn't say goodbye.

Since Archie came from generations of fisherman, saying goodbye to a fisherman was something you didn't do. It was bad luck, and when you were a fisherman from Twillingate Newfoundland, you needed all the luck you could get.

There are plenty of tombstones in the graveyards with no bones beneath them and the words "Lost at Sea" chiseled into them. If you wanted to see your loved one again then you never said goodbye. You never, ever said goodbye.

You could say, "Good fishing," or you could say, "Good luck." You could say, "Calm waters," or you could say, "Watch your top knot," a reference to the knotted ball on top of the French sailors' caps to keep from banging their heads in tight quarters. But you could never say goodbye, so he didn't.

74

Mom was a different story and was not nearly as disciplined as Pop. She said goodbye in a dozen different ways, hung onto him and begged him not to leave, tried to say goodbye another dozen ways until finally collapsing at his feet. Mom could be quite dramatic.

After finally breaking away, he daydreamed about his past and his future while walking to the train station. He glanced up and down the streets and avenues of his beloved Brooklyn for what he knew would be the last for a long time.

He was leaving his family and his friends, his Dodgers and his sort of girlfriend who wouldn't wait for him. He felt sorry for the poor bastard who took the crappy job he left, and even sorrier for whoever was working for his dad at the moment.

His heart started to flutter a little as a wave of anticipation went through him. He was on his way back to his Battalion, back to his gun, back to his buddies.

What was it that Pop said? Stay out of the bars? Somehow I have a feeling I'm going to break that promise.

He took the train and then the bus and finally rolled through the gates of Camp Edwards with two hours to spare. Doug came in an hour later and Herb and John were already there.

Herby smuggled in a fifth of scotch even though Dutch would have him for lunch if he would have been caught with it. The other three helped him drink it, so they were just as guilty. They buried the bottle when they were done.

"We should put a note in there," said Doug. "In case someone digs it up in a hundred years."

"Just don't put my name on that note," said John. "In case someone digs it up in a hundred hours."

"Good point. What did you do this past week, Bob?"

"Well, I hit a few bars and I kissed my girl. Hugged my mom and listened to my dad lecture me about staying out of the pubs in England. That's about it."

"How about you, movie star?"

"Well, I had to go on three different dates to kiss my girls goodbye. I broke a lot of hearts this week, guys, and I'm feeling really bad. Give me another scotch will you, Herb?"

"What a line of horseshit that is," said Bob. "Probably went to church with his mommy."

"Actually I did that, too. What about you, John?"

"I spent most of the week with my girl," he smiled and stared off. "I'm going to come back and marry her. She's been my girlfriend since we were fifteen."

"Well ain't that the sweetest thing you've ever heard?" said Herby sarcastically. "You really think she's going to wait for you?"

"I know she will."

"How about you, Bob? That girl going to wait for you?"

"No Herby, she won't, but that's ok."

"I'm not even going to ask you, Doug. You'll lie anyway."

"How about you, Herb? Have you been saying goodbye to some pretty little Jewish girl from the Bronx all week?"

"I'm actually in between girlfriends. I'm available to all the little English and French girls over there."

"Haven't they been through enough with the war and all?" asked Bob. "They're going to have to contend with you, too?"

"God Bless New York," John said holding up his tin cup of scotch.

"And God help those Nazi bastards," grinned Herby.

"Amen," they all agreed as they did lights out for the last time in Camp Edwards.

Chapter Seven

"We need the Americans," Ted said as he swigged. "I don't think we can hold out without them."

"They won't help us. They don't want to get involved in our war, and I don't blame them. But you are right, a few million Americans would make him crap his bloody lederhosen," and they both laughed.

Ted was right. Even with the British newly invented radar system and their magnificent fighters along with thousands of anti-aircraft guns, barrage balloons and giant spotlights, the Germans waged a war of terror from the air on the British people.

The black bombers would come at night and bomb the cities and factories. They put screamers on the bombs so they would shriek all the way down to terrify the public.

By day they would send the V-1 rockets, which were basically bombs with wings that flew like a plane. It was also a terror weapon because it was inaccurate. They would put a measured amount of fuel in it and when it ran out of gas, it fell.

German spies would report back the location of the impact so the fuel amount could be adjusted. This made them only slightly more accurate. The British pilots would fly high over the channel and watch for them.

If one was spotted, the plane would dive down on the much faster rocket hoping to catch it, and tipping its wing with their own, it would flip it over to crash it into the sea. A dangerous maneuver that the pilots only got one shot at.

Lillian's wages were meager to begin with, and she was worked like a dog. After they deducted her room and board and clothing and everything else they could, she would barely have anything left. Sometimes she even owed them money.

But she did have her Sundays, her wonderful Sundays off to do what she wished. It was the one thing that made the job worthwhile. She loved getting up early and staying up late to get the very most of her wonderful free day.

Sometimes William would drive her into town, but not often — he would be in trouble if he got caught doing so. She would usually just get up early, pack a lunch, and walk down the road into Bath. Sometimes she went to the plaza and sat there eating her lunch, and sometimes she would sip tea at a little café and watch people go by.

She started seeing some of the women of the Royal Air Force, WAF's they called them. All dressed up in their uniforms with the official hats and gold RAF pins on them. She was fascinated.

A group of them passed by her. *I wonder what they do. I wonder how I could be like them.*

Sometimes they would catch her looking at them and they would smile and she would turn away embarrassed. Often the men would flirt and tease her, which mortified the young girl. William and Ted were just about the only men she had ever known, but that was different.

One morning there was a knock at the door and Lillian opened it to find an unexpected work crew.

"Metal, love," the dirty and disheveled man said, tipping his hat. "Everything that's not nailed down, orders from the King, love."

"And most of what is," the other man said and they laughed, clearly a running joke they had developed.

And with that they proceeded to rip the Commander's house apart. They took the fence out and the light posts and the mailbox. They ripped the gutters off the house and the shelves out of the garage and they even took half the pots and pans, which crushed Joyce.

"At least they left the car," said William. "But the ration of gas is so meager that they may as well have taken it. Even the Commander with all his bloody money can't get more gas rations."

The time was shifted forward ahead two hours for more evening daylight. It at least gave you the illusion of a longer day and shorter night with more time to hide the lights from the bombers.

The church bells in the entire country were ordered silent. They were now an early warning system. If the Germans tried to invade, the bells would ring all over England to warn people to take up their arms.

All over the country the civilians were mobilized in the "Home Guard." They vowed to fight to the death to protect their island, young and old, even William and Ted. William had an old shotgun and Ted had a 50 year-old rifle, and an ax he chopped wood with.

William and Ted were no real threat to anyone, but a few million William and Teds might make you stop and think.

There were also tens of thousands of soldiers that had escaped the Nazi invasions of their own countries and made it to England to fight with the British against their sworn enemy.

Margaret came to visit her one Sunday while she was near Bristol, and took Lillian to lunch in one of the nice cafés on the Plaza.

"Such a lovely place," she said. "I see why you like it so."

"It is lovely, Aunt Margaret, and so very different than the convent," said Lillian. "But I have noticed many more soldiers passing through and many more people in uniform visiting the zoo and here in the plaza, even women."

"It's like that everywhere, my dear. Soldiers are pouring in from all over the commonwealth. Places like Australia, Canada, and even countries like India are doing what they can to help."

"Will we win, Margaret?"

Margaret shifted in her chair a little and glanced around the small café. The smell of baked bread and the sips of red wine made her think of France, poor France.

"We may not win child, but we won't lose. Do you understand what I mean? We won't let them take our Island. You must believe that, everyone must."

A chill went through her. "I understand, and I will always believe. I will never surrender, just like the Prime Minister."

"You seem to forget that I know you and I know that you are not capable of surrendering."

Lillian smiled and looked down shyly at the table.

"We found out that your father had two sisters who married well, and were living a comfortable life in London."

Lillian's head snapped back up and her eyes opened wide.

"Their names were Lillian and Rose. Their maiden names were, of course, Bradley. Your mother named you after them in the hopes of getting in their good graces, but it seems not to have worked. Interestingly enough, you are the only sibling in your family with a middle name. I assume that is why."

"And what of them, Margaret?" Lillian asked excitedly. "Have you found them? Do they know anything?"

"I'm sorry, child, there is no good way to tell you this, so I will just tell you. Along with Rose's son, Roger, they were killed in a bombing in London."

Lillian just sat there staring at her, blinking her eyes in shock.

"Oh my God, Oh my God," Lillian said, as she started to feel a panic rising inside of her.

"Did you know them?"

"I never heard of them. I really didn't know Jake either but at least I knew he existed. This is too much, Margaret. I just want my sisters."

Margaret came around the table and hugged her. "Let's go for a walk and you can show me what is left of the Roman Empire here."

Conversation was awkward after that until Lillian said, "I'm sorry for getting upset, Aunt Margaret. You have done so much for me."

"I understand, dear Lillian. I only hope that the next time we speak I will have good news. It has, unfortunately, been difficult to come by."

"It could be worse, Margaret. We could be Romans," Lillian said as they stood in the middle of the ruins, making both of them laugh.

When Margaret left, Lillian, feeling a little numb, went back to the house on the hill and back to work the next day for another week, and a promise of a nice Sunday at the end of it.

This war had stolen three more people from her, two aunts and a cousin to add to her brother. *No more, God. Please, no more.*

On August 24, 1940, German bombers once again launched attacks on strategic targets outside London, but drifted off course and dropped their bombs on the center of the city in populated areas, killing civilians.

Winston Churchill believed the attack was deliberate and ordered that Berlin be bombed the following evening. Over the next few nights Berlin was bombed several more times, killing German civilians. The "Blitz" was on.

Beginning on Sept 7, 1940, the Germans bombed London for 57 consecutive nights, killing over 15,000 British civilians. The people of London would retreat to their shelters and surface again afterwards. They wanted the Germans to see that they would not be terrorized. They wanted life to go on as normally as possible so as not to give them satisfaction, or to show weakness.

King George VI refused to move out of Buckingham Palace though it was bombed several times. He walked among the people everyday with Queen Elizabeth at his side, often wearing a lovely gown, and reassuring them. The people loved him.

Every week the BBC would broadcast the national anthems of each and every occupied nation across the English Channel to honor them, and also send a message to those occupied countries that they were not alone, England was with them. Many patriotic men from those countries made their way to England to stay in the fight.

Bruce Belford was a BBC broadcaster that would start his show with his trademark, "Good evening." Lillian and Joyce never missed his show and the Grishams rarely did either.

As they listened on Oct 15, 1940 there was a loud "boom" followed by silence. Lillian and Joyce looked at each other aghast as nothing but static came through the airwave.

A few moments later he came back on the air and picked up right where he left off as though nothing had ever happened. Joyce and Lillian were relieved and sat back once again enjoying the show and their tea.

Mr. Belford was in fact standing in the rubble of Broadcast House in downtown London because the building was nearly destroyed by a 500-pound bomb in the middle of his show.

It took him a few moments to stand back up and get situated so he could resume with the news of the day. Seven people were killed by the bomb but the show went on so the Germans wouldn't get the satisfaction of silencing him unless they dropped one right on his head.

"Why must we cover all the windows?" she asked Joyce while helping her hang the heavy blackout curtains over every opening in the house.

"The bastards use the lights at night to find us, that's why, love."

"It's torturous to be trapped behind these when I know the lovely green hills are out there."

William strolled up behind them and said, "Every light, every window, every streetlight, every car and even cigarettes can't be lit outside, so we don't give them landmarks to navigate by."

"I wondered if you were about," Joyce said sharply. "Bring your long arms over here and help with these curtains."

Lillian laughed as Joyce scolded William at every move no matter how hard he tried. There would be no sneaking off to Ted's shack tonight.

"They drop incendiary bombs first," William continued as he worked. "They light the bloody cities afire so the next wave can better see what to bomb. Then they go for the water works so they can't put the fires out — bloody nightmare."

"It must be awful in London," Lillian said, shaking her head. "Just awful."

King George VI addressed his nation during the customary Christmas broadcast, overcoming his stutter to deliver this important message: "A new year is at hand. We cannot tell what it will bring. If it brings peace, how happy we shall be. If it brings us continued struggle, we shall remain undaunted."

In London, a fish and chips shop was hit by a bomb overnight and half destroyed. Within a day the stoves and tables were stood back up, the rubble cleared away, and they were back selling fish out of the bombed out storefront.

A makeshift sign hanging out front said, "Because of Hitler, Yer fish will be lit'ler." It seemed nothing could break the British spirit, but on May 24, 1941, the most devastating blow to date came close.

The HMS Hood was the pride of the Royal Navy, and the pride of the people of England, as well. She was a beautiful battleship and she was the very symbol of Great Britain's power and grace on the oceans and seas of the world.

The Hood was fast for a battleship, having sacrificed some of her armor for speed. She was ordered to shadow the new German Battleship Bismarck as it left for its maiden voyage after lingering in the fjords of Norway.

One lucky hit from the German ship exploded the Hood and sank her in moments, leaving 1,415 Royal Navy Sailors dead with only three survivors.

On Churchill's command, every available resource was thrown at the Bismarck and she was soon sunk in retaliation, but the people of Great Britain wept for the mighty Hood, and the brave souls lost with her.

Lillian cried for them. All of England cried for them.

As the bombing continued, and the German submarines tried their best to deny England the supplies she needed. Everything was rationed. Not just food and gas, but clothing, coal, building materials and every other essential. Even toilet paper.

Joyce got very good at making meals for them with very little and she taught Lillian many of her tricks.

"Mrs. Grisham's not used to eating like paupers but there's not very much she can bloody do about it, is there?" she laughed.

"I eat better now than I ever have in my life, so I don't feel much sorrow for them, love," said Lillian, as she smelled the pot of potato and fish soup.

"Bread and cheese for breakfast! William traded some coal for it," said Joyce. "He comes in handy now and then," she said, making Lillian laugh.

"They always manage to come up with some bloody whiskey," she continued. "I think he and Ted would just stay bleeding drunk all day if they could, the no good bastards."

"They work hard, Joyce, you know that," Lillian chided her. "Besides, you love him."

Joyce looked up from her chopping and smiled. "I do dammit, I bloody do."

Lillian smiled and stirred the big pot.

"But they are still a couple of no good bastards," Joyce said, causing Lillian to burst out laughing.

Like the rest of the world, they were astonished to hear about the attack on Pearl Harbor.

"Where the bloody hell is Pearl Harbor?" Ted asked, getting a dirty look from Joyce.

"Excuse me language, mum," he said. "Where is Pearl Harbor? I never heard of it."

"The American President sounded ruddy ticked off tonight, he did," said William.

"I like him," said Lillian. "He reminds me of our Mr. Churchill, don't you think?"

"Roosevelt will never be as good as the Prime Minister. I'd follow him right off the bloody white cliffs of Dover, if he asked," said Ted. "I pray the Americans have the stomach for this war he just declared on the Japanese. Sneaky little bastards, aren't they?"

They all agreed. There was much evil in the world, far too much.

A few nights later, William sat with Ted in his shack and shared a bottle and the latest news.

"Why did he do that?" Ted asked, confused.

"I suppose he wants to be on their side," William pondered.

"By declaring war on America? Hitler must be daft."

"Well, Roosevelt declared war right back. In for a penny, in for a pound, I suppose."

Ted sat back and thought about that for a while. "Well, I suppose we are all in it together now."

"Well then, to the Americans!" William toasted and they both took a swig.

"To the Commonwealth!" said Ted, and the glasses clinked again.

After topping off their glasses they looked at each other and smiled and said almost in unison. "God save the King!"

Few things changed over the next few months in Bath and at the house on the cliff. There was less fish in the soup and less gas in the car. Spirits were becoming more difficult to find, so that made Ted and William a bit cranky.

The Commander was working a lot but still never saying a word to any of the domestics. The kids were growing and Mrs. Grisham was still barking orders at Lillian and Joyce no matter how hard they worked.

"She would have made a good Nazi," Joyce whispered, making Lillian laugh.

But she still had her precious Sundays and she intended to make the most out of each and every one of them. On this particular Sunday she decided to go to the zoo.

Her day was all planned out. She would walk into town and have a cup of tea on the square (about the only thing she could afford — no mere war could ever keep the English from their tea), then she would eat her small lunch that Joyce packed for her on the plaza, and then she was to go and spend the afternoon at the zoo. She hadn't been in some time and she was anxious to see if there were any new animals, and if the ones that were there before were still there.

While it was a chilly April morning, the sun was coming out and the promise of a pretty Sunday afternoon was nice. It was always disappointing when the weather was bad on her only free day.

She walked the zoo and saw many of her four legged friends there. She loved the elephants and wondered how they could feed them when they ate so much but there was so little to be had, but she was glad they managed. She would watch them for a long time and she was fascinated at how close they were.

They are a family. They love each other.

She had these thoughts not out of feeling sorry for herself for her own loss, but out of a great joy for them. A joy from being able to witness true and innocent love that these creatures possessed.

The world needs more elephants. She smiled to herself.

She walked along and made it a point to visit every animal in the zoo, even the ones that smelled really bad.

While she loved watching the animals, she also loved watching the people who watched the animals. There were people with children, and old couples leaning against each other as they looked over a railing and she wondered what they were saying.

There were always plenty of handsome young soldiers with pretty young girls on their arms, and she wondered if they were falling in love.

Then passing right in front of her came four WAF's in uniform walking side by side, chatting and laughing and seeming to not have a care in the world. She was so envious, but too young to join them. And besides, it would mean leaving Joyce and her other adopted family.

"You're one of us now," she remembered William saying to her. Those words meant so much to her, then and now. No, she couldn't possibly leave them behind. She loved them. *They are my elephants.* She almost giggled out loud.

Right at that moment in the middle of her daydream, the air raid siren started to blare. It went from a low moan, and in the short time it took to get to its highest pitch people were scrambling everywhere to find cover.

The unthinkable was happening — the Germans were bombing Bath and Bristol. It was April 27, 1942, and the Germans were retaliating for a bombing in Lubeck, Germany the previous month, a target of no real strategic value.

Now eighty German bombers were homing in on the helpless and undefended cities. Lillian woke from her dream to a nightmare as the bombers terrified her. The screaming bombs were hellish and evil.

Lillian followed the crowd that seemed to know where they were going. In this section of the zoo, the shelter was the gorilla cage. The cage was an inside/outside setup with a big steel door separating the two.

The zookeepers could close the door and clean the side that he was not in, often times giving him a treat to lure him where they wanted. Since the bombing campaign began, the gorilla was kept outside whenever the zoo was open so his enclosure could be used.

The room quickly filled with people and Lillian was pinned against the back wall by the crowd. She could feel herself getting claustrophobic and starting to hyperventilate.

Just calm down. She closed her eyes tight and repeated to herself. She could feel the strangers pressed up against her as they shuffled around, while still smelling the big animal in the dark, dank cage. *Relax, it won't be long.*

But it was long, seeming like forever. The siren wailed on and on and she could hear a group of planes as they buzzed quickly by right overhead shaking the ground as they went.

She couldn't tell if they were German bombers or British Hurricanes chasing after them.

Maybe they have passed. She could only hope. Just then another group of low flying planes went over, shaking the ground as they pushed their powerful engines to the limit. Whoever it was, they were flying low and going fast, their presence triggering the siren to go on and on. Trickles of nervous sweat ran down her neck.

The ground thumped under her feet as the bombs hit in nearby Bristol and Bath. Sometimes the crowded room would startle collectively when the thumps grew too close for comfort.

Suddenly she became aware of another feeling on her neck, a feeling of hot breath, hot bad breath. She strained herself to get turned around and found herself at eye level with the small barred window in the door that separated the two spaces.

With his face right up to the other side of that barred window, stood the gorilla, and he was not happy. She tried to pull away but there was nowhere to go. He growled at her and bared his teeth, but when he tried to work his fingers in between the bars only inches from her face, she screamed.

Other people nearby turned to see what was happening and seeing the ape, tried to pull away, too. Lillian screamed again and the startled gorilla backed off but never took his eyes off her, and hers were frozen on him.

He picked up an old spare tire and held it front of him, twisting it like it was a child's toy, stopping only to pound his chest and stomp his feet. Then he picked it up again and twisted it into a figure eight, never looking away, and seemingly with no effort at all.

Finally the sirens stopped and people started to push their way out of the shelter. One of the zookeepers was standing by the exit and, seeing Lillian, he asked, "Are you alright, love? You're white as a bloody ghost. Was that you doing the screaming?"

"Yes," she answered, still shaking. She relayed the story of her encounter with his gorilla.

He laughed. "Don't worry, miss. Harry is just a big teddy bear, he is. He wouldn't hurt you."

"He looked at me and twisted that tire as though he wanted to do that to me," she said.

"He was just showing off, miss. He always does for the pretty ones," he said and winked.

"Great," she said. "I made a new friend. I need to run, I'm late. Bloody Germans."

"Ta, love," he laughed. "Come back and see us. Harry would like that."

Houses and buildings were afire everywhere and the ruins were even more ruined. She wound her way past the damaged plaza and as the sky darkened, she made her way to the road leading up the hill.

She was already an hour late, and she knew that as fast as she could walk, she would still have another hour to get there, and the pitch-black road was no help, though she could still see the fires burning in Bath.

The house was blacked out with not a crack of light anywhere; they had done a good job. She went around to the kitchen door and tapped gently, but there was no answer. She had tried the door and it was locked so she tapped again, waited, and tapped once more.

How could Joyce leave me out here like this? Can this day get any worse?

Out of desperation she went around to the big oak front door and looked at it as that familiar feeling of panic started to build. She decided to go around to the back and try the kitchen door again, her fear growing at the thought of getting caught breaking a rule that she was told never to break.

"Don't be late, and especially don't come back after dark." It was a rule told to her by Mrs. Grisham herself in the same tone that the nuns would use. She was late, she couldn't get in, and she was terrified.

She had no choice, she had to get in. It was possible to avoid this if the right person opened the door and let her in, but if she were discovered outside in the morning then there would be no doubt.

The big door seemed to loom over her and she once again felt like she was standing in front of the Convent of Saint John, a feeling she never had about this lovely place before.

"Please be Joyce, please be Joyce," she whispered under her breath and tapped. Nothing happened.

"Please Joyce, let me in, love," she said a little louder but still to herself. She tapped and still nothing happened, only silence and dark.

"Well, in for a penny, in for a pound," she said aloud trying to convince herself she was doing the right thing. She knocked firmly on the door, waited, and this time she could hear shuffling inside.

She braced herself for trouble and held out hope that her friend the cook was coming to rescue her, but she would never have imagined what happened next.

The door swung open wide and out stepped the Commander himself. With no expression on his face at all, and not a word from his mouth, he reached out and sharply slapped Lillian across the face, then slammed the door in it.

It so shocked her that she fell to her knees holding her stinging face and cowered, waiting for the next blow, even though he was gone. It was an automatic reaction she had since her convent days.

She sat there and whimpered and cried for a few minutes when the door quietly opened and Joyce appeared and pulled her to her feet and pulled her inside.

"I'm so sorry, love," she said. "Mrs. Grisham was watching for you, she always does. When she saw you were late she ordered all the doors locked and made us go upstairs."

"I wondered where you were. I knew you wouldn't leave me."

"The bloody witch has been listening for you, delighted to catch you. She's so bloody proud of herself."

"So it was her?"

"The Commander could give a bloody damn, so I'm sure she put him up to it. She's been sitting up watching for you. We couldn't get around her to let you in."

"So it was a trap," Lillian said, with anger starting to build in her voice.

"It would seem so, love."

Lillian was enraged, the rest of her face beginning to turn as red as the handprint across it. "Who the hell does she think she is? Who the hell does he think he is, the bastard?"

"Calm down now, love," said Joyce. "Let me get you some tea."

"Bugger the bloody tea, Joyce. I'm going to bed."

The next morning Lillian woke up and got the kids ready, making sure they ate breakfast, and sent them off for their studies. Then she went upstairs and packed her one suitcase, and got ready to leave.

Joyce cried and hugged her and begged her to stay, but in the end, she understood. She went out to Ted's shack and gave him a hug and a kiss on his cheek and was surprised to see him on the verge of tears.

She planned on walking into Bristol but William insisted on driving her. As he put her one bag in the car he grinned, "The Commander is in his study, do you want to go in and say goodbye?"

She looked back at the house for a few moments and then turned back to William and said, "The Commander can bloody well go to hell."

They were still laughing when William dropped her off. "We will never forget you, sweet Lillian," William said, holding back tears, as she gave him a hug.

"Thank you for everything, dear William."

Just before he drove away he abruptly stopped the car and yelled out to Lillian. "Remember to close the window when they blow the whistle, love!"

She laughed and waved and then, lying about her age, she joined the Royal Air Force.

Chapter Eight

That morning the guns were prepared and hooked to the trucks. The four gun batteries were lined up in columns and the headquarters battery was formed out in front, led by Colonel Gibb's jeep.

The men climbed into their trucks that had been divided into gun crews and pulled their own guns behind them. As they pulled into formation it became the first moment that the entire battalion was together in one place, and it was an impressive sight.

One by one the trucks pulled out from the gates of Camp Edwards and started on their way to New York, where they would be shipped overseas.

"Well, here we go boys," Doug said with his trademark grin.

"Skywatchers," said John.

"What was that?" Bob asked, straining to hear in the back of the noisy truck.

"Skywatchers. That's what the Colonel named us. The Skywatchers."

"Skywatchers," said Herby, nodding his head. "I like it."

"Me, too," said Bob.

"Well, I guess you would, Bob, now that I think about it," said Herb, smiling. "You're the only one here that actually watches the sky. They should call the rest of us the Plane Shooter Downers."

"Herby," said Bob. "The safest place to be when you are on the gun is the place you are aiming at."

"Can you pick up any Tommy Dorsey on that radio of yours, Bob?" Doug asked. "I'd settle for a little Glenn Miller."

"Yankee games," said Herb, to no one's surprise. "What good is it if you can't?"

"Hey look, dames," said Doug. As they were winding their way through the streets of New York on the way to the docks, people stopped and waved, as they always did to the soldiers who were shipping out. Most of them were women because most of the men were gone.

Doug pulled off his helmet and started waving back with a big smile, blowing kisses to the pretty ones.

"Hansen," snapped Dutch. "Put that helmet back on and get your stupid head back in my truck."

"But, Sarge!"

"Now, Hansen. Unless you want me to throw your ass of the back of this truck and watch you get run over by the next one. You won't be so pretty then."

Herby laughed. "Friggin' movie star."

"I like the part about the stupid head," Bob chuckled.

"Everybody shut the hell up," said Dutch. "That's where we are going, over there."

The men turned their attention to the direction the Sergeant was looking. Between the buildings and almost to the horizon they could catch glimpses of her. Glimpses of her were all they needed to feel awestruck. It was Feb 2, 1944, and they were about to meet the Queen. The Queen Mary.

As the column pulled in they were joined by many other columns of men and equipment lining up to board, but they seemed like ants alongside the great lady.

All the luxuries had been stripped out, such as artwork, expensive furnishings, and even carpet, all replaced with bunks, mattresses, and pads. Her stacks and her sides were painted grey so she could disappear in the mist as well as any gigantic ship could do. And she was gigantic. By far the biggest ship any of them had ever seen or could have imagined could float, let alone move.

"Jesus," said John, while the other guys were just dumbstruck.

"Get your gear ready, you idiots," said Dutch. "Do you think it's going to wait for you?"

The 386th were among 18,000 American soldiers who were making this crossing. There were also 200 WAF's as part of the crew to help them and find places to jam them in.

"We were just assigned our first official duty," said Lt. Bionde, as he walked among the gun crews. "We're going to protect the Queen."

"Make Gun Six ready as soon as she hits the deck," Dutch ordered as they watched the crane lifting the Bofors into the air.

Twenty-four of the thirty-two guns were to be strapped down to the deck to fend off any enemy planes that may attack her. It was an unlikely scenario because the German planes did not have the reach from any of their bases, but one just never knew.

The biggest threat the Queen faced were the U-Boats. The German submarines were without mercy and would love nothing more than to put the ship and her precious cargo on the bottom of the Atlantic Ocean.

The best defense the giant ship had against this threat was her speed. At an astonishing 30 knots, she could outrun anything the Germans had, especially the very slow U-Boats that operated on batteries when submerged.

To avoid any subs that may be lying in wait for her, she would zigzag across the ocean and take a different route every time, and still make it to Scotland in 17 days or less.

American destroyers would shadow her on the way across, and when the Queen was close enough, British Spitfires would fly overhead. The relief the men would feel seeing those friendly fighters must have been like ancient mariners seeing a seagull after months at sea.

"The Colonel wants to put on a show," said Lt. Bionde to the eight gun crews strapped down to the stern of the ship. "We're going to make some noise."

Gun Six was among the guns chosen, and just like in training, every man was going to get to do every job. The guns were swung out so they pointed away, and hundreds and hundreds of men lined up to watch them fire.

Looking down from the upper deck were a number of high ranking officers, including Colonel Gibbs, with a wide smile on his face and a cigar in his mouth, without his trademark cavalry hat but donning his helmet.

"Get ready, boys," said Dutch as he looked to his right at Sergeant Waltrip, who was grinning back at him from Gun Two.

The order was that each gun would fire five, four round clips in a sweeping pattern, and then rotate each man's position on the gun, fire five more, and continue until all men did all jobs. If done properly, and all the guns in sync, it was like a ballet, and they had practiced this maneuver until they would dream about it.

"The Colonel is watching, boys. Let's get it right," Lt. Bionde shouted out to the ranks as the clock hit 0900. "Fire!"

The aft deck of the Queen exploded in smoke and fire and deafening blasts, making soldiers nearby jump at the unexpected power of the guns. Flames stabbed out of the guns as the smoke curled up into a whirl, left behind by the speeding ship while more and more shot their way through the smoky trail.

The acrid smell of gunpowder filled the deck even as the wind tried to leave it behind. Then in unison, with their proud Colonel looking down at them, every man jumped from his position and rotated to the next as his place was taken in return.

At almost the same moment, with less than three seconds of pause, all six guns started to blast away again. This continued until all eight men on all six guns filled every position in a flawless display. In under a minute after the shooting stopped, the gun crews had removed the now glowing red-hot barrels from the guns and, while throwing them overboard, hissing with steam as they hit the water and then disappeared, replaced them.

The new barrels were affixed as the guns fell silent and the smoke drifted off. The men leapt down from their guns and mustered up with a salute to the officers on the upper deck until the grinning Colonel saluted and dismissed them back under control of their sergeants.

"Nice work, Colonel," said the General standing beside him. "Very nice."

"Thank you, sir," said Colonel Gibbs as the General walked away. Then, smiling as he looked over the rail at his men remounting the guns, he put the cigar back in his mouth and followed him.

"Good job, guys," Bionde was saying as he walked along the rear deck past all six guns.

"You fellas made me look good today," said Dutch. "Way to go, gentlemen, way to go."

"My God," said the elated Herby who rarely got to actually fire the big gun. "That was almost as good as sex!"

"Then I'd hate to see your girlfriend," said Bob.

"Hey, Bob," said John. "Herby hit something this time."

"We finally found a target big enough for Herb to hit," said Doug. "The damn Atlantic ocean."

"Good job, Herb."

"Way to go, Herb."

"Proud of you, Herby."

"Shut up you assholes," Herby said back as they laughed.

Suddenly Dutch yelled out with a booming voice, "Incoming!"

They all scrambled into position and darted their eyes all around the sky seeking the target as the gun spun back and forth and up and down. Doug fumbled with the first clip that was passed up to him and Herb dropped his helmet.

"Just when I start to think you idiots are actually getting somewhere, I look over and catch you standing on your own dicks," said Dutch with his hands on his hips.

It took a few seconds for it to register. This was not a real attack, but their hearts were pounding and hands were shaking and even Doug, the best in the battalion, botched it.

"Yeah, that's right," he continued. "It happens that fast. And just like that you're dead."

Dutch walked away and the men of Gun Six glanced around at each other, and then went back to work.

"And just like that you're dead," Bob imitated the gruff Sergeant. "What a prick."

They were off duty and walking around on the foredeck, taking in the sights, snapping pictures, and watching the water part beneath the bow of the magnificent ship.

It was cold and windy but the salty air smelled good and it beat being cooped up in the crowded bowels beneath the deck. The weather was a little like walking the docks on his old job, but the similarities ended there — this was a whole different life, and that was a lifetime ago.

Then Bob squinted as he spied some little specs on the horizon, elbowing Doug as he nodded towards them.

"Spitfires," he said. "Three of them. Coming out to say hello, I would guess."

"How the hell does he do that?" John asked, scratching his head.

"You think that's good?" asked Bob. "The pilot on the left has blue eyes and a brown mustache that's turned up at the ends. The guy in the middle is clean shaven, and the one on the right is an ugly bastard, looks a lot like Herby."

"Very funny," said Herby, as they all had a good laugh.

A minute later the three Spitfires screamed over the Queen in a flyby to honor her and the Americans she was bringing to the fight. The British fighters gunned their powerful Rolls Royce engines and made the men cheer.

They passed by so low the gas fumes could be smelled moments after they were gone. It was the first time any of them had ever seen a British fighter in the flesh. They had seen plenty of pictures and mockups so they would not shoot one down by accident, but this was the real deal.

"Good Lord, that was close," said John.

"Did you get a good look at them, Herb?" asked Bob.

"Hell yes, how could I not?"

"Did you see that ugly bastard on the right?" asked Bob.

"I did," said Doug. "Looked just like Herby. They could be twins."

"You guys can just all go to hell," said Herb.

The ship docked at Firth Clyde, near Greenock, and it took a couple of hard days of work to get all the equipment offloaded. The great "Grey Lady" would steam off again and back to help bring the war to Hitler.

The trucks were loaded with spare parts, food, and, of course, ammo, and lined up on the dock. Last but not least, the great guns were hooked on and the column slowly pulled away.

The long drive brought them to Wattisham Airfield where they were to join up with several other battalions of AAA to protect the vital base and nearby town. The important base was ringed with about ninety guns determined to fight off any attacks by German fighters or "Robot Bombs."

The high-flying bombers would be out of range for the 40mm's, but the Brits had some 88mm and fighter cover, if needed.

This very large airbase had been turned over to the United States as a base of operations for its own strategic bombing against Germany, launching thousands of planes and dropping thousands of tons of bombs.

It was, to say the least, a juicy target for the Luftwaffe, but they would pay dearly for any attempt to strike it. That's not to say they didn't try from time to time.

Gun Six of "C" Battery was set up between the edge of town and the outskirts of the airfield and was manned 24 hours a day with six hour rotations of the two crews.

Bob's crew came in after their quiet shift as the light was fading and, after pulling off their boots, grabbed a quick meal. There would be no hot showers tonight, just a quick splash off and a nap.

"I hate being dirty," said Doug. "I should have joined the navy."

"What a prima donna," said John, shaking his head.

"Better get used to it, pretty boy," said Bob.

"I may be able to get used to it, but there is one thing I will never get used to," said John.

"What's that?" asked Doug, as he tried to pull a comb through his hair and grimaced.

"The smell of Herb's feet when he pulls off those boots."

"You could drop those boots on Berlin and the war would be over," said Bob.

"I have a better idea," Herby replied. "Why don't all you guys just go to hell."

They all sat there laughing when the sound of a distant thumping hushed them, and they looked at each other, and snapped back into reality.

"Is that what I think it is?" whispered Herby.

"Sounds like bombs. I didn't think we were that close yet," said John.

"Holy crap! Bombs!" said Doug. "This is real, isn't it?"

"We better get some shut-eye," said Bob. "We are going to need it."

Before their next shift a few hours later, John came back into the farmhouse laughing. "Notice how the bombs stopped after I went to go crap?"

"I'm not sure I want to hear this story," said Doug, shaking his head.

"Somebody left the rope off the shithouse door and it was thumping in the wind all night."

"Damn it," said Herby. "I really wanted to fight some Germans."

"You are even fuller of crap than that outhouse. And your boots smell worse," said Bob.

"Go to hell, Bob." And they went back out to the guns.

While all shifts here were boring for the most part, night shifts were mind numbing. The only excitement came when they watched wave after wave of American Bombers taking off for God knows where and then coming back in, sometimes smoking or even burning.

100

The Germans didn't dare attack the field during the day, but sometimes the bombers could be heard in the distance heading for London or parts unknown. Without line of sight on the targets, they couldn't shoot at them.

Hitting one was almost impossible with the shorter range 40's, so the danger was greater to the local population. Millions of tons of AAA were fired into the air during the war, and every single ounce came back down somewhere, of that it was certain.

One morning, Dutch pulled Bob aside and told him to paint a sign for the Colonel's office. A sign with a hook on it so he could take it with him wherever they went. "386th AAA AW Battalion, Headquarters Battery," he said.

Bob carefully painted the sign on a plank, and then turned it over and painted it in a mirror image on the back side. He hung it up for the Sergeant to see with the backwards side out.

"Anstey, you shithead. What the hell kind of sign is that?" he roared.

"What's the matter, Sarge?"

"It's backwards, you wiseass. Now fix it before I kick your ass up around your ears."

"No, no, it's not backwards. You're just looking at it the wrong way," he said and flipped the sign around, blinking at him innocently.

Dutch looked at it and after a few moments he said, "Get the hell out of here."

After Bob left Dutch smiled to himself and whispered under his breath, "I've got to try that one on Lt. Bionde. He'll get a kick out of it."

Then he flipped it around again, and hung it over the door.

Chapter Nine

Airman Bradley's bus pulled into the gate of the Royal Air Force Training Camp at Morecambe, Lancaster, on May 1, 1942. They were marched off the buses and formed into ranks as orders were barked at them so fast and so loud it made her head spin. Standing at attention in an open field being yelled at from all different directions was a new experience for her.

This is not exactly what I thought it was going to be like. She now questioned her decision to leave that oppressive employ.

As ordered, she was told to leave her suitcase on the bus. Now there were women coming up and down the line pushing things into her arms as she struggled to hold onto all of it.

One airman walked along with another who carried a box. The first would glance a girl up and down, size her up, reach in the box and pull out two uniforms and a hat and shove them into her chest before going to the next girl.

How can she tell what size I am? As it turned out, she couldn't.

In the same manner she was given a mess kit, a bag of toiletries, and a "frightfully ugly" pair of shoes.

A bedroll was then wedged into her already stuffed arms, and she had to claw her hand out to grab the month's worth of ration coupons that were being passed out by the airmen walking up and down the line.

The girls were marched single file as they waddled like ducks clinging to their huge armload of supplies; some, including Lillian, were unable to even see where they were going.

A group of them were split off and pointed into a small, cramped quarters. She was assigned a bunk that she instantly filled with her new belongings by just letting go. She looked down at the mess of newly issued gear that was spilling off her tiny bunk and realized the only thing she was still holding were the ration coupons.

The building was a ragged old rusted metal building with a few filthy windows that were uncovered, but high enough that it was unlikely anyone could see in. There were no chairs for changing or sitting, no drawers or lockers, and no other furniture of any kind.

The only things in the room were these cots, wooden cots with folding legs that were probably left over from the last war. The dozen or so cots were spaced inches apart except for a narrow walkway down the middle.

The cots were no more comfortable than the ones at the convent, but at least they didn't squeak, but the floor sure did. The loose planks on the wooden floor squeaked and creaked as it bounced up and down on the nails that now didn't hold them down like screws would have.

The building was, quite simply, not built to last this long and should have been torn down years ago. The slight smell of something dead under the floor, the complete lack of any lights other than the filthy windows, and the holes in the roof that were sure to drip, made her miss her room back in Bath.

In a matter of seconds the thoughts of Joyce and William and sometimes Ted, listening to the radio and snacking, of the clean fresh air and the view from her window, of the children, of the ruins and the plaza and the people walking by and of the zoo and even Harry the ape, almost made her cry.

Then it started to rain and she could hear the tapping of the drops on the metal roof. This day was going from bad to worse and that slap in the face was beginning to pale in comparison to what she'd given up over it.

"Well, this is certainly not what I expected," a voice said standing next to her.

"I was thinking the same thing," she replied without looking up as she arranged the things on her bed. "I guess we are to put our things under our bunks, unless they give us lockers or the like."

"Where is a girl supposed to bloody pee around here? They'd best bring us a bloody bucket or something or I'll go squat back there in the bus."

Lillian started laughing and said, "Please don't make me laugh or I'll pee right here. Let's run outside and see if they have a place."

They trotted out into the rain and went along with another group of girls that were suffering from the same problem long bus rides cause, and saw the line in front of the little outhouse. All the girls were hopping up and down in obvious distress.

"I'll never make it to the loo if I have to wait in that line," the girl said. "Follow me, love."

The strange girl darted off along the back of the next old metal barracks, splashing through the growing puddles, and turning to disappear between the buildings. Lillian watched her run off, turned back to the line of girls standing in the rain, and then ran off after her.

Lillian found out that day that her new friend was not shy, and when she had to pee, she had to pee.

When they got back inside they were both laughing and Lillian's mood changed; perhaps she had made a good decision after all. This was the first time she got a look at her new friend, and they both stood there dripping wet with their hair stuck to their heads.

"Sarah," the girl said, while sticking out her hand. "Sarah Jane Prescott."

"Lillian," she said, and took her hand and shook it. "Lillian Rose Bradley."

"Nice to meet you, love. I'd share a pee with you anytime," Sarah said, and they both giggled.

Sarah had glowing white skin like a porcelain doll, strawberry hair, and emerald green eyes. She had the innocent face of an angel, but she was anything but angelic, and far from innocent.

Lillian was so taken aback by her new friend's beauty because she seemed so out of place here that she asked, "So what made you join up and come to this God-awful place?"

"Well, I suppose it was because daddy made me mad," she said with a sly grin.

"I think I'm going to like this story," said Lillian, as she sat on the cot and pulled off her wet shoes. The other girls were starting to file back in, one by one. "Where are you from?"

"London. And you, love?"

"I was born in London, but I grew up in South Wales."

"A lovely place. I've been there on holiday with my mum," said Sarah.

"Well then, you probably didn't go to the part of South Wales where I grew up — The Convent of Saint John."

"Oh bloody hell no, you wouldn't catch me dead in a bloody convent."

That made Lillian laugh. It was the first time she could remember ever laughing about growing up in a convent.

"So there were no boys in this bloody convent of yours? Only those fat nuns that walk like big fat ducks?"

Lillian started to laugh out loud and some of the other girls moved closer in to join the fun. "Like big fat penguins," she said.

"Well, I had a big fat nanny looking after me, but she wasn't a penguin," Sarah said, and they all laughed.

"I had a nanny, too," said one of the other girls. "But she wasn't fat, she was just mean."

"Well, I was a nanny, but I wasn't fat and I wasn't mean, but the woman I worked for was both," Lillian said, and they all laughed even more.

Lillian told her story to the little group of girls who huddled around her, from losing her sisters to the slap on the face. She decided not to mention the Polio.

They all told their stories about where they came from and how they wound up here. Every story was different and every story was personal. Some of the stories had never been shared before, and every girl was fascinated with every other girl's life.

Lillian had shared much of this with Joyce, but that was different. That was Joyce, who was almost her adopted mother. The convent was a cold place of mind-numbed girls, devoid of feelings and of friendships, so that was different, too.

This was a new experience for her, and it was exciting.

Sarah told her story of growing up in a beautiful house in a lovely area and of being spoiled with everything she could ever want. "He used to call me his little princess," she said with a grin.

"But when I met a boy I liked," she continued, "he sent me off to private school far away so I couldn't see him."

"Did you go?" asked one of the girls.

"Well, of course I went, silly. I didn't want to but I had no choice, now did I? But I didn't speak to daddy for six months, and he wasn't too happy about that."

"So did you see your boy again?" asked Lillian.

"Oh no, love. But I found another one soon enough. And then I found another one after that, actually. He's the one that daddy got mad about, real mad."

"This sounds like the good part," Lillian said, rubbing her palms together. "Keep going, love."

"Well, daddy came to pick me up for the spring holiday, and he arrived a little early. I was still in my room, shall we say, saying goodbye to the lad. I think it was the first time I ever saw my daddy turn that color."

"Then what happened?" They all wanted to know. Sarah had a lovely way of telling her story and she had a captivated audience.

"That poor naked boy jumped out of that bed and tried to cover himself as he ran out while daddy was screaming at him. Then he turned and started screaming at me. He said he was taking me out of school and bringing me home. I thought he was going to have a heart attack!"

Lillian was shocked, but she loved it and hung on her every word.

107

"That's when I said the hell with you and I went down and joined the bloody RAF."

The girls were all laughing so hard there were tears running out and some were holding their sides, never having laughed like this in their lives.

"But first," she continued, "I went and spent a few nights at that boy's flat and gave him a proper goodbye. Hung like a bloody mule, he was. He was harder to leave than daddy."

Lillian had never heard girls talk this way before but she was loving it, and she was having so much fun. She had never met anyone like Sarah before, and she just couldn't get enough of her.

Sarah's new uniform was a little too small for her, and Lillian's was a little too big, so they traded. The hats being one size fits all were fine, but the gold RAF pins that were to be affixed to them were not to be passed out for another four months of training. Upon graduation, at the "Passing Out Parade," they would go from cadet to airmen and earn their wings.

Sarah's shoes actually fit her, but Lillian's were too big so she had to line them with paper and a little cloth; the paper to tighten them up and the cloth to keep the paper from scratching her feet.

"They're a little uncomfortable but I've had worse," she told Sarah.

Sarah was mortified at the thought of having shoes that didn't fit.

"You have to learn a lot of little tricks to get by when you grow up poor," Lillian said, teasing Sarah.

"I'll tell you what, love," Sarah said with her sly smile. "You teach me some of your tricks, and I'll teach you some of mine."

"I would say you have a deal," Lillian said, and they shook hands once more.

The next morning they were mustered up on the parade ground in front of the buildings with uniforms on and hats off, standing at attention in the rain. It was then that they were introduced to Sergeant Major Beatrice Moreland, a woman they would come to loathe and fear. She was everyone's worse nightmare.

She made "Dutch" Van Holland look like a box of puppies.

"I think I'd rather be locked up with your friend Harry the gorilla than with that monster in pumps," Sarah said, making Lillian bust out laughing as they stood there in line.

The Sergeant heard the laughter and snapped her head around, but couldn't tell where it came from. She walked up and down the line right in the general area of the sound, stopping and staring for a few moments into each girl's face, nose to nose.

Lillian was petrified, her heart pounding as her throat went dry. But the Sergeant had made her point and just walked away. From that moment on, they all knew to not dare get caught crossing the Sergeant Major, and though unspoken, that was their only warning.

Before breakfast they had to be fitted for gas masks. While it didn't really matter to the higher ups if their uniforms didn't fit right, or if their shoes were uncomfortable, the gas mask had to be perfect. It had to seal around the face and had a hood that went back to form a raincoat-like cover, and all this was rolled up and fit into a canvas bag that was carried on the hip.

Sometimes the girls would pull out the contents and use them as a purse, but it meant big problems if they got caught doing it. Sometimes the authorities would cordon off entire sectors in London and inspect every gas mask case, and levy fines if it was not properly equipped.

When they returned to their old barracks building they found all the suitcases in a pile and each girl had to find hers and stow it under her bed. Each suitcase had been thoroughly searched and the contents just stuffed back in.

The next few months became an unending nightmare of drilling and marching and marching and drilling. The girls were often too tired to laugh or act up, which was most likely the idea.

Lillian's legs were really being put to the test. She had not, of course, let on that she struggled with polio while growing up. Her legs were not as strong as the other girls, but to admit that would get her booted out.

She had to grin and bear it and while all the girls were tired, she was tired and her legs were on fire. Sometimes she hurt so bad that she couldn't get up to eat, but Sarah made sure she did.

Sarah knew there was something Lillian wasn't telling her, but she never asked, and brought her food back from the mess hall on the days Lillian just couldn't push any further, though there were few days like that. Pain was no stranger to her, and like the tree, she wouldn't complain.

A few months later it was getting a little easier. The girls had their marching skills honed and Lillian's legs were getting stronger, so with less than two months to go in training, it looked like she would make it after all.

"Are you up for a jailbreak next weekend, love?" Sarah asked Lillian, with a devious twinkle in her eye.

"What are you up to now, Sarah Jane?"

They were on the parade grounds on a routine clean up assignment just out of earshot of the other girls. The big white grandstand where the cadet class would march past upon their graduation was just in front of them.

Lillian glanced up at it, and a tingle went through her as she thought how grand it will be when she will get to march in front of the generals and VIP's assembled for the spectacle. How proud she will be to get that RAF pin on her hat, making her an airman in the Royal Air Force. A WAF.

"Are you going to stand there and bloody day dream all afternoon?"

Lillian snapped her head back to Sarah, and then looked once again at the grandstands.

"I can't believe it's almost time. I can't believe in about six weeks I will be one of them. Like the girls I saw at the zoo, I wanted to be them, Sarah. I wanted to be just like them."

Sarah just stood there and shook her head. "You're bloody daft, do you know that? Do you want to hear my little scheme or not?"

"Yes, yes, of course. Sorry."

"Alright, well try to stay with me, love. My daydream is better. Do you see that shed over there?"

"That's the contractors' shed, is it not? I've seen them bring equipment in and out of there."

"Do you trust me, love?" Sarah asked, almost in a whisper as she leaned in close. "Do you want to have some fun?"

Lillian did but she didn't. She didn't want to get in trouble, and in fact was petrified of getting into trouble. Perhaps it was all the years at the convent. The way the punishment was doled out there was enough to fear causing trouble.

But there was something about Sarah. Something that was very hard to say no to. Sarah was delightfully devilish, adventurous and infectious. In her mind she could picture the stern face of Sergeant Major Moreland, and it made her shudder, but in her ear whispered Sarah, like a siren beckoning the sailors to the rocky cliffs.

"Well, do you?"

"Trust you or want to have some fun? I want to have fun, but even your daddy knew not to trust you."

Sarah laughed and put her hand on Lillian's shoulder and said, "Then it's settled, love. Over the wall we go on Friday night. Do you have any cute little dresses in that little suitcase?"

"What's settled? We didn't settle anything."

"Just trust me, love, and get your little dress ready. We're not bloody soldiers yet, but we could go play with some." Sarah winked and strutted away leaving Lillian standing there bewildered, worried, and yet somehow, exhilarated.

It was Friday afternoon and Sarah whispered to Lillian she was to gather up her little dress and a change of clothes. "Pull out your gas mask and put in a few essentials and then stuff them in."

"Then what?" asked Lillian, as her heart started thumping with anticipation.

"To the contractors' shed. They don't lock it, and I figured out a way to slip out of the gate from there."

"Past the guards?" she asked, as she saw most of the civilian contractors walking off the base for the day.

"Past the guards, through the gate, and off to the pubs, love. Morecambe is a town full of pubs, little hotels, and lovely little shops. With any luck, there will also be lots of soldiers. Lots and lots of soldiers."

By then they had slipped into the contractors' shed. It was dark and smelled like motor oil, mowed grass and paint. Sarah guided her to the back of the shed and the floor felt squishy like wet hay.

"Alright, love, take off your uniform and fold it up tight. We're going to hide them up on that shelf so fold it small. Hat, too," she said as she stripped.

"Take off my bloody clothes?! Right here?"

"Of course right here, then put on your dress. Then we will put on those bloody siren suits," Sarah said, and nodded at the row of suits hanging on the wall.

A siren suit was a coverall type outfit with a built in hood designed to cover everything but the opening for the gas mask. They were made famous by Winston Churchill but were not necessarily widely used.

Wearing the siren suits with the hoods up, not uncommon on a chilly day, the girls slipped out of the shed and walked right through the gate blending in with the workers leaving for the day, casually talking and attracting no attention to themselves as they went.

They slipped into an alley nearby, pulled off the hooded coveralls, and rolled them up tight. They then checked into a room with two beds under which they shoved the siren suits.

"Time to have some fun, love," said Sarah.

Lillian wanted to walk around town and see the sights because they only had a glimpse of the place on the bus ride in. There was one thing in particular she wanted to see.

"I want to go to the beach," she said to Sarah. "I want to see the channel. I've never been to the sea before."

"Tomorrow, I promise. Tonight we have some real fun. Let's go have a pint."

Within a block of the hotel they found a very loud, very full pub, with lots of singing and lots of drinking, and lots and lots of soldiers. Exactly what Sarah was looking for, and as soon as she walked in she became the life of the party.

It smelled like beer and cigarette smoke and a haze hung in the air within.

Lillian tried to keep a lower profile, but the soldiers buzzed around her and bought her drinks and tried to get her to dance, and one even asked for a kiss. She relaxed a little bit after a couple of beers, but there would be no kissing tonight.

Sarah, on the other hand, was having the time of her life. While there were other girls in the bar, there were none like Sarah. All the guys loved her, and all of them thought she loved them right back.

They ate and drank and with all the soldiers and airmen there trying to impress them, they didn't pay for any of it.

Lillian felt a tap on her shoulder and she turned around to see Sarah who asked, "Do you remember how to get to the hotel, love?"

"Yes, I think so."

"I'll meet you back there in the morning," she said with a wink, and then darted out of the pub with a soldier in tow.

Lillian was flabbergasted and then suddenly terrified at the thought of being left alone, so she worked her way to the door. She wound up being escorted by four airmen sworn to protect her but she wondered who would protect her from them.

Safe and sound back in her room, she stretched out on the soft bed and fell asleep, wishing her cot back on base was nearly this nice. She didn't even have a pillow back there so she was determined to make the most of this while it lasted.

Just after dawn, as Lillian lay there not wanting to get up but not able to go back to sleep, she heard the click of the lock and lifted herself up to see Sarah coming in with a big guilty smile.

She carried in a package of French bread and cheese, the warm bread filling Lillian's nostrils and making her aware of just how hungry she was.

"Compliments of my new friend," said Sarah.

"So how was your night?" asked Lillian.

"Well, love, they can't all be bloody mules, but it's much better than bloody marching, I can tell you that. If the Sergeant Major got a good "Rogering" now and then she might be less of a sourpuss."

"You may be right," Lillian laughed.

They sat and ate that wonderful warm bread and nipped at the cheese that she had wrapped up in a piece of cheese cloth. They shared a tea bag and stretched it into two cups using hot tap water. It was a marvelous breakfast compared to the fare on base so they savored every bite.

"Next stop, the beach," Lillian said with an authority she didn't know she had. "My turn to choose, and it won't be another pub."

"Good idea, love. Let's go see your beach."

"Oh my God," Lillian said in awe as they reached the cliffs and looked out over the English Channel.

"The channel is an amazing place, love," Sarah said. "Sometimes it's as calm as glass and sometimes it churns like a cauldron, but it's always lovely."

"I had no idea it could be like this," she said as she looked at the gulls flying overhead and breathed in the salty air. "It feels almost alive. It's so big."

"It's a bloody shame they have to do all that," Sarah said as she looked down at all the barbed wire and defensive obstacles built along the beach, as well as the soldiers on alert and the patrol boats offshore. "Goddamn Nazi bastards."

"It seems to go on forever. As far as you can see, even the little boats on the horizon."

"Not forever, love, only to France. And I don't have to tell you who is in France, and I'm sure their beaches are looking like ours, full of soldiers and all that mess. Now come on, we have to get back. We are back on duty in the morning."

On their way back to the little hotel they passed by a little outdoor café where some soldiers were having a birthday party for one of their own. The soldiers made a big fuss seeing these two beauties walking by and invited them to join in.

Sarah pulled Lillian into the party where she hugged the birthday boy and stayed just long enough to spirit away a piece of cake. When they got back to the hotel room she put the cake in her gas mask case and then they both put on the siren suits and headed for the gates.

Hoods up again, they chatted and casually walked through the gates past the guards, intending to return the suits to the contractors' shed and retrieve their uniforms. But one of the guards noticed them and called for them to stop.

They both had their heads down as the guard approached and Lillian's heart was pounding out of her chest. Sarah turned to her and gave her a wink and a little smile.

When he walked up he demanded to see their passes, expecting to catch a couple of guys sneaking onto the base. Sarah pulled back her hood and looked up at him blinking, and his whole demeanor changed. He melted like almost every other man that she came in contact with.

She reached up and put her hand on his arm and said, "Just going for a little walk, love."

"Well, I'm going to have to inspect your gas mask cases," he stammered out, unable to break eye contact until she opened the case and he looked down into it, seeing no gas mask. All he saw were some ladies' undergarments, and a big piece of cake perched atop them.

"Where is your gas mask? Where you get this cake?"

She looked at him with a little smile and blinked her eyes and said, "Cake, love, what cake?"

He stared into her eyes and she stared right back. About a minute went by before he said, "Off with you now. Next time you sneak out for some cake come pay me a visit first."

When they got to the shed both of them burst out laughing.

"Cake, love, what cake?" Lillian mimicked her and they laughed again.

"Men are so bloody easy," said Sarah.

After changing back into their uniforms, Sarah pulled the cake out and they split it and each took a bite. They looked back up at each other and laughed again.

"This is the worst bloody cake I've ever had in my life," said Sarah, while Lillian laughed and nodded in agreement.

Due to rationing, eggs and sugar were hard to come by, so the cake was hardly sweet, perhaps a little honey mixed into it, and it was so doughy it was gummy. But it was, after all, cake, and even though it was awful, they ate every bite.

Sunday, Lillian and Sarah went back to work as usual, their adventure over. While Sarah tried several times to convince Lillian to repeat it, Lillian was just too worried about being caught right before they finished training.

Unlike Sarah, Lillian had to succeed. Just like when she left the convent, she simply had no place to go back to, so failure was not an option.

"There will be time for that soon," she would tell Sarah.

"But you don't understand, love. I want to go now AND I want to go later."

"I'm sure your little guard would love to see you again, but next time I walk through those gates I'm going to be pinned."

As the training came closer to the end, the physical part slowed down some and the education of military rules and regulations was stepped up. How and when to salute. How to recognize ranks and how to address officers. Chain of command, ethics and even punishment. All the things a young airman must know when in service of the King.

The "Passing Out Ceremony" had the entire cadet class, led by their sergeants, march in high step past the grandstand with the band playing and the flag flying high. The girls received their RAF pins and affixed them to their hats, now official WAFs in His Majesty's Royal Air Force. God save the King.

When they got back to the barracks a few hours later, Lillian cried with joy as she stared at the pin. Sarah shrugged as she looked at hers.

"All that work and all we get is this crappy little brass pin. We should get a bloody gold one for that."

"Look at the bright side, Sarah. At least we get to leave. At least we don't have to worry about Sergeant Major Attila the Hun."

Sarah laughed at that one. "You have a point there. I wonder where they will send us."

"Maybe we could drive tanks! I would love to drive tanks and run over things, wouldn't you?"

Sarah just looked at her for a few moments and then said, "Are you bloody daft? Have you completely lost your mind?"

Lillian laughed and said, "I'm just kidding, you wanker. Do you think I'd want to drive a bloody tank?"

"I'd like to go back to London, but quite frankly the bombs terrify me."

"Maybe they will let you stay here and get a job in a pub," said Lillian. "You'd be good at that."

"Well, aren't you the funny one today? The truth is I *would* like that."

That's when the senior airman popped into the door of the barracks with a handful of envelopes. He was calling out the girls' names as he handed them out. Since they were in alphabetical order, Lillian was one of the first to get hers, but Sarah had to wait a few minutes.

"What is it?" she asked as Lillian scanned through the contents.

"Orders," she said. "Bad news, very bad news."

"Oh my God, what now?" asked Sarah, with a look of sheer terror on her face.

"I'm not going to drive a bloody tank, dammit."

Sarah sat there blinking at her, and Lillian broke into a laugh at the look on her face.

"Bloody wanker," said Sarah, shaking her head.

"Prescott!" the airman called out and handed the orders to Sarah as she tore it open in a frenzy, not sure what to expect, and then smiled as she read it.

"Where are you going, Sarah?"

"Bournemouth. I'm going to Bournemouth."

"Is it nice there?"

"Oh yes, love. It's by the sea, the channel that is. It's a lovely place."

"That's good," said Lillian, as Sarah looked away from the papers and into Lillian's smiling face. "Because I'm going there, too."

Chapter Ten

"Anstey!" Dutch was yelling. "Where the hell is Anstey?"

He found him hunched over the Morse code handbook still trying to get it down. It didn't help that every time one of the other guys would walk by, they would make "deet, deet, deeeeeet, deet, deeeeeet," noises until he got mad and ran them off and started again.

"I have a job for you. I volunteered you, so come with me."

The two men walked across the field and Bob realized they were heading for the headquarters battalion building, and while he was a little worried about going to the Colonel's office, he couldn't help but smile when he saw his sign over the door.

"I have another little painting assignment for you, soldier, but no fucking around this time, you got it?"

"Ok, Dutch."

"What did you call me?" he asked, stopping in his tracks.

"Sergeant, I called you Sergeant."

"That's what I thought. Between that sign and the little pictures you draw on your V-Mail, I think, or rather hope, you can help me surprise the Colonel."

"Anything you say, Sergeant."

"Good answer. Bionde came up with a little bottle of gold paint and I want you to paint an eagle on the front of Colonel Gibb's helmet. Think you can do it?"

"Yeah, I'm pretty sure I can do that. I need a small brush, smaller the better."

"Got it," Dutch said as they walked into the office. The Colonel wasn't there and he sat Bob down at a desk in front of the helmet. "Now paint."

Bob took out a pencil and thought about what a colonel's eagle was supposed to look like. He did a few sketches on a piece of paper until he felt like he had it right, and did a light outline on the front of the helmet.

He wasn't too worried about drawing and painting the eagle, but getting it in just the right place and making it not too big or too small was a challenge, and he wanted to get it right.

Last thing I need is Dutch on my ass right now. He can be a real horse's ass.

The helmet itself was perfect, not a scratch or dent on it. The leather liner had no sweat stains in it like his and all the other guys. Of course, the Colonel had aides to keep it clean and shine his shoes and press his uniform. It's good to be in charge.

His cavalry hat, however, was no man's land, as were his western boots. Don't mess with a Texan's boots. And the hat was weathered and shaped to his head, as all good hats like that should be. It was broken in, and he liked wearing it when protocol allowed.

Protocol allowed it when he was the highest ranking officer in the vicinity, so no one could tell him any different, but the rest of the men had to wear their helmets anytime they were outside.

As Bob was finishing up the pencil outline, Dutch and the Lieutenant came over and stood over each shoulder and watched his progress, until Bob looked up at them and asked, "Do you mind?"

The two looked up at each other and then back down. "What?"

"I can't do this while you watch. Go away."

"Goddamn prima donna," Dutch grumbled as they stepped away.

"Hey, Sergeant," Bob leaned over and said. "I have a question. If I do a good job, what's in it for me?"

"How about if you do a good job I won't kick your ass?" said Dutch.

Then Bionde pulled Dutch aside and whispered a few words in his ear and the Sergeant scowled and looked back at Bob. "How about a weekend pass, would that make you happy?"

"It would make me real happy if I could bring the movie star with me."

Dutch's face got red and Bob thought he would explode, but the Lieutenant nodded a yes so he gave in and agreed to give Bob his passes.

When the Lieutenant stepped away, the Sergeant leaned over Bob's shoulder and said, "That better be one fucking good eagle, asshole."

Bob just smiled and got back to work. He got what he wanted, and couldn't wait to tell Doug. He would have loved to have gotten four passes, but he knew that was pressing his luck, so he and Doug would just have to go have fun for them.

Two hours later they were all staring at the perfect eagle emblazoned in gold on the Colonel's helmet, and it was, quite frankly, beautiful.

"I have to admit, I never thought it would come out this good," said Bionde.

Dutch just stared at it, unable to decide if he was glad it came out so well, or if he was disappointed that he didn't get to bite Bob's head off. "That's pretty damn good, Private. I don't think you should get two weekend passes out of it, but that is pretty damn good."

"Look what I got," he showed Doug, holding them up to his face.

Doug was speechless, but Herby leapt from his cot and said, "Where is mine?" John just looked up and listened.

"Sorry fellas, but these are all I could get out of Dutch, and he didn't want to give me these."

John shrugged his shoulders and Herby sulked, but that wasn't about to ruin their weekend.

"Way to go, Bobby boy, I owe you big time," said Doug with a big grin on his face as he shined up his shoes.

"The passes are for Dartmouth, a little place near the coast not too far from here. Maybe we can find a pub or two."

"Private Anstey," Doug said with a very serious voice. "Just be glad you decided to bring with you one Private first class Douglass Hansen or you wouldn't have any fun at all. We are going to London, not some old people's town."

"Come on Doug, Dutch is itching to hang my ass out to dry and I don't want to hand it to him on a silver platter."

"Trust me Bob, it will be worth it. To hell with Dutch, to hell with Dutch for the weekend anyway. To hell with the whole goddamn army."

"To hell with the whole goddamn army!" repeated Bob with enthusiasm. "Let's go to London. Hide your daughters, here comes the movie star!"

"Amen brother. Now come on, we have a train to catch."

With help from the Red Cross, and a little smooth talking by Doug, they were able to get a room at The Washington Club.

As they danced and drank and flirted, it crossed Bob's mind that this was the most fun he'd ever had in his life and he was supposed to be going to war. He would have spent the rest of his life in The Washington Club if he had a choice of that or going back to the base.

The girls couldn't get enough of Doug. Soon his tie was loose, his shirt untucked, his hair was mussed up, and he had lipstick kisses all over his face. The last time Bob saw him he was stumbling up the stairs with a redhead on his arm.

"Goddamn movie star," Bob smiled to himself.

After a few more beers, well, a lot more beers, Bob somehow made it up to the room and Doug wasn't there. No big surprise.

He kicked off his shoes and hung his jacket and tie over the bed before flopping down onto his back, staring at the ceiling. He had to keep one foot on the floor to try to keep the room from spinning, but it wasn't working very well.

As he drifted off he smiled as Archie's words came into his head about staying out of the bars over there, and he smiled a guilty smile. *Sorry, Pop. You old bastard.*

When he came down for breakfast after a nice hot shower, he saw Doug standing there talking to a couple of military cops. He walked over. *What kind of trouble did he get into now?*

When he walked up smiling he discovered they had asked Doug to see his pass and they saw that it was not for London, which meant he was in big trouble. Bob's smile quickly went away with the "oh shit" moment he had when they asked to see his.

"Bob!"said Doug, with a nervous grin and a wink. "I was just explaining to the Sergeant here how I had to come see my girl."

"Your girl, eh?" the MP said skeptically.

"C'mon fellas," he said, flashing his big toothy smile. "Haven't you ever been in love?"

"So now you're in love?" he asked, as he looked down and saw the lipstick still staining Doug's collar. "I bet."

"I just had to come see her," he lied. "If you had a girl like mine you would come see her, too."

"Give us a break," Bob pleaded. "We'll go straight back to our battalion, I promise."

"I promise, too," said Doug.

"And we won't see you here again, right?"

"You might see me in the movies someday, Sarge, but you won't see me here."

"What about your girl that you love so much?" he asked Doug sarcastically.

"Well, I guess I'll just have to find another one."

The Sergeant laughed and clapped him on the back while the other MP stood there grinning. "Ok pretty boy, you and your friend here be on the next train to Dartford or I'm throwing both your asses in the clink."

"Thanks, Sarge," they both said as they rushed away to the station.

On the train ride back Doug wouldn't shut up about what a great time he had with that wild redhead, what he could remember anyway.

"I can't wait to get back so I can tell Herby just how much better sex is than firing the guns."

"Just don't tell him it's better than baseball or you might have a fight on your hands. So what was that little redhead's name, anyway?"

"To tell you the truth, I really don't remember, and she was still asleep when I left this morning."

"So you never even said goodbye?"

"No, I suppose not. I guess I should have but I didn't."

"You dog," Bob said, as he punched him in the arm. "No wonder the Brits don't like us."

The next morning was May 1, 1944 and Privates Hansen and Anstey were back on station with none the wiser.

"I guess those guys didn't send word back to Dutch or he would have us cleaning latrines."

"Cleaning latrines from the inside," Bob agreed in a whisper.

They were cleaning and greasing down Gun Six when Herby called over it from the other side, "So how was your night in London?" He was still a little miffed about it, by the tone of his voice.

"Quiet, Herby, Goddammit," Bob and Doug both chimed in. They could see Dutch walking towards the gun but still too far to hear. "Dartford, you dumbass. We went to Dartford. Van Holland will eat us for lunch if we get caught."

"Shut your pie hole, Herb," said John.

Herby smiled as Dutch walked up. They knew he wouldn't say anything but he still enjoyed jacking with them when he could.

"You sorry bastards shoot down any planes for me today?" Dutch asked with a broad grin.

"Not today, boss," said Bob. "But we have the cleanest gun in the battalion."

"I heard a rumor that we will be moving the battalion soon. Maybe in the next few weeks, so don't get too attached to this place."

"I have news for you, Sergeant, you don't have to worry about us getting attached to this place," said Herby. "Where are we moving to?"

"Nobody is allowed to know where we are going, they are keeping it hush-hush. So that means some bad news, boys, there will be no passes. As of now everyone is confined to base," said Dutch.

"Ok, so let me get this straight," said John. "You won't tell us where we are moving to, and we are not allowed to go off base because they are afraid that we might tell somebody where we are moving to. Is that about right?"

"That about sums it up," said Dutch, nodding his head and smiling. "You didn't expect the army to make sense, did you?"

"Let's just hope the guys in charge know a little more than we do," John said, shaking his head.

"The ironic thing," said Bob, "is that the more you know, the more they let you walk around."

"That's true," said Herby. "You have to kiss the Colonel's ass if you want to get a pass around here."

Dutch looked up at Herby with his trademark scowl. "Let me make this clear, Private. Your buddy kissed MY ass to get those passes, not the Colonel's."

Nobody said anything.

"I'm the one that kissed the Colonel's ass," he said and smiled. They all laughed at the Sergeant's rare display of humor.

"Next time you have some free passes just let me know and I'll kiss your ass for them. I'll kiss your ass in Macy's window if you like," said Herby.

"I'll keep that in mind, Private. In the meantime, get my gun ready to deploy. Double check the spare parts and go ahead and get the 50cals loaded up and ready. We won't use them here."

"Ok, boss," said John.

A week later the word came through and Dutch passed the orders to his gun crew. "Get my gun ready to roll right now, and get the truck loaded and gear stowed. Gun Six, "C" Battery, is going to be the best gun in the battalion or you birds will wish you were never born."

"Too late for that," whispered Herb.

As the 386th AAA A/W Battalion secured the guns and mounted them to the thirty-two 2-½ ton trucks with the tow bars, locking down the barrels, swinging in and locking the rear wheels, and raising the jacks, a large squadron of B-24 Liberator bombers began lifting off from Wattisham airbase.

"They are really loaded down," said Bob. "It's taking everything they have to clear the field."

They watched in awe as the planes clawed at the sky while all four engines screamed, and in seemingly slow motion, became airborne. One by one they carried their heavy burdens to the sky and onward to points unknown.

"Was anyone counting?"asked Herby, speaking for the first time since the first plane started down the runway.

"Had to be well over three hundred," said John. "Well over."

"I would hate to be sitting there eating my nice kraut lunch and see them coming."

"No shit," said Herb, as more planes behind them started spinning up.

"There goes the fighter escorts," said Bob, as he nodded downfield. "Those are the new P-51 Mustangs, see the drop tanks?"

"For long range?" asked John.

"Those babies can fly all the way to Germany and kick the crap out of anything the Krauts can fly," said Bob.

"They are going to put the 386th out of business," said Doug. They won't leave us anything to shoot down."

"I hope the hell you're right, Doug," Herb said. "I hope to hell you're right. Bomb the shit out of them and let's go home. I'm fine with that."

After all the 40mm Bofors guns were loaded on the big trucks, the 32 quad 50cal machine guns were hooked onto the jeeps set up for them. Four more jeeps and two more trucks made up the headquarters battery to lead the column, now seventy vehicles long.

On May 25, 1944 they lined up and passed through the gates of Wattisham and headed down the road to a place known to only a few of them. All the gun crews riding in the back of their trucks pulling their guns could only wonder as they bounced along.

"Where do you think we're going?" asked Herby.

"Based on where the sun is, my guess is to the coast, but it's hard to tell with all the twists and turns," Bob said. He was sitting in the far rear of the truck, and while that made it easier to see out, it also made for the bumpiest ride.

"Coast?" asked Herby.

"The English Channel, you lunkhead," said John, shaking his head.

The truck smelled like canvas and grease as it bounced along and heaved and pitched with every hole and every bump. Doug was sitting on the rear end as well, across from Bob and was looking a little green. He always fought the motion sickness but this ride was especially rough and it showed on his face.

"Watch this," Herby said, grinning as he elbowed John in the ribs.

"Hey, Doug," he said. "Hey, hey Doug, over here."

Doug took a few deep breaths and, glad for the distraction, he looked at Herby and said "Yeah?"

"Want some oatmeal?"

That did it. Doug first put his hand over his mouth and clenched his eyes closed, and then he stuck his head out the back and threw up everything he had in him and then some.

"Herby, you asshole," Bob said. When he glanced back he noticed Dutch had a little grin on his face. Herby laughed out loud and even John couldn't help chuckling a little.

Doug sat back up with his eyes watery and his face red but he managed a smile and looked at Herby and said, "I owe you one, you bastard."

"Ok, play time is over. What the fuck is this, fourth grade?" asked Dutch. "Herby if you do that again I will tie you to my gun for the rest of the way."

"Do you know where we are going yet, Sergeant?" asked Herb.

"You fellas want to know where we are going? Is that right?"

"We all do," Herby said, and as he looked around the truck all the other guys were nodding and looking at Van Holland.

"Ok, I'll tell you then. We are on our way to none of your fucking business, England. Any other questions?"

The men smiled and shook their heads.

The Colonel was in the front jeep leading his column when he said to his driver, Staff Sergeant Mitchell Hayes, "Let's give the men a piss call, Mitch."

"Yes, sir, Colonel Gibbs," he said, and slowed the jeep down as he pulled over to the side of the road.

Mitch got out of the jeep and looked back at the column slowing down as well, and he shouted to the driver of the next jeep back, "PISS CALL!"

That driver nodded and turned back yelling, "PISS CALL" to the next vehicle and the word went back the line, jeep by jeep, truck by truck, until every vehicle had men pouring out of them and heading to the side of the road, the Colonel included.

The road ran alongside a green meadow, lined with trees, popping with the spring wildflowers, and the fresh spring breeze gently swayed the tall grass back and forth. It was truly a little piece of heaven and a welcome sight to the mostly cooped up soldiers.

Just over eight hundred men stood shoulder to shoulder between their trucks with the guns and the field of green to answer the call of Mother Nature. The sounds were of birds chirping, leaves rustling, and pee hitting the ground.

128

Suddenly out of nowhere came the roar of huge engines over the treetops, and flying at almost eye level, two B-24 Liberator Bombers, one smoking badly from the left outboard engine, zoomed past them from left to right, right in front of their eyes.

Both planes had their bomb doors open and full strings of 500-pound bombs were pouring out of their bellies. The bombs, dozens of them, hit the ground just a few hundred feet from the battalion, clanking and bouncing on impact as they rolled across the meadow, finally coming to a halt.

It happened so fast the men didn't even have a chance to zip up, but wasted no time in doing so. They all clambered back into the trucks, while the Colonel, unfazed, climbed back into his jeep.

"Begging the Colonel's pardon, sir, but what the hell just happened?" asked Mitch.

"Those planes were a bit shot up, Mitch. Probably trying to get back to Wattisham. They drop the bombs to lighten the load so they have a better chance at landing, or even making it there."

"Why didn't they go off? We could have been vaporized standing that close."

"They didn't arm them. They have to arm them before they drop them or they don't go boom."

The same basic conversation was going on in every truck, including the one pulling Gun Six of "C" Battery. "I thought I was going to die with my dick in my hand," said Bob.

"I can think of worse ways to go," smiled Doug, as the truck lurched forward, swinging the soldiers rearward and then forward again.

"I hope those guys made it," said John. "They were smoking pretty badly."

"Hey, you guys want to see something funny?" asked Doug.

"What?" asked Bob with a smile, wondering what his friend was up to.

"Look at Herby. He's got piss all down his leg."

"He does have piss all down his leg!" laughed John. "Hand get a little shaky there, Herb?"

Herby just sat there with a frown but didn't say anything.

"Cat got your tongue there, Herb?" laughed Doug.

Bob was beside himself laughing and even Dutch was laughing it up. There were 18 men in this truck and the only one not laughing was Herby.

"The truth is that it's so damn big that I couldn't get it back in my pants quick enough," said Herby.

"It didn't help that you were running while you were trying to do it," said Doug, and the other guys laughed out loud.

"Ok I have an idea," said Herby. "Why don't you all just go to hell, how would that be?"

The 386th got back on the road and bumped along, dragging her guns behind her. They went through a few small towns and started running into traffic — other units heading the same way they were. There were artillery battalions of every type, tanks and trucks, a lot of supply and command vehicles, but mostly infantry units.

"There are a whole lot of boys out there, fellas," said Bob as he peered out the back of the truck. "And a lot of hardware."

Aircraft were going overhead so often and in such numbers that it was almost a constant droning noise by now and they had to shout over it. The roads were getting thick with troops and they were approaching a larger town so the Colonel ordered another stop.

It had been a few hours since they last stopped for a break and he was afraid of getting jammed up, so he told Mitch to once again pull the column off to the right. The shout of "Piss call," went back from truck to truck and the Colonel stepped to the road and unzipped.

He stood there next to Mitch, donning his cavalry hat, and he looked here and there down the road at the row of trucks and jeeps with guns in tow. This time there were only about forty men out there instead of the eight hundred from the first stop, the rest choosing to stay in their truck.

Dutch and John were the only two men of Gun Six taking advantage of this break, while the others swore they didn't need to go.

"Suit yourselves," Dutch laughed as he jumped down. "I hope you all wind up like Herby with piss on your leg."

Herb just sat there sulking.

The Colonel turned to his driver and said, "Looks like we have some strong bladders in the 386th, Mitch. What do you think?"

"Stronger than mine, sir. I'm just glad you stopped when you did."

As the Colonel zipped up he nodded at the town just ahead and said, "I'd rather not stop again until we get past that. I'd hate for the boys to be peeing on some old lady's rose bushes or across from the playground."

"I know what you mean, sir. I don't think my wife would be too happy if she looked out the kitchen window one morning and saw eight hundred guys peeing on the lawn."

"Well, Sergeant, I suppose that is all of them."

"I suppose so, too, sir."

"Let's give them a few more minutes to think about it, Mitch. If we just sit here then they will wonder if we are lost and will worry about when we will stop again."

"Whatever you say, sir," Mitch grinned. The Colonel always seemed to know how to handle the situation, even the unusual ones.

It was more of a trickle than a flood, but the men of the battalion were jumping down, here and there, taking a quick pee and jumping back up to the safety of the truck. The trucks were not really any safer than the side of the road should they be attacked, but they felt safer, like an ostrich does when he buries his head. Perception is everything.

"Ok, let's get rolling, Sergeant. They had every chance and we have to make it before dark."

"Colonel, sir?"

"Yes, Mitch?"

"Just where is it that we have to make it to?"

"We are going to a town on the coast. On the English Channel. I suspect many of the units we have seen today are also heading for the coast."

"What town are we going to, sir?"

"We are on the way to a place called Bournemouth. To the China Hotel in Bournemouth, as a matter of fact."

"Reservation for eight hundred?" Mitch asked with a smile.

"Reservation for eight hundred, Mitch. Reservation for eight hundred."

Chapter Eleven

The girls were sent to Gloucester Air Force Camp for some advance training of their new assignment. They were to be assigned to the "Personal Receiving Station" in Bournemouth to process bomber pilots and crews as well as their support crews.

They helped them to find quarters and rations, as well as travel, leave and passes. They helped them in getting to their assignments and they helped them get back. Anything that had to do with the logistics of keeping these guys on track, fell on them.

Lillian was a little concerned about keeping Sarah out of trouble. Gloucester was a little easier to sneak away from, but that was mostly due to the fact that they were no longer cadets and no longer on such a short leash.

"We are Airmen now, Sarah. If we get caught this time it will be big trouble, trouble you may not be able to talk your way out of."

"When we get to Bournemouth then, love?" Sarah smiled.

"When we get to Bournemouth. Don't worry, I'm sure there will be lots of boys for you. Lots of pilots."

"Good, I like pilots. I like pilots a lot. You have a deal," and they shook on it.

When it was time to go to Bournemouth they traveled by convoy at night, so there would be no lights, or they would be sitting ducks. A few dozen trucks carried hundreds of airmen, mostly male, and tons of supplies.

A few men had to walk down the road in front and alongside the trucks to keep them crawling along. Lillian could feel the hum of the engine as it crawled along in first gear, and she could hear the crunch of the gravel as they slowly plowed through it.

The worst part of the journey was the constant smell of diesel fuel wafting up from the pipes — fumes that would normally be left behind as they drove, but that could not be escaped at this pace.

This terrible and slow journey only made the arrival that much better as they stood outside what was to be their home and workplace until assigned otherwise.

It was The Grand Hotel, and grand it was. The downstairs lobby area was used for the receiving station and the upstairs rooms were used for the girls' housing. Lillian and Sarah were assigned a room with two other girls.

Their two new roommates were Rebecca Elizabeth Hamilton, or 'Becky', and Emily Susan Church, who sometimes went by 'Em.' There were twelve girls in total on that floor, in three different rooms.

The hotel itself was a beautiful hotel in a one-time resort town of seventy-some-odd hotels, and many quaint little attractions, quiet little parks, a theatre, and of course, the sea wall and beach. There were also more than a dozen churches and Bournemouth was well known as a place young lovers went off to get married.

Paintings had been taken down from the walls, expensive furnishings moved out, and expensive rugs rolled up. Beautiful draperies were taken down and replaced with blackout curtains.

Desks with metal tops, filing cabinets, bulletin boards and telephones were moved in. Standing in the lobby with its great winding staircase the splendor could still be felt, and if looked for, the glory could be seen, but it had taken on a utilitarian purpose.

The place became a streamlined, well-managed processing center with a huge workload dealing with British, Canadian and Australian flight crews. All the girls and the mission of the Personal Receiving Station came under the command of Major Martha Bishop of His Majesty's Royal Air Force, and command she did.

By the spring of 1943, Lillian and Sarah were feeling quite at home with their new roommates and settling into the new job. There was always a great deal of work to do, and always an endless line of air crews coming and going.

In between the hard work with countless hours on their feet, they had to deal with the rationing system. Everyone had to do their part to conserve the few resources available to an island nation under siege.

Each girl was allowed one egg, and one half a cup of sugar per month, but those items were often nowhere to be found even if you had the ration coupon. Clothing was rationed, which killed Sarah because of her fondness for shopping.

They were allowed only two baths per week, and there was a mark in the tub at the six-inch line, which, if exceeded, could cost them a fine. Spam was a treat when it was around, as was fresh bread. Sarah said she never thought she would see the day when she would look forward to Spam. People waited in line for powdered eggs as well.

There were usually plenty of potatoes, and leeks and onions. Usually there was some kind of fish around as well, dried or cooked into a soup to stretch it out. And there were porridges and various other kinds of gruel to be had to keep them barely sustained. It did no good to complain, nobody listened. Everybody was in the same boat.

One good thing about Major Bishop, is that if you worked hard and did your share, in the off hours you could come and go as you pleased. There was no need for a pass to leave the Grand, and the best plan was to keep the Major happy and not wind up being confined to quarters.

"If you are going to misbehave," Sarah would say, "just don't let the Major see you doing so."

By now the English and the Germans were in a fight-to-the-death-winner-take-all war that seemed to have no end in sight. Air raid sirens would go off all hours of the day and night. While Bournemouth was not a strategic target, its location on the coast put it in the path of many German bombers on their way to London.

They would fly inland from there until they reached the Thames River and follow that right into London. If some of those German planes were intercepted by British Hurricanes they would dash for the channel. The bombers would often dump the bombs to lighten their plane to escape their pursuers.

Sometimes Bournemouth would be the place they would drop them, and sometimes people were killed. Day after day the sirens would blare, and almost always there would be no bombs, almost. It certainly kept you on your toes.

Even so, Sarah and Lillian loved the new assignment, especially since the town kept swelling with soldiers until the girls were outnumbered ten to one. The mere sound of a woman's shoes clicking down the street attracted men from blocks around.

"They are like bloody sharks, love," said Sarah as she and Lillian walked the few blocks back to the hotel from the department store.

"I think you like sharks," came the reply while looking over her shoulder. There were men behind them and men in front of them, and they all stopped and looked when the pretty girls went by.

"I do," Sarah smiled. "But you must remember to never fall in love with a soldier. They will promise you everything and then never come back. They will break your heart and never even say goodbye."

"I will remember that," said Lillian with a nod, then they both turned their heads as a group of soldiers whistled at them.

Sarah turned back to Lillian and said, "They are so very fun to play with, love, but don't fall in love."

By June of 1943, Major Bishop's receiving station was also processing French and Polish air crew members as well as a few other nationalities. These soldiers had escaped their homelands, now occupied by Nazis, and fought alongside the Commonwealth to try to win them back.

The Americans were starting to filter into Bournemouth as well, and they set up a receiving station for the American airmen in the hotel next to the Grand. Word spread that a lot more Americans would come to be stationed here, but rumors were rampant and one could not believe everything one heard.

Canadian and Australian crewmen made up the bulk of the non-British forces at the time, and they did not play well together at all. Some of the hardest fighting in Bournemouth at the time had nothing to do with the war.

They couldn't have them at the receiving station at the same time or there would be some words back and forth, some pushing and shoving, and then sometimes a bar room style brawl.

The British airmen didn't particularly care for anyone and the Americans seemed to like everybody, but the Canadians and the Australians would rip into each other at the drop of a hat, though they were both there to do the same job.

They were there to fly the Handley Page Halifax bombers made by the British, and they formed entire squadrons of them to fly deep into the heart of Germany and bring the war to the Nazis. Quaint and quiet little Bournemouth near the sea was just not the same with all these different soldiers here.

Lillian came to love the sea, and would spend many hours down at the seawall just staring out into the channel. She found a certain inner peace in the churning waves, and often times she could look out and not even see the heavy defenses and coils of razor wire that covered the beaches.

One day while sitting there in an almost trance-like state, a voice came from over her shoulder and asked, "Excuse me, miss, may I sit with you?"

She turned around to see a very nice looking Australian lieutenant standing there with his hat in his hand and a smile on his face. She was a little surprised by his sudden presence there, but his gentle demeanor disarmed her.

"I'd just like someone to talk to, miss," he said. "Just a friendly face far from home, is all."

"Lillian," she said sticking out her hand. "Lillian Rose Bradley. Airman First Class Bradley."

He smiled broadly and reached out, taking her hand and replied, "Jim. Jim Pendleton. Lieutenant Pendleton. So very lovely to meet you, Airman First Class Bradley."

Jim was a bombardier on a bomber. The Halifax, or referred by its crew as the "Halibag," was the stalwart heavy bomber of the Royal Air Force. The bombardier on the big plane actually had three jobs.

He sat up in the glass bubble nose of the aircraft, ahead of and below the pilots. In front of him was a machine gun in the bubble if they came under attack and needed a nose gunner. Behind him was the navigator's table from which he plotted the course to and from the targets and relayed the positions to the pilots above him.

At his feet was, of course, the bombsite. The reason for the trip over the channel through anti-aircraft fire, past enemy fighter planes trying to shoot them down, through all kinds of weather and unpredictable mechanical failures, all laid at Jim's feet.

If Jim's efforts missed the target, the whole dangerous mission was for nothing. And no one wanted to go through all that for nothing, so in many ways, the bombardier was the most important crewmember aboard.

"He is very sweet," she told Sarah. "He's from Perth, and his father is a minister, and he has three younger sisters."

"He sounds like no bloody fun at all," said Sarah.

"He sounds nice," said Becky, and Emily nodded her agreement.

"He is nice, very nice. A perfect gentleman."

"Don't you go off falling in love with him now, you silly girl. You look a little starry-eyed. Just remember I warned you."

"Warned her against what?" asked Emily.

"She told me not to fall in love with a soldier. She told me they would leave and never come back."

"What about you?" Emily said to Sarah. "You fall in love with a new soldier every week!" All the girls laughed except Sarah.

"That's the whole point, silly girl. But I only play with them and I let them buy me things. Then I get bored and go find another. But I don't fall in love."

"Well, how do you know I'm not going to just play with Jim?"

"Well, for one thing, you're a bit of a stick in the mud when it comes to playing with boys, and for another thing, you have that silly faraway look on your face. Don't do it, love. You'll be sorry."

"Well then, I will just have to be a stick in the mud. I like him, and he likes me. We are going out again tomorrow."

"Don't say I didn't warn you."

Jim and Lillian started going out on a regular basis, and she could tell he was growing quite fond of her, but he was always a perfect gentlemen, unlike many of the Aussie soldiers in town, which were more often than not, wild men.

When soldiers marched in platoons through the streets of Bournemouth, the Americans, Australians and Canadians always marched with the sergeant alongside the column, but the British sergeants would stand out in front. A typical sergeant marching this way would carry a long baton and make exaggerated motions full of pomp and circumstance.

It can be quite a spectacle watching a British column of very well drilled troops going down the road led by such a man. British troops were disciplined enough to have no need of a sergeant walking beside them to keep an eye on them. However, the seargents of the other troops knew better, especially the Australians.

One morning while Sarah, Lillian and Rebecca were standing out in front of the Grand, a column of fresh Australian troops were, for some reason, being led by a British sergeant major as they marched down the street.

The sergeant major high-stepped down the middle of the street in full regalia, shouting a spirited cadence, swinging and pointing his baton while his charge of Australian troops marched unseen behind him.

The sergeant major was perfect in every way. From his head held up high, to his spit-shined boots and everything in between. Every motion he made was perfect, every step was flawless, with his eyes locked in front of him.

When he wanted his column to turn, he put his baton in the air, shouted the right turn, and pointed the baton right as he stepped into the direction with a shuffle that must take years of practice to perfect. Then he marched on, never looking back, shouting the cadence and high-stepping again.

The Australians, however, did not share the sergeant major's enthusiasm for marching. They figured out he wasn't going to look back at them, so they just strolled along, talking and joking, pushing and playing like high school boys on a playground. One of them was right behind the sergeant, mimicking his every move while a whole row of them were walking backwards.

"Look at those silly wankers," Sarah nodded towards the group coming down the street.

"Oh my God, that is so funny," Lillian giggled, and Becky turned to see what they were looking at, then she smiled, too.

"He looks like he's marching all by himself down the street with a clown circus parade following him."

"He has no idea," Lillian started laughing out loud. "He has no bloody idea at all!"

"I think I might pee my bloody pants," Becky said, laughing and holding her side.

Sarah couldn't say anything, she was laughing too hard as the procession was passing in front of them. The girls did not go unnoticed, and a few of the Aussie's trotted over and introduced themselves.

"No worries, love, we'll catch up," one said and Sarah had tears in her eyes from laughing so hard. They flirted for a minute or two, and seeing their comrades getting further away, they tipped their hats and with a smile, promised to return.

"They all say that," Sarah said, still laughing.

When the group came to the end of the street and the sergeant major made an abrupt right turn in his grand fashion, he started leading them up a steep grade. The men paused at the bottom of the hill, not at all happy with the prospect of marching up it.

As luck would have it, a trolley came by just at that moment and turned to climb up the same hill, giving the men the break they were looking for. They dashed for the slow moving trolley and all twenty-four men made it aboard with their packs and guns.

Lillian and her friends, as well as all the other onlookers, were doubled over with laughter as the trolley full of men rode right past their sergeant. They tucked themselves behind a fence until he passed by totally unaware of their presence.

"That's the funniest thing I've ever seen," said Lillian, as the men fell in right behind the sergeant major, still marching proudly and still oblivious to the undisciplined fools he was leading.

"That made my bloody day," said Rebecca, wiping away tears.

"I'll have to tell Jim about that tonight," said Lillian, making Sarah roll her eyes.

"Tell me you didn't," said Sarah, shaking her head.

"She didn't what?" asked Emily, as Lillian slipped off her shoes and hat with a dreamy little smile on her face.

"You bloody did it, didn't you?"

Lillian just shrugged her shoulders and milled around still smiling. Becky knew what Sarah meant but Emily was bewildered by the whole conversation.

"You fell in love with him, didn't you? You went off and fell in love with a soldier. A bloody Aussie soldier at that. Are you daft?"

"I don't know if it's love, but I do like him. He makes me feel good. He makes me feel…safe?"

"Safe! What the hell does that mean?" bellowed Sarah.

"When will you see him again?" asked Emily, now catching up on the conversation.

"He has one more mission and then he gets a two week pass. He wants to take me to London for a few days."

141

"Are you daft? You're not going, are you?"

"I'm going to beg the Major for a pass for a few days. Just a few days. I know I can't get two weeks but a few days would be nice."

"I was talking to a Canadian yesterday when a bloody Aussie bumped him away so he could make my acquaintance. The next thing I know they are rolling around on the floor beating each other silly. Bloody Aussies," Sarah said.

"Those Australians are all crazy," said Emily.

"Not all of them," said Lillian.

The call for lights out went through the halls and Becky reached over and clicked off the blue light.

"Don't fall in love with a soldier, love," Sarah said in a whisper. "They will bloody well break your heart every time."

The next day Lillian pitched her case to Major Bishop. The Major was reluctant to allow one of her charges to run off to London with an Australian flier — she had seen them in action enough times around the receiving station.

Airman Lillian Bradley stood there in front of the Major and suddenly felt the same feelings she had as a child when she had to stand in front of the Mother Superior for one reason or another, and that rarely worked out well for her.

The Major just stood there looking at her.

"I will be careful, Major. I promise to stay out of trouble," Lillian said as if she were reading the Major's thoughts.

After a long and painful pause Major Bishop said, "Alright then, I will trust your judgment, don't disappoint me."

"Is that a yes?" Lillian asked rather shocked.

"You had better go tell your flier, I'm sure he is waiting."

"Thank you, Major Bishop. Thank you very much," she said and left the Major with a little smile on her face, hoping she had made the right decision.

Lillian left the Grand that evening to meet up with her handsome lieutenant and tell him the good news.

That night Lillian slipped into the room just before lights out and found the other three girls sitting and talking around the little blue, blackout light. Lillian was as white as a ghost and her hands were shaking.

"What is it, love?" asked Sarah, after seeing tears on Lillian's face.

The black curtains covered every inch of window while the Home Guard patrolled the streets, seeking to darken any telltale crack of light, but just enough light always made its way in so that once used to the dark, they could see each other, and Sarah could see the shock on her friend's face.

"Lillian my love, what is it?" Emily asked as she sat up and put her arm around her friend. Becky did the same and Sarah stood in front of her.

Lillian started to sob and she couldn't answer their questions so she just shook her head and looked at the floor.

"Did something happen to Jim?" asked Sarah. "Is that it?"

Lillian nodded and had to sit down as the girls huddled around her. They were all just quiet for a little while as Lillian cried. They didn't know what happened, and yet they did know. It happened every day.

"His plane," Lillian finally choked out. "His squadron. They were ambushed on the way back. He's gone. I can't believe it, but he's gone."

"It's alright, love," the other girls said as they huddled around her and cried with her. "We are here with you."

"I can't believe it, he was just here, and now he's gone, and we never even said goodbye. I never said goodbye."

Sarah hugged her friend and let her cry on her shoulder. "It's alright, love. It will be alright."

"No more bloody soldiers, Sarah. No more. I should have listened to you. Never again."

Sarah held her and patted her back until she stopped sobbing and finally drifted off to sleep.

Chapter Twelve

During the winter of 1943, the Americans were starting to pour into the Bournemouth and surrounding area. As winter turned into spring, tent cities went up everywhere and heavy equipment started to roll in, such as tanks and trucks and artillery.

Up until now, Bournemouth had been the home of more aviators than anything else, but now more and more infantry and mechanized units were showing up every day, almost bursting the town at its seams.

Lillian still loved the seawall, even though it was like running a gauntlet to get there and back, through all the American soldiers. She would sometimes think of Jim, but the feelings started to fade away, and she wondered if she ever really loved him.

She was having trouble remembering his face — it all seemed so long ago. It was a lifetime ago. There would be no more soldiers, of that she was sure. No more bloody soldiers in this lifetime.

Sarah and Lillian stood outside the Grand Hotel talking one evening and watching a group of American soldiers standing around up the street laughing it up and acting like teenagers, the way all Americans seemed to act.

"Those yanks are some odd ducks, are they not?" asked Sarah.

"They act like they are here to play," replied Lillian. "Maybe nobody bothered to tell them that there is a war going on here."

"What the bloody hell are they chewing? They look like a bunch of cows."

Lillian started to laugh. "I wondered about that myself."

"I can't believe they walk around outdoors with their hat stuck through that loop on their shoulder, and no tie. A British soldier wouldn't be caught dead like that."

"They say we need them if we are to win this war."

"Good lord," said Sarah. "We must be worse off than I thought."

Lillian laughed. "Look at them, Sarah. Just look at them."

Sarah stared at the boys standing up the street chewing whatever it was they were chewing.

"They're not afraid Sarah. They think they're here to save the bloody world, and they're not afraid."

"Thank God they're here, love."

"Thank God they're here, Sarah. Thank God."

"You know why they are bringing all those tanks and soldiers down to the sea, don't you? Down to the channel?"

"Either we are going to get them, or they are coming to get us."

"Let's hope it's the former, love."

"Let's hope."

"Just look at those crazy buggers, Lil. They have everything they could ever want. It's no wonder they are happy."

"They certainly don't look like they go hungry."

"They certainly don't. One tried to give me a pair of silk stockings if I would go out with him. Silk stockings! I may have said yes if his two front teeth hadn't been missing."

Lillian laughed.

Just then Becky came walking up with a frown on her face. "What is it, love?" asked Lillian.

"Do you remember my friend Shirley? The widow with two kids that lives in that old house off the square," she said and her friends nodded.

"She ran out of coal for her stove and her ration is used up. Her kids are always sick lately and these chilly nights don't help any, plus she can't even boil her potatoes. I wish I could do something."

"The Americans have coal," said Sarah. "They have lots of it in a bin behind the hotel up the street. I've seen it."

"Do you mean the one with the guard outside all the time?"

"That's the one. Lillian, could you, let's say, distract that guard while we sneak back there and get that coal?"

Lillian's heart started to thump as an adrenaline rush went through her. She thought about it for a few moments, then smiled and said, "Sure, why not. It just might be fun."

"Alright, here is the plan," said Sarah, immediately taking charge as usual, and already with a plan worked out. "Becky and I will grab a couple gas mask cases, dump them out, and stroll with them down the side street by the hotel."

The other girls nodded their heads listening carefully to all the details. Lillian could feel the sweat beading on the back of her neck as Sarah told her what her part would be.

"Walk right past the hotel," continued Sarah. "Walk right past him. When you know you are just past him then snap you're head around, and I promise you will catch him looking at you."

"Won't that embarrass him?"

"That's the idea, love. But then you give him a little smile, like an 'I-caught-you-looking-but-it's-okay' smile, and he will get all shy and silly with you. He will look at the ground and glance up at you and rock back and forth and try to stammer out something to say."

Lillian giggled. "And what do I do then?"

"Just stand there and smile and nod. Just stand there and flirt a little bit while Becky and I sneak down the driveway and load up. When you see us coming out, then we are good to go. Don't worry, love. Men are so easy."

They all laughed, took their positions, and off they went. When Lillian snapped around to see the soldier looking at her, she almost laughed as she saw Sarah and Becky slip around the wall and down the sloped driveway that led around back.

"You look a little cold, Yank," she said, showing some concern, trying to make him feel important.

"No, no, it's nothing, I can handle this, I've been in a lot colder places than this," he said, trying to look like a big, strong soldier. He was more like an overgrown boy, like most of these Americans. "Maybe I can take you out sometime?"

Lillian had to keep from laughing as she saw the two girls lugging their heavy bags up the hill then around the wall, then disappearing from sight. "Perhaps."

"Hey listen, doll," he said as he glanced around like he was about to do something he wasn't supposed to. "I have something that I was going to trade for some booze, but I want to give it to you."

He reached into a nearby truck and pulled out a package wrapped in wax paper, and brown paper below that. It felt like a big soft bowling ball when he dropped it in her hands.

"What is this?" Lillian asked, rather stunned.

"It's a rump roast. A good one. Now you and your girlfriends have something to cook with the coal," he winked at her.

"Thank you," she stammered out. She stretched out and gave the yank a kiss on the cheek and then hurried off to meet the girls.

"I told you men were easy," grinned Sarah as she watched Becky and Lillian head off to deliver the goodies to Shirley and her kids. After a short visit, Lillian decided to leave but Rebecca stayed with her friend for a while. It was May 6, 1944. One month before D-Day.

Lillian strolled along in a bit of a daydream, thinking about how she got to this place at this time in her life, and she wondered again about her sisters, although the pain of it was subsiding. There is only so much pain you can carry and still go on with your life, so on she walked, deep in thought.

"Oh I don't want to set the world on fire. I just want to start a flame in your heart!"

Lillian almost jumped out of her shoes as this American soldier had snuck up behind her and started singing as loud as he could. She snapped around and jumped back a step.

"In my heart I have but one desire, all that one is you, no other will do," taking a step forward as he sang.

"You bloody crazy yank," she shouted at him. "You scared the shit out of me."

He just smiled and sang even louder, now spreading open his arms and drawing the attention of everyone on the street. *"I've lost all ambition for worldly acclaim, I just want to be the one you love. And with your admission, that you love the same, I'll have the goal that I've been dreaming of."*

Lillian pulled her hat down and headed straight for the Grand as fast as she could walk, but he just trotted alongside her and never stopped singing. *"I don't want to set the world on fire, I just want to set a flame in your heart."*

When she got to the Grand she darted straight inside to the safety of the hotel, a place he couldn't come, but he stood out there for a few minutes and bellowed out another chorus before trotting away. The other girls stood there, mouths agape, after watching the whole little show.

"What the bloody hell was that?" asked Sarah.

"I don't know. I think he's bloody daft. Scared me half to death."

"Well who was he?" asked Emily.

"I haven't the foggiest. He popped out of nowhere."

"Did he say anything?" asked Sarah.

"Not a bloody word," said Lillian, still a little shocked. "He just sang to me the whole time."

The girls broke into a roaring laugh and giggled about it all night. Crazy yanks. They were as bad as the Australians. They didn't fight as much, but they were crazy.

Over the next few days the singing soldier appeared behind Lillian three more times, each time making her jump, each time singing the same song, and each time never saying a word.

Once while sitting on the seawall looking out at the growing flotilla of warships, and thinking that there were as many ships that she could see as stars in the sky, he jumped out of nowhere once again.

149

"Oh I don't want to set the world on fire. I just want to start a flame in your heart."

"How in the hell did you find me here, you bloody bastard?" she yelled at him and ran away, leaving him standing there grinning. He seemed to be everywhere she was. "How the hell does he do that?"

The next night, Sarah was carrying some boxes down to the basement when she smelled that smell. That irresistible, tantalizing, alluring smell that she loved so much but had been without for so long.

"Cake!" she whispered. "I smell cake!"

She tracked the smell around the dark basement to the common wall between the Grand, and the hotel next door occupied by the Americans. She looked up to see cracks of light flickering through a damaged area about six feet off the ground.

The bricks in the wall were bulged out indicating that whatever damaged the wall was caused by an impact from the other side. She looked around the cluttered basement for a chair, and found a stack of them, covered in dust and cobwebs.

"This will work," she said out loud to herself, dragging one to the wall.

She stepped up on the chair and looked through the crack at the commercial grade kitchen on the other side, and was intoxicated by the rush of air bringing the lovely smell to her hungry nose.

Sarah leaned back a little and looked at the bricks. She could see the little pile of broken mortar on the floor beneath her, so she decided to wiggle a couple of the bricks, but had to be quiet because there were cooks on the other side still working.

"They are loose," she told the other three girls that night while huddling together in the middle of the room.

"We can do this," she continued.

They all laughed as Sarah told them how she stuck her nose in the crack and smelled the divine smell, and they

150

giggled nervously as she told them the scheme to help get their hands on it.

"It sounds like a dangerous proposition just to get some cake," said Rebecca. "We are sure to get caught."

"Just cake?" said Sarah in a raised voice. "It's not just cake, love. It's stolen cake, and stolen cake is the sweetest cake of all."

"What the hell, count me in," said Emily.

"Lillian?" asked Sarah, as she stared at her with the same look she had from their last cake caper.

"Sure," she said reluctantly. "Count me in, too."

The three girls turned and looked at Rebecca, who darted her eyes back and forth from girl to girl.

"You know what they say about the Americans, don't you? That they have just too much for their own good. Spoiled, they are," said Sarah. "I think we should help them with that little problem."

"Alright, count me in, too, then," she said shaking her head.

Sarah leaned back and smiled and said, "Alright then, it's all for one, and one for all."

"And all for cake," said Lillian, and they all laughed.

Midnight. They all agreed on midnight, midnight in stocking feet. They would slip out the door at midnight and tiptoe towards the dangerous cake.

Sarah, always the eager leader, eased open the door and it made a squeak that seemed to echo up and down the empty hall, sounding much louder to the frightened girls than it really was.

They inched out onto the hardwood floor, casting long shadows on the walls ahead as they walked towards them, squinting in the dark to see. They walked past two rooms just like theirs and turned the corner to face the top of the long staircase.

Three steps down the first landing and Sarah's weight on the stair made a terrible squeak, freezing the terrified girls in place. Lillian could feel her heart beating in her chest, the adrenaline pumping through her brain.

With the girls frozen and wide-eyed, Sarah pointed to the step she was standing on and shook her head no, and the girls nodded their heads, indicating that they understood to avoid that squeaky spot.

A few steps later, another squeak, another point, and three more nods before pressing onward to the cake. They made it down to the first landing, and then the second with three bad squeaky spots they would remember to avoid on the way back up.

They crept silently along the wall in the hallway that led to the basement steps, but they had to pass their commanding officer's quarters on the way, without a doubt the most dangerous part of this journey.

Sarah stopped them just short of the door and made the shush sign with her finger but made no actual sound. The girls nodded. Then she made the cutthroat sign and they nodded again, and Sarah moved quietly forward. One by one they crept past Major Bishop's door and held their breath as they did so.

Lillian felt a fear so intense it made her ears ring and her throat as dry as dust. *I must be daft.*

Becky was the last girl to pass the Major's door, and paused while the other girls were bunching up in front of her. Lillian glanced back to see Becky holding her hands over her mouth and her eyes squinting almost closed, like she was trying to hold in a sneeze. She bent over and tried desperately to move ahead.

Once they turned and went down the basement steps, closing the door behind them, Becky broke into a side splitting laugh that made her eyes water, as the other three just stared at her.

"What the hell are you laughing at?" asked Sarah Jane.

Becky was trying to compose herself as she coughed out the reply, "Did you hear her snoring?"

"Hear what?" asked Lillian, while Emily looked back and forth at the girls, then up the stairs, then back at them again.

"She snored like a bear. When I heard it I almost burst out laughing."

Emily and Lillian laughed at the thought, and Sarah smiled and shook her head with her hands on her hips. "Are we finished now, ladies? Can we get our bloody cake?"

"Show us where," said Lillian, and the other girls nodded.

Sarah pulled the chair over to the wall and lit the candle she had brought with them, then handed it over to Emily. Lillian jumped up on the chair, examining the bricks and looking through the cracks into the kitchen.

"Can't see a thing. It's black in there."

Sarah traded positions with her and started jiggling the bricks until one came loose and she slid it out and handed it down. After the first two or three were down, they started to come out easier.

"Does that look big enough?" she asked, and Becky nodded as the other two girls shrugged.

"It is pitch black in there," she continued. "Give us a candle, love."

As soon as Sarah held it up to the hole, it blew out. "Light it again, will you, Em?" she said, as she passed it back down.

She held it up again and the air rushing from the other side once again blew it out. "Well, this is not going to work," she said. "One of us needs to climb through and find a light. Any volunteers?"

The four of them looked back and forth at each other with wide eyes and blank stares when Becky looked up at the black portal with so much promise awaiting. But it was a dark promise.

"Bloody hell," she said. "I'll do it."

"That's the spirit, love," said Sarah, grinning broadly.

Becky climbed up on the chair and put her hands on the edges of the opening, and after glancing one more time back down at the three other girls, boosted herself up and through the hole.

She was halfway in with her legs dangling in midair when Emily asked, "Can you see anything?"

"Not a bloody thing," she said, and just a second later, she slipped through the hole and disappeared.

CLANG! BANG! CLANG! CLANG! The noise from the other side echoed through the basement like the tin man rolling down a hill, then went deathly silent.

Sarah jumped up on the chair and whispered through the hole, though whispering now seemed rather pointless, "Are you alright?"

A few more seconds went by, and then another small clang, and then a giggling Becky said, "Hand me the bloody candle."

"Good lord," said Lillian. "If that didn't wake up the Major then nothing will!" Suddenly a light flickered on in the American kitchen as Becky lit the candle.

"See if you can find a light, love," said Sarah. "And maybe a chair so we can climb over and down."

Becky found the light in no time and flipped it on, and there leaning against a wall was a step ladder, presumably for reaching things on high shelves. Becky carried it over to the hole in the bricks and one by one the remaining cake bandits scurried up the wall and down the ladder to their treasure.

"So that's what that was," said Lillian as she glanced around at the big mixing bowls scattered around the foot of the ladder. It seemed Rebecca had crashed into a shelf on the way down and cleared it of its noisy contents.

"They are lucky to have them," she continued, thinking about the gap tooth pair of metal collectors who came to the Commander's house and relieved Joyce of most of her tools of the trade.

"Look," said Sarah to the other girls as she pulled the lid up on a large tray. "Just look at that, ladies. Is that lovely?"

"Oh my God, chocolate! How in the world did they get all that chocolate?" Emily asked, as she stared at a huge slab of cake already half eaten, but still enough to feed an army.

"Good lord, look at that," said Lillian as she pointed to a mountain of hard-boiled eggs, more than she had eaten in her whole life. "Where on earth do they get all this?"

They were amazed as they looked around the room and saw sacks of sugar and flour stacked against the wall, and bags and bags of potatoes.

"The bloody Americans seem to get anything they want," said Sarah. "Tonight they are going to share some of it. They can keep their potatoes, but they are going to make a little donation to the Royal Air Force. Who wants cake?"

Lillian carefully cut a long strait slice off one end of the slab of cake so they wouldn't notice it missing. Then each girl dropped two eggs in their pockets, picked up the mixing bowls, and three of them scurried up the ladder and out the hole, leaving Lillian behind.

She put the ladder back, turned off the light, and made her way back to the hole where the other girls pulled her up and out, leaving no evidence behind.

Then they got to work putting the bricks back in place, putting the chair away, and ascending up the basement steps hoping to make a clean getaway by slipping undetected past the Major's quarters.

Trying not to giggle, and in their stocking feet while remembering the squeaky spots, they eased back upstairs and crept into the safety of their room.

"Oh my God, we did it!" exclaimed Lillian. "I can't believe we actually did it! My heart is pounding, and look, my hands are all sweaty."

"Well, of course we did it," Sarah smiled. "Now, thanks to me, we all get to eat some lovely cake!"

"Magnificent!" said Emily. "You should be working for Mr. Churchill himself. He could use a diabolical mind such as yours."

"Brilliant," Lillian proclaimed as she broke off a piece of her cake and popped it in her mouth. "Oh my God, this is divine."

The others all agreed and the room fell silent for a few minutes as they relished every morsel of the freshly baked chocolate cake.

"Eggs for breakfast," said Sarah, and they all nodded and smiled.

"When do we go again?" asked Becky, and they all turned and looked at her and then to Sarah, who smiled and nodded.

"Tomorrow night, ladies. Tomorrow night at midnight." They laughed and, after turning off the blue light, went to bed.

The next day Lillian tried to keep a straight face as the Major told them what a great job they were doing, handling the greater workload and staying out of trouble. *If she only knew.*

The next night at midnight the girls slipped out of the room once again, and avoiding the carefully mapped out squeaks, and the bear's cave, they made it to the basement door. This time they brought with them a couple of pillowcases.

After exposing the hole again, and boosting Lillian through, they all gathered in the kitchen and looked around as if they had just discovered King Tut's tomb and all its riches within.

"Oh my God, apples! Look at all those bloody apples," Lillian said.

"And cookies, for Christ's sake," said Sarah. "How the bloody hell did they get all these cookies?"

They filled the pillowcases with apples and eggs, half of the cookies, and a few cups of sugar from an open bag. They filled their pockets too, and started passing their loot back through the hole and covering their tracks.

Once they were safely back in the room, they divided up the loot and with gentle taps on the other two doors, the other eight girls that had been sworn to secrecy earlier in the day, eagerly awaited their share.

The girls were suddenly rich with luxury foods they had only dreamt of a few nights before. The only dilemma was that out of fear they would be caught, they had to get rid of the evidence as soon as possible, so they ate until they could eat no more.

"One more time," Sarah pleaded. "Just one more night and then we take a break for a while."

"It's too much," Emily protested. "They will miss it."

"The other girls are counting on us," said Lillian. "We can go one more time. They have so much."

"They won't miss it, Em. They won't."

"Come on now, love. Remember it is one for all, and all for one."

"And all for cake!" they said, almost in unison.

Emily looked around at the three girls and finally relented. "There's no point in stopping now, I suppose."

Four pillowcases this time went out of the room with the girls — four pillowcases that were destined to be as chock full of American goodies as the sacks over Santa's shoulder on Christmas Eve. The four shadows danced on the wall, and the four pairs of socks slid along the hardwood floor.

They stood there in the American's kitchen with bags so full they may have to take out a few more bricks to shove them out. More apples, more eggs, and more sugar. The real treat today was the brownies. Thick and rich brownies that would have made any baker proud.

They took a full two dozen eggs, a dozen brownies, and eighteen apples. They also took a piece of cheese that was well over a pound, two sticks of butter, and finding six fresh loaves of bread, they took two of them.

"This is the crime of the bloody century, ladies," said Lillian, as the girls gathered to make good their escape.

One by one the full pillowcases went through the hole, and one by one went the girls as well. All except for Emily. Emily stood there and looked around the kitchen and seemed not to even hear when Lillian whispered through the hole for her to come on.

"It's too much," she finally said. "They will miss it, it's just too much."

"What are you waiting for? Come on now," said Lillian with some urgency in her voice now, but Emily still ignored the heed.

"Get down off that bloody chair," Sarah said to Lillian and traded places with her. "Emily, have you gone daft? Are you planning to surrender to the bloody Americans in the morning?"

Emily looked up at Sarah's face in the hole, blinked her eyes a few times, and without saying another word, she walked away and out of sight.

"Em wait. Emily! Dammit Emily, come back here," Sarah said, and then turned and looked at the other two with an astonished look on her face.

"What's wrong?" asked Rebecca.

"Bloody hell," said Sarah, shaking her head, and then she started climbing back through the hole. Lillian and Rebecca followed close behind.

Emily had pulled up a stool in front of a giant pile of potatoes and, with a knife she found in a drawer, was peeling them. The three girls came over and stood around her but she never looked up from her work.

"Are you going to peel all those potatoes by yourself?" asked Lillian.

"No, you are going to help me. And so are you, and you," she said looking at Sarah, and then Rebecca, and then down again.

"We need to go," said Sarah. "We don't have time for this."

"The knives are in that drawer," she said as she nodded towards it, and then placed the perfectly peeled potato into the huge stainless steel sink and picked up another.

"Let's get on with it then, ladies," Sarah said as though it were her idea, and they did.

One after another after another, the mountain of potatoes turned into a mountain of peeled potatoes. Whatever the soldiers thought about the purloined groceries in the morning, they were going to have a lot less work to do while they thought about it.

After finishing their chore, washing the knives, wiping down the counters, and moving the stools back in place, they were finally ready to leave.

"Happy now?" Sarah asked Emily, who didn't respond.

"We thought you got caught," said one of the girls from another room. "We were so worried when you didn't come back."

"Sorry, love," said Lillian. "Emily decided to go all domestic on us, but we made it back with treats for days."

The next day after work, a very tired Lillian was making her way from the store back to the Grand for a much needed good night's sleep. She was within a hundred feet of the entry when she was startled once again, almost throwing her bag in the air.

"Oh I don't want to set the world on fire, I just want to start a flame in your heart."

She wanted to scream at him, but he suddenly gave a timid nod and tipped his cap and scurried away, much to Lillian's surprise, but definitely to her relief. Then she turned and saw why he chose to take off.

A British Major was standing in the doorway, and he would rather avoid the trouble a call to his commanding officer would surely bring. It was a female British major — Major Bishop, as a matter of fact.

Standing behind the Major were her three best friends in the world, and they were all looking at the ground, none of them looking happy.

"Now that your boyfriend is done serenading you, may I have a word with you, Airman Bradley?" The Major was asking, but not really asking.

"Of course, Major. But he is not my boyfriend," she said as the other girls looked up. Only Sarah smiled.

"You look rather tired, Airman. Have you been working too hard? Or maybe not sleeping enough, perhaps?"

"No, Major, I'm fine."

159

"Good, good. Because I would hate to think you have been up past curfew, wouldn't I?"

"No, Major, I would hate for you to think that," she said as she looked over the Major's shoulder and the other girls just shrugged.

"Well, that is good, Airman Bradley. Since you and your roommates have so much energy after sleeping so well, I need you to polish the brass on that upper level."

"All of it?"

"All of it."

"Tonight?"

"Tonight."

The four tired girls with their heads hanging low and their feet dragging made their way to the staircase.

"Oh and ladies, one more thing." The girls turned to look at her. "In the morn I expect to find an apple and a few eggs on my desk, and some cookies would be lovely, too. I have a lot more brass to polish if you would prefer."

"I told you it was too much," said Emily, as they rubbed the brass fixtures with polish to shine off the tarnish that had built up. So much brass, more than Lillian had ever noticed before. Door knobs and knockers, light fixtures and handrails, and even fire extinguishers.

"Maybe so," said Lillian. "But it was worth it."

"We will be here all bloody night," said Sarah, shaking her head.

"Maybe not," Rebecca smiled and said. "Look."

The other bedroom doors had opened and the other eight girls quietly slipped out into the hall, each with a rag, and each taking on a small dab of polish before hunting down anything that didn't shine.

They all worked in silence and with grins as the luster filled the landing, and Lillian couldn't help but think how proud she was to be one of these girls. It truly was all for one, and one for all.

When they were nearly done, as Lillian looked around and smiled while she polished, she accidently hit the discharge on

160

the fire extinguisher, and it shot a stream of foam over the rail and down to the lobby below.

A terrified Lillian raced to the rail, quickly joined by the other girls, to see a dozen flight officers with globs of foam on their shoulders, pants and hats. And standing there with them was Major Martha Bishop. This was going to cost a lot more eggs, and a lot more brass, and it was going to be a very long night.

It was May 23, 1944. It was two weeks before D-Day.

Chapter Thirteen

The 386th pulled into Bournemouth and started working its way through the crowded streets. The air was thick with the smell of diesel fuel, and the streets were lined with tanks and trucks.

There were thousands of soldiers camped just outside the town, and thousands more packed in everywhere as they got to the outskirts of the once pretty little seaside hamlet.

They rumbled past the remains of the Metropole Hotel, an iconic six story magnificent old hotel, once a landmark but now reduced to rubble. The St. Ives Hotel was a burned out shell that was destroyed during the same air raid.

A Focke-Wulf 190 fighter bomber crashed into the St. Ives during the raid, and sat on the roof with the pilot just sitting in the cockpit looking straight ahead as if he were still flying. The fire brigade tried to bring the flaming hotel under control, but then noticed the full complement of bombs still attached to the plane, so they ran for cover.

Eventually the flames were extinguished, and the unharmed pilot, Lt. Leopold Wenger, climbed down from his plane and was taken into custody. He had to be protected from the angry crowd who would have torn him to shreds had they gotten their hands on him.

John and Doug had their heads sticking out the back of the truck watching the town go by as they worked their way towards Boscombe.

"All these guys are not here to guard Bournemouth," said Doug.

"That's a lot of hardware out there," said John.

"They must have a lot of boats somewhere," Doug grinned. "Tanks don't swim."

163

"Shit," said Herby. "We are actually going, aren't we? Shit."

"Relax, Herby," said Bob. "Taking beaches is a job for real soldiers, not Skywatchers. They'll bring us over later, if at all."

"Shit," Herby said again as he looked out the back of the truck at the big gun they were dragging behind them. "Shit."

"C'mon Herby," said Doug. "You're not gonna meet one of those little French girls if you don't take that boat ride."

Herby didn't laugh or even smile. He didn't have one of his trademark come backs as he usually does. He just fell silent, as did the others, when the English Channel suddenly came into view. They all just paused and stared.

"Shit," said Herby.

"Shit," said Bob, and the other guys nodded their heads.

"Look at all that," John said, as he nodded toward the barbed wire and mines strewn across the once pristine beach. This was a place where eleven miles of beautiful white sand met blue sea during peacetime, but now looked like the Alamo.

"I wonder if the French beaches look like that, too," said Doug.

"Worse than that, I bet," said Bob.

"Shit," said Herby.

Just then the trucks started pulling up in front of their new home, The China Hotel. Before they could even come to a stop the men were pouring out of them as fast as they could, emptying the vehicles in record time.

For the next few minutes, nothing was safe as nearly eight hundred men peed on everything they could find — every tree, every bush, behind every corner, behind every truck, and right out in the open. A collective sigh of relief let out, and the steam rose up in a cloud.

"Do you think they got hot water and maid service in this joint?" Herby asked, as he stood next to Bob peeing into some bushes.

"Right now I'm just glad they have bushes."

The battalion was mustered up and the guns were placed and set up at the locations the Headquarters Battalions' intelligence guys had mapped out prior to the crews getting there.

They were manned 24 hours a day and were all pointed out over the channel. The four guys were assigned a room together to bunk in, and quickly felt right at home guarding the China Hotel.

Sitting on their gun position, the guys were amazed as they looked out over the channel at the traffic in the air.

"I never thought there were this many planes in the whole friggin' world," said Bob, shaking his head.

"Do the Krauts have that many, too?" asked Herb. "We're gonna need a lot more guns."

Every few hours the full alert siren would sound and all the men would rush out to the guns. The shift that manned the guns would be joined by the shift that was off so replacement gunners were standing close by in case they were needed.

Bob hated that part of the job. "I don't like standing here while they work," he said.

"Doesn't bother me a bit," said Herby.

"It's not that," said Bob. "It's just that I feel like a sitting duck on the pond here. I'm having to leave it up to those guys to protect me while I just watch."

"Got nothing to shoot back with. I get it," said John.

"Well, it could be worse," Doug said, with a serious look on his face.

"How could it be worse?"

"We could be depending on Herby, then we'd all be fucked."

They all laughed except Herby.

"Why don't you all just go to hell," said Herby, and they all laughed again.

"C'mon guys," said Bob. "Don't pick on Herby. I bet he could hit the English channel from here."

"Maybe," said John. "But I wouldn't bet on it if I were you, Bob. The Atlantic is a lot bigger, you know."

165

"Like I said, you guys can just…."

Herb was cut in mid-sentence when the air raid siren started to blare again, and everyone jumped to their feet. They were facing out over the water with the seawall to their backs.

"Is that them, Bob?" John shouted and pointed at a cluster of aircraft out almost to the horizon and flying parallel to the shoreline.

"No, those are Hurricanes," said Bob, looking through his binoculars. "Don't shoot at them, the Brits will get pissed off."

Everyone continued to scan the sky for targets as the siren moaned its plaintive wail. The siren tower was close to them so the sound seemed to vibrate through them with an unnerving hum.

Bob had heard air raid sirens before, but this one was just off key enough and just close enough that the sound really disturbed him and he wished it would stop.

"God I wish they would fix that thing," he said. "It's making my bones ring like a tuning fork."

"It feels like touching the electric fence at my dad's place," said Doug.

"You have an electric fence?" asked Herby. "What the hell kind of New Yorker has an electric fence?"

They heard them before they saw them. They were coming up from behind and the roar of the engines was different than that of any of the other planes they had heard before. It got so loud that it drowned out the air raid siren, and with a deafening scream the planes flew right over them. There were three of them.

"Bad guys!" Bob yelled as he jumped up and down. He was so surprised he could barely talk. "Shoot at them, shoot at them!"

The guns started to blast at the German planes now trailing away from the shore, as two foot long bolts of flame and balls of smoke came ripping out of the barrels. Empty shell casings from the Bofors guns were clanging away from the guns and bouncing down to the beach.

"Out of range, out of range," Bob yelled, and the guns began to stop firing as all the other gun crews came to the same conclusion.

"What were they, Heinkels?" asked John.

"Yeah," said Bob. "HE One Elevens. Probably just did a raid somewhere."

The big twin-engine German bombers had just buzzed right over their heads at full throttle, flashing a shadow over them, and leaving behind the smell of burnt fuel and ringing ears. They still flew low and fast over the water and took a slight track to the left to avoid the Hurricanes.

"They are going after them, guys," said Doug. "Those Brits don't put up with this shit."

"We may get to see them shoot down a couple of Krauts," said Herby, now all excited.

The Heinkels disappeared over the horizon, and a few moments later the Hurricanes did as well.

"You think they'll catch them?" asked Herby.

"I guess we will never know," said Bob.

"Hey Doug," asked Herby. "You really have an electric fence?"

"Yeah, I really do."

"And you touched it?"

"Yeah, lots of times."

"You better hope they let dumb bastards become movie stars or you don't stand a chance," Herb said as the other guys laughed.

"It's to keep the cows in, Herby. You do know what a cow is, don't you?"

"I have an idea," said Herby. "When we get upstairs, let's all stick our finger in a light socket. Hey Doug, you go first."

The guys all laughed while Doug shook his head, and they made their way back upstairs to the China Hotel. The 386th had fired its first shots.

Colonel Gibbs signed off on an order that anyone off active duty could go into town, either Bournemouth or Boscombe, to visit a few pubs and walk around town. They had to stay out of trouble and they had a 10:00 pm curfew. One infraction of these rules and they would permanently lose all privileges.

That afternoon Doug pulled Bob aside.

"Not another one of your crazy schemes," said Bob. "Last time you almost got me locked up in London."

"Nothing like that, Bobby boy. Besides, I seem to remember that you had a pretty good time."

"You're right, I did," he grinned. "Ok, so tell me what you have cooking this time."

"Did you see that theatre in Bournemouth? We drove past it on the way in."

"No," said Bob. "But I'll take your word for it."

"Well, how would you like to meet a couple of dames? Are you up for that Bobby?"

"At the movies? How do you meet girls at the movies?"

"Ok, so this is what we do: We get all shined up, you know — boots spit-shined, ties, hats, everything perfect. Like we are going on parade. Like we went to London."

"Yeah, I get it. Go on."

"Then we go down to that theatre and we buy four tickets, you see. And when a couple of skirts go by, we tell them our friends couldn't make it and ask them if they would like to see a movie."

Bob looked at him and blinked a few times. "That's your big plan? They will just take our tickets and go in and see the movie. Probably never even talk to us."

"Yeah Bob, but here's the thing. That's not your average run of the mill movie theatre. It's a fancy place with assigned seats. They take our tickets and they have to sit next to us."

Bob thought about it for a minute. "This just might work. But we have to separate them. If they sit together they will just talk to each other."

"Now you're thinking, Bobby boy. But we can't break up the seats, either. If we get two pairs of seats then you and I will be sitting together, and I don't like you that much."

"Well, we will just have to be careful when we sit down to get in between them. I think we can do that."

"Good plan. Now let's not tell Herby and John about this, because I don't think this will work with too many guys out there."

"Ok," said Bob, nodding his head. "Besides John is already in love, and Herby can go try tomorrow."

The two spit-shined privates were on the way out of the gate laughing and goofing around when Doug reached over and tipped Bob's hat forward. Bob shoved him and they both laughed again.

"It's going to be a good night," said Bob." "I can feel it."

"Of course it is, Bobby boy," said Doug, flashing his big toothy smile. "What do you expect when you run around with a movie star?"

"Hey boys!"

The two of them turned around to see Lt. James walking up behind them, so they saluted and replied, "Good evening, Lieutenant."

"Listen boys, I need a volunteer. I'm a man short on Gun Two so who is going to help me out?"

"We sure would like to help, sir. We really would, but we have big plans in town tonight. I'm sorry, sir, but I'm sure you understand," Doug said.

"Ok good, you then. Follow me and get out of that dress uniform, Private. Maybe you'll get to use it tomorrow night."

He knew Doug couldn't talk his way out of it this time. *Shit. Now what the hell do I do?*

Doug slumped his head over and since there was no point in arguing, he started back to the China Hotel with the Lieutenant. After they walked a few steps, Bob slowly started to walk back as well. Then he saw Doug turn around, and with a big smile and a thumbs up signal, he waved Bob back towards town.

He wants me to go anyway. He looked at his watch and glanced toward town, then looked back at Doug just in time to see them disappear from sight. *It's a great plan. A really great plan. I would love to come back tonight with a story that would make Doug proud.*

He looked back at his watch, turned and started toward town, not looking back this time. He was all shined up, he had a pass and a few bucks in his pocket, and he had a great plan.

What the hell. Even if it doesn't work I'll still have time for a few beers, and it beats sitting in that room with Herb's stinky feet.

And so with a purposeful gait from his new found confidence, he set off for Bournemouth to put Doug's plan to the test. On the way there he thought about Herby trying to do this tomorrow night.

Maybe Doug will even go with him. He laughed to himself as he tried to picture the two of them out there together, and he tried to imagine what pair of girls could possibly match up with that duo.

He glanced at his watch as he arrived at the theatre. *Time to spare. I should be able to meet some dame within forty minutes.*

"Two tickets, please. Best ones you have."

"Six rows back in the center, sir."

"I'll take them," he said, but gulped when he heard the price. It was going to eat up most of his cash.

This better be one fancy theatre like Doug said.

No sooner than when he turned away from the box office did he see her. She was standing there, her elbow bent, with a cigarette between her delicate fingers. She had long red hair with big green eyes and Bob could smell her perfume from where he stood. Not a man walked by without stealing a glance of her.

Bob's heart raced and his throat went dry while his brain scrambled for something to say as he stepped towards her.

"Hiya, doll," he said with a big smile, and she turned to face him. "I have an extra ticket, care to join me?"

"Nice try, yank," a British lieutenant said as he hooked his arm into hers and led her off toward the entrance.

170

She glanced back over her shoulder and gave Bob a tiny smile and a wink as she went in on the officer's arm.

Ok, that was a practice run. I'll get it right next time. Although I have to admit, that limey lieutenant is a lucky bastard.

And so it was back to work on the movie star's plan. He strolled back and forth in front of the theatre. Most of the people going into the place were groups of British airmen. He found that odd since the movie was "Buffalo Bill".

I guess Brits like westerns, too. But where the hell are all the girls?

He saw a few other girls. Some were on dates with other guys, like the redhead he saw earlier. Some girls came along in groups, giggling and laughing. That wouldn't do. Some even came by in pairs, often times with their arms locked together as they walked and talked.

That would be perfect if Doug was here. He could unabashedly stop a pair of girls in their tracks and strike up a fun conversation and then pull Bob in. He was a master at it, and the plan sounded much better with Doug as a factor.

Bob's luck was running out. It started to drizzle and a breeze picked up. The crowd started to thin out and the box office closed. The movie was about to start and he realized that his time had run out.

He lit up a cigarette and puffed on it as he stood there alone under the marquis. He looked around one more time. The street was empty, and he noticed a trash bin on the corner.

Looking down at the tickets he spent too much for, he headed towards the bin. *Well, so much for the grand scheme.*

Lillian had been running a few errands and was now heading back to the Grand Hotel. It was misty and damp and starting to drizzle, so she stepped up the pace and pulled her hat down.

Her mind was wandering as she pushed her way into an ever stronger blowing breeze, thinking that she just wanted to get back and get dry. Of course, she first had to run the gauntlet of soldiers lining the streets. She tried to just ignore them as they whistled at her or tried to talk to her.

She plowed ahead. *I'm in no mood for this nonsense tonight.*

Then she heard him, she heard that voice. It was that unmistakable voice that she had heard too many times. He was loud as he was talking with some other soldiers and his voice was carried to her even half a block away. She had no doubt whatsoever that it was him. No doubt at all.

It was the singing soldier. That crazy bloody yank that would surely follow her all the way back to the Grand if he saw her. He was driving her out of her mind and the girls would tease her about him all the time.

He seemed to pop out of nowhere, making her jump out of shoes and make her run back to the hotel or he would follow her all night. She never knew when she would have her next encounter with the "Kentucky Crooner."

But this time she saw him first and apparently he hadn't seen her yet. The problem was that he was between her and where she had to go. There would be no getting around him on this busy street.

A few ideas raced through her head.

Maybe I could take off my shoes and walk quietly down the other side of the street and he won't notice me. Maybe I could hurry past with my hat pulled down and he won't recognize me. Maybe he will get hit by a bloody bus before I get that far.

Lillian was getting irritated.

I'm going to have to take the long way, bloody yank.

She could backtrack to the corner, bypass this street and take a long loop around and avoid this guy altogether. She reluctantly resigned herself to the fact that this was the only way.

The drizzle was coming down heavier as the air turned chilly. She resented the fact that this crazy American was forcing her to do this. She could have been home by now.

172

She went around the block and cut across the square. As she muttered to herself she kept looking back over her shoulder wondering if she had lost the guy.

She turned up the street that ran alongside the old movie theatre. *I think he's gone.*

Just as she was starting to relax and feel like she got away, she was shocked to hear his voice again. It was not as close, and she was not sure it was him, but she didn't want to take a chance so she started to trot away as quickly as she could.

She took a hard right turn at the movie house, and she ran right into Bob.

Chapter Fourteen

She was startled because she smashed right into someone almost in a trot while looking behind her, and with the impact she was pushed back a step. The hat that had been pulled down over her face was now cocked back on the crown of her head.

She looked up at him into his big brown puppy dog eyes that were wide open, and she could see he was as startled as she was.

His boots were shined, his uniform pressed, his jet black hair was slick and his face was clean-shaven. Even his tie was straight.

After working all day, she was disheveled and tired. Her hair was damp and hanging there, out from under her hat. Her hat was crumpled and her uniform was a faded and slightly frayed RAF issue that was once crisp and blue and pressed. Her eyes were bloodshot, she had no makeup on, and the only thing she carried was a gas mask case.

She was the most beautiful girl he had ever seen.

His brain took a few seconds to reset. He was but two feet from the trash bin with his arm outstretched to ditch the tickets he wished he had never bought. Now he had a wet spot on the front of his uniform shaped like her.

He glanced around quickly and realized she was alone. Alone and just in time. Alone and a little bit late, actually, but better late than never. He was at a loss for words so all he could manage to do was smile a big smile, a big goofy smile.

He stepped a half step towards her, more of a shuffle actually, not even realizing he was moving. They were now face to face and eye to eye.

Look at those beautiful blue eyes.

He could feel her breath and smell her blonde hair, and as his heart jumped a little bit, he felt suddenly intoxicated by her.

She was momentarily frozen in place by the shock of the impact and the soldier she ran into. She looked up into his handsome face with that silly smile and almost laughed, because she had seen that speechless look on soldier's faces before, plenty of them.

But in just seconds, she shook it off and snapped into her mission of getting back to the Grand without too much drama. All she did was crash into a stranger, that's all, no more than that, and now it was time to press on again.

He seemed nice looking, but he was, after all, a soldier. What's worse he was an American soldier, and there would be no more soldiers in her life, she was done with that. And there was certainly not going to be any American soldiers.

"Sorry, Yank," she said as she flashed him a polite but uninviting smile, pulled down the brim of her hat again, darted around him and started back on her way.

Good Lord, I hope this one doesn't start singing to me, crazy bloody yanks. She made herself smile, but not so he could see it.

By this time Bob had composed himself and his brain was desperately searching for something to say. She would never have gotten away from Doug. He realized that in a few moments she would be gone and gone for good. Just another pretty face to forget, but a very pretty face indeed.

"Hey, what's your hurry?" he asked as he took off his cap and stuck it under his arm and trotted a few steps to catch up with her.

"Excuse me?" she replied, as she stopped and half turned back to him.

"C'mon, doll, where's the fire?" he asked, taking a step towards her, putting them eye to eye once again.

"Fire?" she asked. " What fire?"

"Would you like to see a movie?" he asked, holding up the tickets. "My friend couldn't make it and I hate to waste them."

"But what about the fire?"

"Don't worry about the fire, it's just an expression."

"Of course I worry about fires, and so should you. The bombers look for anything that glows. Don't you know that?"

"Ok, listen, Blondie," Bob said grinning. "There is no fire. Nothing is glowing and everything is dark."

This American is talking in riddles. First there was a fire and now there is no fire.

"Look, doll, here's the thing. I got these two tickets to see 'Buffalo Bill', good tickets. My friend and I were supposed to go but he couldn't make it, he had to go do some army stuff."

"Maybe he had to put out a fire," she said back.

"Then I suppose he did a very good job, because there ain't no fire."

"That is a lovely barbaric form of English you speak. Where are you from?" she asked.

"I'm from Brooklyn, home of the Dodgers."

"Brooklyn, that's in New York, is it not?"

"Well, we prefer to think about it as New York is part of Brooklyn."

The rain started to pick up and the wind was bringing a chill to the air. Lillian wrapped her coat around herself a little tighter. Then she started hearing loud laughter like a bunch of unruly drunken fools, and they would be turning the corner any moment.

Lillian quickly weighed her options. She could take off running through the cold rain to the Grand a few blocks away, she could wait just a moment and get sung to all the way to the Grand a few blocks away, or she could see a movie.

"It's supposed to be a good movie," he said. "Buffalo Bill. It's a western. Do you like westerns? Do you know who Buffalo Bill is? And look at these seats, six rows back in the middle, great seats, perfect I'd say."

Bob was shuffling his feet and looking at the ground then back up at her and couldn't stop talking as he seemed to get more and more nervous. *Shut up, you big dumb bastard. You're going to talk yourself right out of this date.* She was nodding her head and shaking her head and nodding again, trying to keep up with him.

Then he saw it, the subtle change, the faint smile and softening in her eyes. His confidence came bursting back along with his big smile, and he was able to look into her pretty eyes without turning away.

"C'mon, you like me, I can tell," he said, which made her smile even bigger.

"Ok, Yank, let's see your movie then. We better hurry, it's going to start soon."

Bob was flabbergasted. "Are you sure?" he asked.

"Yes, I'm sure," she said and took him by the hand, pulling him into the theatre just before the loud group turned the corner, the loudest one almost certainly him.

Bob handed the tickets to an usher who guided them down the dark aisle and pointed out their seats. Bob led the way with his hat in one hand and her hand in the other, only letting go after he got her seated and then sat himself.   *Jeez. When Doug makes a plan Doug makes a plan.*

She hadn't realized it until the moment he let go that he had been holding her hand the whole time. As soon as they sat down he took her hand again, and she let him. The cartoons had started so the theatre was dark.

There were four RAF airmen sitting in front of them when they sat, and one turned to Bob and asked, "Say Yank, do you have a fag?"

Bob blinked his eyes and turned to Lillian and asked, "Is there something about you that I'm missing?"

"A fag," she said, and he just stared at her.

"A cigarette. He'd like a cigarette."

"Is that what you call them here? You people talk funny over here."

"Silly American," she grinned. "You are the ones that talk funny."

"Ok, fellas," Bob said, leaning forward. "I'll make a deal with you. I don't have any matches, so I'll give you some cigarettes, or fags, whatever, if you give me some matches."

With that all four of the airmen were holding out matches with big smiles on their faces in anticipation of getting some American cigarettes, a hot commodity.

"Ok, two each," he said. "That's all I can spare."

They eagerly agreed so he doled them out and dropped a handful of matches in his pocket, and passed Lillian a "fag" as well.

The four airmen immediately fired up their smokes. Bob struck one of his new matches and lit his own, then held the flaming match in front of Lillian's face. She had no idea what to do, and only a second to do it, so she stuck the cigarette in her mouth and puffed it alight.

Then she spent the next five minutes coughing, coughing until her eyes watered and she almost threw up, all from one puff.

"First time, eh?" he asked.

She nodded, still wiping the tears away and croaked out, "And last."

"Sorry."

"Trying to kill me on the first date doesn't leave a very good impression, Yank."

"Would you rather be home?" he asked, smiling again.

She paused for a minute and looked at him and smiled back, "No."

"See," he said. "I told you that you liked me, you can't help it."

"Cheeky bugger," she said and she elbowed him.

He shifted around in his seat and leaned towards her. She leaned towards him and they got cozy and comfortable as the cartoons stopped and the newsreels started to run.

All the things one came to the movies to escape from were now coming alive on the screen in front of them. The war was raging all over the world, and the carnage was being reported right here.

Battleships and submarines, beaches and jungles and cities . . . tanks and soldiers and planes . . . bombers . . . she hated the bombers more than anything. She hated how they brought the war from the front line to the innocent and how helpless one felt when underneath a raid. It was when the bombers were shown on the screen that she slid her hand back into Bob's, and he let her.

Finally the movie started, and so now she knew who Buffalo Bill was.

"You yanks and your cowboys, that's another thing I'll never understand."

"You are just jealous because you don't have cowboys here in England," he laughed.

"From what I understand you don't have cowboys in Brooklyn either, but you still seem to like them an awful lot."

"I never thought of it that way, but I do like cowboys, and you like me, so you must like cowboys, too!"

"You're daft, Yank. All of you are."

"I don't know what that means, but thank you, I think. It's funny how we both speak English but can't understand each other."

She smiled and said softly, "You don't speak English, love, you speak American."

They shuffled out of the theatre with the rest of the crowd and started walking slowly towards the square. She would go right from there to the Grand, and he would turn left and go back to his battalion.

She stopped and turned to him and said, "Well, I guess this is goodbye then. Thank you for the show, I had a lovely time."

"No, no, not goodbye," he said with alarm. "It's too early for that. I only just met you."

"I'm sorry, but I really must go. I have a curfew and I'm sure you do, as well."

She was right, he did, and it was coming up soon.

"I'll tell you what, I'll settle for goodnight, but don't make it goodbye. I want to see you again," he said with those puppy dog eyes.

"I don't know, I don't see how."

"Let's meet right here," he replied. "Right here, tomorrow night at seven. We can walk and talk, have dinner. You can tell me your life story."

She just looked at him and thought about it.

"Say yes. You like me, I know you do."

"Why should I trust you?" she asked. "You tricked me earlier to get me into that movie."

"Tricked you?" he asked, wondering how she figured out Doug's little scheme.

"Yes, tricked me. You told me there was a fire."

"Oh that," Bob laughed, relieved. "Well, see that was an example of how you speak English and I speak American. You can trust me."

"You yanks tell stories. You'll say just about anything. Are you going to tell me you have a bloody ranch in Texas, or that you are really some big movie star or something? I've heard it all before you know."

He smiled at her and said, "No, I must admit that I have no ranch in Texas, but I do have a tree in Brooklyn. And as for the movie star, well let's just say he couldn't make it tonight."

She stood there shaking her head with her arms crossed. "What am I to do with you, you crazy American?"

He took a step forward and said softly, "You're supposed to meet me here at seven tomorrow night, that's what."

She just stood there. He could hear the pigeons flutter around him, and the clicking of shoes on the stone streets as other couples walked by. He could smell the sea air from the channel, but all he could see were her blue eyes.

"Say yes," he finally said to break the silence.

"Alright then, Yank, seven. Seven right here, and don't be late. Goodnight it is, then."

With that she spun on her heels and walked away, leaving him speechless . . . almost speechless that is.

"Wait," he yelled and ran to catch up. "What's your name?"

She stopped briefly and said, "Lillian. Lillian Rose."

Then she was off again, disappearing into the night.

Lillian Rose. The prettiest girl I've ever seen.

He couldn't wait to tell Doug how well his plan worked out, and to tell the other guys how he was in love with the prettiest girl in England. They will think he's crazy, falling in love at first sight, but he didn't care.

"Lillian Rose," he whispered out loud, and trotted off towards the hotel.

Chapter Fifteen

Bob walked back into the hotel room to find Doug already back from his unexpected duty, laying on his bed and staring at the ceiling. There was no telling what he was daydreaming about, but he had a little smile on his face, so it was probably girls.

Herby was in a chair tilted on its back legs, leaning against the wall reading a comic book and humming the whole time. John was sitting on his bed shining his boots, the smell of shoe polish wafting through the air as Bob walked in.

Doug glanced over at Bob walking in and looked down at his watch.

"Wasn't sure if you were going to make it, Bobby boy," he said. "Only a few minutes before curfew."

"Where were you, Bob?" asked Herb, looking over his comic. John glanced up and then back down and continued to shine away.

Bob just grinned and shrugged his shoulders at Herb's question.

Doug saw Bob's little smirk and the dreamy look in his eyes and jumped to his feet.

"It worked, didn't it? I told you, didn't I?"

Bob just grinned. Herby dropped the comic to his lap and John stopped shining to look up and see what they were talking about.

"So tell me what happened. Did you get laid?"

"Who got laid?" asked Herby as he leaned forward and dropped the front legs of the chair to the floor with a clunk. "Bob got laid?"

"Yeah, he did. You got laid, didn't you, Bob?"

"Did you really get laid, Bob?" asked Herby, while John sat there shaking his head and smiling at the conversation.

"No, I didn't get laid, it's not like that."

"Then why are you smiling like that?" Herb challenged.

"Oh no, don't tell me," said Doug, shaking his head. "You didn't, did you?"

"I didn't do what?"

"You went and fell in love, you poor dumb bastard. Get that idea out of your head."

"He's only been gone five hours," said John. "How the hell did that happen?"

"Bobby boy, listen to me on this one. If you didn't get laid, you didn't get anything."

"Well, I got to see Buffalo Bill," Bob said, grinning.

"The movie?" asked Herb. "They have movies here?"

"You got laid, and you saw Buffalo Bill?" asked John. "That was some five hours, Bob."

"How did you do that?" asked Herb.

"Well actually, it was Doug's plan, but I didn't get laid."

"So now you think you're in love, you big dope?" asked Doug. "There is like a million soldiers here and what seems like only a few dozen broads, and you are telling me she fell for you?"

"Maybe," said Bob. "And I don't think the odds are quite that bad."

"She'll be in love with someone else tomorrow, you knucklehead," said Doug. "Besides, she hasn't met me yet. So what kind of bullshit story did you give her to get laid so fast?"

"I told her my best friend was a movie star," Bob grinned. "And I didn't get laid."

"Very funny," said Doug. "So you just told her you were some poor Joe Schmoe from Brooklyn?"

"Yep. And she loves me anyway."

"Are you going to see her again?" asked John.

"Yeah, tomorrow night. We are meeting at the square in town at seven."

"She won't show up," said Doug, and John was nodding his head in agreement.

"I want to go to the movies," said Herb. "How much was it? I'm broke."

"She won't be there, Bob," said Doug. "You're not getting laid two nights in a row."

"She'll be there, and I didn't get laid, it's not like that."

"Unless she looks like Herby in a dress," said John. "Then she might show up."

"If I put on a dress, will you take me to the movies, Bob?" asked Herby while batting his eyes.

"I'm telling you guys, she is the prettiest girl in England."

"Then she's definitely not coming," said John.

"Hey, Herb," Doug said. "If I take you to the movies will you put out?"

"Now, Mr. Movie Star, you know I'm not that kind of girl," he said, making them all laugh.

"Even if I buy you dinner?"

"Just because Bob got laid doesn't mean you will, too."

"I didn't get laid."

"Well, don't feel bad, Bob," said Herb. "I wouldn't have put out for you, either."

"Thank God for that."

"What does she look like?" asked John. "Better than Herby I hope."

"Well, she's kind of short, with a face like an angel. She has blonde hair, and blue eyes, a little skinny, but she has nice boobs."

"I like her already," said Herb.

"Oh, and by the way, she's in the RAF."

"Was she a good lay?" asked Doug with a big grin.

"I didn't get laid."

"So she's a WAF, eh?" asked Doug. "I never laid a soldier before."

"Well then, maybe you should take Herby to the movies," said Bob.

"I still want to know more about this movie house," said Herb.

"Well, I hate to tell you this, Bob," said Doug, shaking his head. "But in my professional opinion, and we all know that I am the professional here, she won't show. Just don't say I didn't warn you."

"She will be there."

"She got a sister?" asked Herb. "I'd like to get laid, too."

"I don't know, I only just met her. And I didn't get laid."

"If she does happen to show up," said Doug, "which she won't, can I be your best man?"

"Herby can be a bridesmaid," said John.

"She'll be there, I know she will. You guys will be singing a different tune tomorrow."

"Now what about this movie theatre?" Herby asked, and John nodded with seemingly renewed interest.

"Do they have newsreels? Any Yankee game highlights?"

"Yeah, they had newsreels, and some baseball highlights, including those bums of yours. I thought about you, for about two seconds anyway."

"How did you hear about this place?" asked John.

"Doug told me about it."

John and Herby turned around and looked at Doug and he grinned and shrugged his shoulders.

Just then the air raid siren went off, and they jumped into their boots, pulled on their flak jackets, grabbed their helmets, and ran out the door. As they were running down the stairs they could hear and then feel the rumble of the four FW-190's scream out over the coast, followed in hot pursuit by a half dozen British Spitfires.

The British fighters were so close behind that the battalion couldn't fire on the German planes, but the entire battalion let out a cheer when a fireball appeared in the sky just seconds later.

"Score one for the Limey's," said Dutch.

Herby stood there frozen while the others were clapping and celebrating, and he turned to see Bob smiling and looking out at the sparkling debris falling down towards the water.

186

Bob turned to look at him and saw his face was pale and his eyes were wide open.

"What's the matter, Herb?"

"Holy shit, Bob. They just killed a guy. We just saw them kill a guy."

The smile went off of Bob's face and he looked back out over the channel to see the last trickles of light disappear in the darkness, and he realized Herby was right. Suddenly he didn't feel like celebrating anymore.

"Yeah, Herb," he said softly. "They just killed a guy."

Lillian was back in her room at the Grand when she heard the siren in the distance, the same one that bought the guys down to Gun Six. While there weren't many shelters here in Bournemouth, at least they had the basement, so in their pajamas they made a dash for the staircase and filed down to the makeshift shelter with all the other girls. Lillian was still in her uniform because she had just gotten back.

"Do you have any idea how many hearts in Bournemouth would be broken if a bomb hit this basement full of girls?" Sarah laughed.

"Probably half the single girls in town are packed in here right now," said Emily.

"Well, we know there is at least one American that would never sing again," said Sarah and they all laughed.

"Maybe two," said Lillian with a little grin.

Sarah looked at her suspiciously and asked, "Are we up to no good now, love?"

The four girls were standing under the bulge in the wall that had once been their way into the American kitchen and Sarah backed her up to it and said, "I noticed you were awful late getting back tonight for just going to market."

"I got a little busy," Lillian said and tried to look away, but Sarah was right in front of her.

"You didn't actually go out with that bloody wanker, did you?"

Emily and Becky huddled around grinning and listening to all the details. There were no secrets among this group.

"No, no, not him. I would never go out with him."

"So who then? Don't even tell me it's some other yank."

"Alright, I won't tell you then."

The other two girls giggled. It was always fun to watch Sarah get herself all worked up.

"Are you going to see him again?" asked Becky, stoking the fire.

"Yes I am, tomorrow night. His battalion is down at the China, so we will meet at the square."

"I thought you said no more soldiers. Don't you remember saying that?" Sarah asked.

"I remember, but this one is different."

"All those yanks are bloody different," said Sarah. "Just look at your singing soldier. Why don't you just go out with him?"

"I'll let you have the singer, I have my own yank now."

"That soldier comes near me and he'll be singing bloody soprano," said Sarah, and they all burst out laughing.

"What does he do? Is he a pilot?" asked Emily.

"Is he a general?" Becky teased.

"He's a private. I don't know what he does."

"A private!" Sarah yelled, going into a rage. Everyone else in the basement turned at the sudden outburst.

"A bloody American private at that," she continued. "Have you gone completely daft?"

"He may be just a private, but he is fun. You told me to play with them. You told me to have fun, and so that's what I'm doing."

"Don't trust him, love. Those Americans will say anything to get in your knickers," said Sarah. "They use that line about having a ranch in Texas as if we haven't all heard it before. They think we're bloody stupid."

"All soldiers are like that, not just the yanks," replied Lillian.

"You have a point there. Just don't go falling in love with him. He will leave you and he won't even say goodbye. He will break your heart, mark my word."

"What about you and your Canadian pilot?" challenged Becky. "You seem to be getting pretty dreamy-eyed over him here of late."

"I am not in love," she said, but the change in her body language was obvious. "I'm just playing with him and I will trade him off when I get bored."

"Of course you will."

"I don't believe her."

"I don't either."

Sarah looked around as the three of them ganged up on her but she was not about to be cornered. "Well, you can all bloody well go to blazes then, don't listen to me. I hope you all wind up in the middle of Texas with some stupid wanker singing to you all night."

"That sounds kind of nice," said Emily, half meaning it.

"Not if he sounds like a wounded cat," fumed Sarah.

"Actually, he's not a bad singer" said Lillian. "He's just daft."

"Well then, you can go to bloody Texas with your bloody singing yank, and you can stand out there chewing with his bloody cows."

All the girls laughed, and when they heard the all clear they started heading back up to the room. It was already past lights out so as soon as they got there they climbed into bed, except for Lillian, who still had to get into her pajamas.

When she climbed into bed and pulled the covers over her, Sarah whispered in the dark, "Bloody yanks." They all giggled and went to sleep.

When the all clear sounded the men went back up to their room and took off their gear. John cursed when he saw the big scuff mark across his boot that he just shined.

Doug said, "I just wish that if we go through all the trouble to rush out there, that the Krauts would be decent enough to let us shoot a few of them down."

"Those bastards," said John.

"By the way, how was that movie, Bob?" Herb asked.

"Best damn movie I ever saw," Bob said, smiling.

"What was it about?" Herb asked.

"I have no idea," Bob grinned.

"Well, at least tonight wasn't a total loss," said Doug. "At least Bob got laid."

Bob just smiled and shook his head and climbed into bed. He could hear the other guys snickering like boy scouts on a camp out.

"She ain't coming," said Doug.

Bob didn't answer.

"She won't be there," said John.

He still didn't answer.

"Anybody want to go to the movies tomorrow night?" asked Herb.

"No."

"Me, either."

"I'm busy."

"Fine," said Herby. "Just fine. You guys can all just go to hell, then."

"Just another night in paradise," Bob murmured to himself as Herby started snoring. *She'll be there. I know she will.*

It was June 2, 1944. It was four days before D-Day.

Chapter Sixteen

He was so anxious to see her again that he got to the square twenty-five minutes early. He tried to sit there on a bench but was so fidgety that he was on his feet again in just a few seconds.

He was pacing like a tiger in a cage and a thousand thoughts were going through his mind. He wondered if she was going to show up, that perhaps she lost her nerve. He wondered if she had ever intended to show up at all. He wondered if she met someone else. He even wondered if that was her real name.

Lillian Rose. He smiled. *Yeah, that's her name.*

He decided to walk around the square to kill some time and burn off some anxiety. He didn't want to come off like a schoolboy on his first date, although that's exactly how he felt.

Even though it was almost seven o'clock, it was light outside and would be for hours because of the time offset. It took the romantic edge off the evening, but it kept the bombers delayed, so it was a good tradeoff.

There were crowds of people moving through the streets, most of them soldiers, and most of those soldiers were American soldiers. On the walk here, Bob passed over twenty Sherman tanks pulled over on the side of the road. They were pointed in the general direction of the channel, and they were not there yesterday.

He looked around in awe at the ever-growing swarm. *My God, it's going to be a hell of a fight.*

As he walked around he could hear music playing, and while he didn't recognize the song, it sounded like beer drinking music. He took a few dozen paces towards the pub it was coming from and sure enough, there was beer drinking going on.

There was a group of Australians drinking and singing and hanging onto each other. They were filthy drunk, uniforms a mess, one was puking on the side of the building while another stood next to him peeing. The only thing that distracted them was when a pretty girl would walk by, or even an ugly one, they would hoot and whistle and act like monkeys in the zoo.

Bob stood there and watched them for a few minutes, smiling and shaking his head.

Look at those crazy bastards. And I thought we were bad.

He looked at his watch and decided to stroll back towards the bench in case she got there early, as well. He thought about his dad's advice about staying out of the pubs over here. And to stay away from "Those Women."

He had just sent him a V-Mail telling him that he didn't have to worry because the beer here was terrible, and that he wouldn't give a plug nickel for anything but a Brooklyn girl. Of course, neither of those things were exactly true, but he hadn't met Lillian yet, and never imagined he would meet anyone like her anywhere.

He tried to write his mom every week, but that was the first time he had written to his dad. He wasn't sure why he did, and Archie was probably surprised to get a letter from him, but he wanted him to know he was safe and following his advice, which he wasn't.

I have to pick up some more V-Mail forms. I'm fresh out.

During the war the soldiers were given V-Mail forms, ten to a box. That was how they wrote home to the states. Each form was letter size, and they were allowed to write one page letters. The forms would then be censored for content, to make sure they were not saying where they were or what they were doing, and then sent on to be processed.

They couldn't possibly fly hundreds of thousands of letters home to America every month, all different shapes and sizes, because of the enormous amount of resources it would take to do so, so they came up with V-Mail.

They would take the original letters and photograph them, then put the photographs on microfilm. They could get thousands of letters on one small roll of film, and fly those home, taking up only a fraction of the space.

When they got back stateside, they would develop the film into photographs and the end result would be a postcard size photo of the original letter, and they would be distributed from there. It might even be called the first e-mail. V-Mail, of course, stood for Victory Mail, and was a welcome sight for every mom to see in her mailbox.

He sat on the bench and looked around. *This could be a nice little place. Unless the Nazis get their paws on it.*

Bob suddenly snapped out of his daydream and looked down at his watch. It was five minutes after seven. He jumped to his feet and his head turned around like it was on a swivel as he scanned in every direction, especially the one he saw her disappear into the night before.

Oh shit, she is five whole minutes late. Now what do I do? She was only five minutes late, but because he had arrived so early and was so anxious, it seemed like hours.

Ok, just calm down there, you dumb bastard. It's only five minutes, she's just running a little behind. She'll be here, I know she will.

As five minutes slowly turned into ten, he was starting to feel some panic rising up inside him. *Was Doug right? Was he standing in the right place? Did she change her mind?*

He started pacing again and looking around all the while. Every now and then he could see a WAF going by and he would squint his eyes, but it never turned out to be her.

He looked down to see it was now 7:21 p.m. *I don't understand. She liked me. I know she liked me. I could tell.*

A few more minutes went by and his hope was fading fast. He took one more look up the street he last saw her on and then sat back down on the bench they had promised to meet by. There were a few couples walking around the square, and that just made him feel worse.

He pulled his hat back on, put his elbows on his knees, and hung his head, looking down at the flattened cigarette butts between his feet that littered the square since all these soldiers took over.

It was now 7:38, p.m. and he sighed a big sigh. *Shit. Story of my life. What the hell do I tell those guys now? I'll never hear the end of it. I should tell them I got laid. That would shut them up.*

"Excuse me, Yank, have you the time?"

He looked up, and there standing over him, was Lillian Rose. He jumped to his feet, pulled off his hat, and his big dopey smile once again filled his face.

"For you, doll," he said, "I have all the time in the world."

"Were you worried I wasn't coming, love?"

"Never crossed my mind," he lied.

She called me love!

"Well, knowing you bloody yanks, I thought I would find you standing back over there with two more tickets," she said, as she nodded toward the theatre.

"Now why would I do that? I already have a girl," he smiled and winked at her.

"Sorry to be so late, love. The Major was in rare form tonight."

"I wasn't worried, I knew you were coming. I know you like me too much, you just can't help it," he said, grinning.

She called me love again.

"Don't get too cocky now, Yank," she said with a grin. "You might find yourself standing out in front of that theatre tomorrow night."

He laughed. "Let's go get something to eat. You must be hungry."

"Well, there is not much around, I'm afraid," she said. "Thanks to Gerry, we are just about down to eating our shoes."

"There's a little café over there," he said, pointing to the other side of the square. "There's people in there so they must have something."

194

"Don't get too hopeful, love. We may leave as hungry as we came. Sometimes all they have is tea. Sometimes a little potato soup, fish if you are lucky."

"Oh, I'm lucky, love. I'm very lucky," he said, taking great delight in calling her love as well.

"You're not that lucky, Yank."

"No, no, that's not what I meant," said Bob with a big grin. "I like you, I really like you."

"I like you, too, you silly yank."

"Besides, we can have sex tomorrow night, no rush," he said with a big grin.

"Since you don't have a ranch in Texas, you can just forget that idea," she came back at him. "I'm really hungry."

"Ok, let's go see what they have. Here, take one of these to hold you over," he said, as he pulled out two sticks of Juicy Fruit.

"What is that?"

"It's chewing gum. Don't you have chewing gum here? I thought everybody had chewing gum."

"I've never seen it before. Is it candy?" she asked.

"No, doll, it's gum. Just pop it in your mouth and chew the flavor out of it. Then you can just keep chewing it if you want. Gives you something to do."

"This is what we see you yanks chewing on like a bunch of cattle?"

"That's it," he laughed. "Everybody likes gum, especially Juicy Fruit."

She unwrapped it and put it in her mouth and began to chew. It suddenly burst into the most wonderful flavor, one that she had never tasted before. Her eyes went wide and she nodded to Bob to show him how much she liked it, and he laughed at seeing her delight.

They walked into the café, chewing their gum and holding hands.

"Any grub left, Mac?" Bob asked in between chews.

"Excuse me, sir?" said the polite but clearly irritated waiter. Like most of the locals around here, he didn't care much for the Americans.

"May we have a table, love?" she asked.

"Of course, right this way," he said, smiling at Lillian and then giving Bob a sour look.

She called him love, too, that's odd. Does she know the old grouch?

They sat down and the waiter explained that they had rabbit tonight, and though they had fish earlier, they were fresh out.

"It comes with some boiled potato, and some spinach, but not much spinach. No bread, either."

"What about hot dogs?" Bob asked with a big grin, knowing they had none. "Don't you have hot dogs?"

"No, sir, we have no hot dogs. This is England, we don't eat dogs here. We use them to catch rabbits, which is why we have rabbit."

"That sounds wonderful," said Lillian. "And a cup of tea, please."

"And you, sir?"

Rabbit, yuck. Bob managed a smile and said, "Sure that sounds great. And water for me, Mac, unless you have beer."

"No beer, sir. No beer and no dogs."

The waiter left and Bob turned to Lillian and smiled wide, then kept on chewing, which made her giggle.

He looks like a bloody camel. I must tell my mates about this, they will just die.

"Alright, Yank, what do I do now? I seem to have chewed all the flavor out of it."

"Well, you could do this," and he rolled the gum around in his mouth and cracked it so loud that everyone in the restaurant turned and looked at them. The waiter poked his head out of the kitchen and frowned.

"Oh my God, you crazy yank. Don't do that again," she said, embarrassed, but she couldn't help laughing.

Bob glanced around the café to see the diners turn away from him, shaking their heads. The waiter was doing the same thing, clearly losing his patience with this American.

Bob leaned over the table and whispered to her and asked, "Doesn't anyone in this country have a sense of humor?"

"Are all yanks as crazy as you are?" she whispered.

"Nah," he said. "Worse. I'm one of the normal ones."

"Well then, God help us."

They were now leaning over the table looking into each other's eyes, and Bob's big dopey grin turned into a soft smile, and so did her giggle. The little round table with the red and white checkered tablecloth, next to the window, with the setting sun casting an orange glow, made it feel like the only place in the world. There was nowhere else, there was nothing else.

"I like you, do you know that?" he asked.

"I like you, too," she said. "I don't know why, but I do."

They stared silently into each other's eyes for a few moments, and then Bob started to chew again. "I wonder what's taking the food so long," he said, glancing back at the kitchen.

"You're so romantic," she said, shaking her head.

"Thanks," he said, smiling. "You, too."

"Alright now, what do I do with this chewing gum of yours?" she asked.

"You just do this," he said, and pulled the gum out of his mouth, reached under the tablecloth, and jammed the gum up with a thunk that made the silverware jump and the teacup jingle in its saucer.

"Oh my God," she gasped. "I can't do that."

"Sure you can, doll. Just wad it up in a ball and stick it up to the table. It will stay there, don't worry."

She was shocked. "I cannot and I shall not do that. You can't possibly think I could ever do such a thing."

"Why not? Everybody does it."

"Everybody does not do it. Actually, nobody does it. Nobody should do it, that's horrid."

"Horrid?" he laughed. "It's not horrid."

The waiter was clinking around some dishes and stacking them along his arm, about to bring out their rabbit.

"He's about to bring out the food, now what do I do with this, Yank?"

"Stick to the table," he said, grinning.

"I'm not sticking it to the bloody table."

"I know," he laughed, "it's horrid. Here, give it to me."

Bob stretched out his hand and she looked down at it and then over at the waiter who was just turning their way. She reluctantly took it from her mouth and started to pass it to him.

"What are you going to do with it?" she whispered.

He almost had the gum in his palm when with a grin he said, "I'm going to stick it to the bottom of the table."

"No," she said a little too loudly and popped it back into her mouth.

The patrons glanced over at the sound, and then the café settled back into a murmur. The waiter was just getting to the table with the food. Lillian looked at Bob with pleading eyes, but he just chuckled at her predicament.

Then he saw the expression on her face change: her chin tilted up, her eyes closed, and she swallowed the gum. When she looked back down and over at Bob he had a big grin on his face.

The waiter was now setting the plates down on the table when Bob asked, "Did you swallow that?"

She shushed him and darted her eyes towards the waiter, which Bob just ignored.

"You swallowed it, didn't you? Didn't you?"

The waiter stood over them, looking from one to the other.

"Well?" asked Bob, ignoring the waiter.

She gave Bob the tiniest nod, hoping that he would see it, and hoping the waiter would not. Bob noticed it, the waiter didn't need to. Bob banged his fist on the table and started laughing, making all the dishes jump and tinkle again, and getting the heads to turn and the murmur to stop.

Bob laughed out loud and banged his fist a few more times, making the horrified waiter back off this crazy yank.

"I can't believe you swallowed that," he finally said.

She started laughing, too, and that only made him laugh harder.

"What's going to happen to me?" she asked. "Is it going to poison me or anything?"

"No, doll, it's not going to poison you. But next time give it to me, ok?"

"I will not give it to you, and there won't be a next time."

"Ok, ok, doll," he said. "You never had gum before tonight, and this is my first rabbit."

"Well, listen here, Yank," she said quietly, as she leaned toward him. "For God's sake, if you don't like it, don't stick it to the bottom of the bloody table."

He burst out laughing again and so did she. As they were just getting composed, the sour faced waiter stood over them and asked if they needed anything. They looked up at him and then back at each other and burst out laughing again.

Lillian couldn't help it. She laughed harder than she ever had in her life, making the tears flow and her face cramp, using every smile muscle she had. Bob was laughing and snorting and trying to answer the waiter, but he walked off shaking his head.

They had a few more laughs over dinner, and a few awkward moments of silence, but not many. Bob could usually salvage any awkward moment with his big dopey grin. They started to share a little bit of their lives with one another.

She told him about her life growing up in the convent. She told him about her struggle with polio, a fact she hadn't even shared with her friends. She told him about losing her family, and leaving the convent, and then winding up here with new friends that were like her new family. Then she told him about Jim.

He let her talk, and he listened to every word. He knew he wanted to know everything about her, but the most important thing was that she needed to talk right now, and he was going to let her.

"So how do you like rabbit, Yank?" she asked, changing the subject.

"You know, doll," he said. "I have to admit, it tastes pretty good. Everything was kind of bland, but it was okay."

"Well, we don't spice up our food too much like you Americans, but even salt is hard to come by nowadays. Sugar is almost impossible."

As they relaxed around each other, there was more eye contact, more little smiles and even a few winks. A few times Bob intentionally let her catch him glancing at her boobs so she knew he was interested. She already knew that.

Bob patted the table as he waved to the waiter indicating he was ready for the check. The waiter rolled his eyes and a few minutes later, dropped it in front of Bob wishing them a good evening, and then strutted away.

"I don't think that guy likes me," said Bob with a grin.

"And why should he?" she replied.

"I think he likes you, though."

"And why shouldn't he?" she said with a mischievous smile.

"I guess he likes English dames, eh?" he asked with a wink.

"Much more than he likes vulgar yanks sticking things to the bottom of his table."

Bob laughed and looked at the bill. He needed a little help from her to convert the money, but once they figured it out, he left it there along with a small tip. A very small tip.

Before they left, Lillian held up her teacup and said, "Long live the King."

"And short live the Furher," Bob said, as he clinked his water glass with her.

"Amen to both," she said with a giggle.

They shuffled towards the front door with the waiter right behind them. It had gotten dark out so the blackout curtain was stretched across the door and he had to gap it back a little so they could slip out without betraying Bournemouth to the sky.

The waiter gave Lillian a little smile and nod and then turned to Bob with a look of disdain before snapping the curtain closed again, making both of them start laughing again.

"You were right," she said, smiling. "He doesn't like you."

Bob stopped and grabbed her by the hand and spun her around to face him and with that puppy dog smile he said, "Yeah, but you like me, I can tell."

"Maybe, Yank, maybe. I haven't decided yet."

They turned and started walking down the street again, hand in hand. She had already decided, but she wasn't going to tell him that. This was a cozy and fun little relationship they had going, but it was only two days old, and it was common knowledge that all these Americans were going to be gone soon.

Common knowledge, yet a secret that everyone had to keep. It was so crucial that the Germans didn't know where and when the invasion was to take place that even the American soldiers had no idea. Many would die on beaches they never knew the names of.

"So do you want to be my girlfriend?" he asked. "I'll write you love letters every week."

"You're not wasting any bloody time are you, Yank?"

"Time is something I'm afraid I don't have much of, so I'm going to make the most of it. I like you, and I don't want you slipping through my fingers. Hell, maybe my battalion won't even go, but I'm afraid they didn't bring us here for sunbathing and surfing at the China hotel."

"How much time do you think we have?" she asked.

"Not enough, doll. Not even nearly enough."

"I've lived through this war for the last five years," she said. "It's funny, sometimes there are days you think will never end, and sometimes there are moments that you wish would never end."

"Is this one of those moments?" he asked.

"I learned a long time ago that moments are all you get," she said. "You learn to live every moment you can. Tomorrow Gerry might drop a bloody bomb on your head while you're sitting on the loo and blow your bloody bum off."

"Bum?" he said. "Do you mean ass?"

She shook her head and said, "Vulgar bloody yank. Have you ever even had a girlfriend before? Do the girls back in Brooklyn all talk that way, as well?"

"What the hell is a loo, anyway? Over here you have fags and bums and loos. At least the girls from Brooklyn know how to speak English."

"If you are trying to win me over you are not doing a very good job," she said with a smile.

"Ok, let me try again. I really hope Gerry doesn't drop a bomb on your loo, while smoking a fag, and blow your bum off. It is, after all, a very nice bum."

"Much better, Yank. I may be able to train you yet."

"And a nice ass, too," he said with a wink.

"I was wrong, you are bloody hopeless I'm afraid."

"So what do you say, doll? Would you like a vulgar American boyfriend?"

"Well, aren't you the romantic one," she said sarcastically.

"I'm going to take that as a yes," he said beaming.

They sat back down on their favorite bench and she said, "Well, let's just call it a trial run, shall we?"

"Wait until Pop finds out I met an English dish that I'm over the moon about. His head is going to explode."

She looked at him and blinked her eyes a few times and said, "I have no idea what you just said."

He laughed and said, "I can't wait to tell the guys about you swallowing that gum. They are going to laugh their asses off."

"I beg your pardon," she said.

"Bums. I meant bums. They are going to laugh their bloody bums off," he said with a big toothy grin.

"See, I told you I could train you."

"Speaking of gum," she said. "Why do you insist on sticking that bloody blob to the bottom of the table? Do they do that in Brooklyn?"

"Of course! That's what tables are for."

"Why not throw it in the rubbish?"

"Why not throw it in the rubbish?" he said, mocking her British accent.

She punched him in the arm and asked, "No really, why?"

"I don't know why, it's just something we do. It's an American thing, I guess. I grew up chewing Wrigley's gum. I didn't think we would have any here, but Mr. Wrigley decided that every soldier would have gum in his ration. Every single American soldier. They don't even sell it back home anymore because they don't have enough to sell after taking care of all of us. I think it's ironic that I was worried about not getting any gum over here, when there is none back home."

"So what you are telling me is that there will be gum stuck to tables all across Europe?"

"I'd like to see gum on every table in Germany, at the very least. Japan, too."

"I'd like that, too," she said, smiling at the notion. "You can stick a piece on Hitler's nose."

"I think Mr. Wrigley would like that," he replied. "But it is an awful waste of a good piece of gum."

She giggled and shook her head.

"I like when you giggle," he said. "I think you're cute."

"You probably say that to all the girls you meet outside of movie theatres."

"Every single one of them," he said. "But I was lying to them."

"How do I know you are telling the truth now?"

"I'll tell you what," he said, as he scooted over closer to her and looked into her blue eyes. "It's okay if you don't believe me, I don't care. All I ask is that you give me a chance to prove it. Give me a chance to earn your trust and I will."

"Well, since you think I'm cute," she said, "I just may have to give you a chance. One chance, mind you, Yank, just one. My mates think I'm bloody daft, I dare say. But I will give you your chance so don't muck it up."

"One is all I need, doll. One is all I need. My buddies think I'm crazy, too, and my dad warned me about girls like you."

"About girls like me? I suppose he thinks you can pick up girls like me on any street corner."

"No, not any street corner," he grinned. "Only the ones with movies theatres on them."

"Oh well, aren't you the funny yank?"

"Yes I am," he said proudly. "But looks aren't everything."

"Lucky for you," she laughed.

"Hey," he snapped up straight and said. "How about some dessert?"

He fished around in his pocket and pulled out a Hershey Bar, unwrapped it and broke it in half. She was shocked when he handed her the biggest piece of chocolate she ever had. She was even more shocked when he bit off half of his in one bite.

"Good Lord," she said, staring down at her piece. "Give us the wrapper, will you love?"

"Afraid I'm going to stick it to the bottom of something?"

"I only want a little nibble, then I'm going to bring the rest back to my mates. Sarah might even like you if I bring her your chocolate."

"I have a better idea," he said, after popping the rest of his chocolate into his mouth. "You eat that, and give them this."

She was astonished when he pulled out a second candy bar and handed it to her. "Where in the world do you yanks get all these goodies?"

"Well, I think Mr. Hershey was not to be outdone by Mr. Wrigley, so he made sure we have plenty of chocolate, too."

"I think I'm beginning to like your friends Mr. Wrigley and Mr. Hershey. What else do you have in those pockets of yours?"

"I'll let you look for yourself if you'd like," he grinned.

"Nice try, Yank, but I'm afraid it's going to take a lot more chocolate than that."

"I'll bring you more tomorrow night, and don't worry, I won't make you search me for it."

"Chocolate is like gold here," she said. "There will be some happy girls in my room tonight."

"Why don't you eat yours? You barely took a nibble off the corner, as though a mouse has been chewing on it."

"I eat my chocolate like a mouse, and you eat yours like a bloody crocodile. Do you even taste it as its going past?"

"No sense wasting all that time chewing when I have a pretty girl to flirt with," he smiled. "A pretty mouse that is."

"Are you making fun of me again, you cheeky bastard?"

"Mickey," he said. "That's what I'm going to call you from now on. Mickey Mouse."

"Mickey Mouse?" she replied.

"I'm going to name you after the great Mickey Mouse."

"And whom might this Mickey Mouse be, exactly?"

"You don't know Mickey Mouse? You have been thinking that we Americans are barbarians when you don't even know Mickey Mouse."

"Well," she said, "you are a bit barbaric. We can go ask your friend the waiter if you don't believe me."

"NO, no, no, I don't want to go back there. I gave him a shitty tip. He was acting like a horse's ass anyway.

"Well, that's ironic," she said. "That shitty tip you gave him may have been the only one he's gotten in months. You made his day."

Bob looked at her somewhat confused about the tip.

"Not much tipping going on around here, Yank. Surviving is all we care about, and not starving to death. That waiter must think you really liked him," she giggled.

"Do you want me to go beat him up and take my tip back?" he asked, grinning.

"I don't know why for the life of me I would have ever taken you for barbaric," she said, making him laugh.

"A loveable barbarian, you must admit," he said. "A barbarian with a girl named Mickey."

"I don't know if I like this Mickey Mouse thing of yours. You Americans are odd ducks."

"Well, I'm not going to call you Mickey Mouse, I'm going to call you Mickey. I'm going to call you Mickey and I'm not going to tell anybody why I call you that. That will be our secret."

"Our secret?" she asked. "I rather like that."

"Good, I thought you would. Besides, Lillian is so formal. It's a beautiful name, mind you, but I want to have my own special name for you. You can call me Yank, and I can call you Mickey."

"Alright then, Yank, Mickey it is. You have yourself a deal," she said, as she stuck out her hand and shook on it. "But I'm afraid it's getting late and I must be off."

"Same time, same place, tomorrow night?" he asked.

"Of course. But tomorrow, let's go down to the seawall. I would love to sit there and talk while we watch the waves rolling in. I can never get enough of the channel, its rough water somehow gives me peace, ironic as that may seem."

"To the seawall we shall go," he said. "Your wish is my command. I'll bring some food and we can have a picnic. Some of your favorite gum, and some fags, as well."

"No fags, please. Never again for me, and you will never kiss me if you have been puffing on those stinky things, so you may want to consider that. If you bring gum, then you must also bring a German to stick it to," she said, and they both laughed.

"Ok," he said. "No cigarettes, and no gum without Germans. How about chocolate?"

"All you can carry," she smiled. "I really must run, now. I don't want to, but I must."

"I understand. I do, too," as the smile fell from his face for a moment, but he quickly recovered. "Goodnight, Mickey."

"She smiled back at him and said, "Goodnight, love. Go straight home now, and no movies on the way. Don't forget you have a girlfriend now."

He watched her walk away. *Girlfriend. I have a girlfriend.*

After a few more steps she snapped her head around and said, "I caught you looking, Yank."

"I can't help it if you have such a nice ass, I mean bum, now can I? It's not very high off the ground, but it's very nice."

She smiled at him again, threw back her head, and started off for her hotel, swishing her bum a little extra just for him.

He stood there smiling, and watched her until she was out of sight, then he stood there watching a little bit longer just in case she might appear again for a moment. He didn't want to take the chance of missing that.

On the walk back, Bob popped his last piece of gum in his mouth and chuckled to himself when he thought of how she had swallowed hers. He looked down at his watch again. *Oh, shit, I better haul ass if I am going to make curfew.*

Making it back just in time he found his three buddies playing cards on a crate they turned upside down and made into a table. When he walked in they all stopped talking and looked up at him, Doug sporting a big grin.

"So did she show up, Bobby boy?"

"We saw Buffalo Bill," said Herby. "How come there are never any Jewish cowboys?"

"I bet she stood him up," said John, looking back at his cards. "I bet you a dollar."

"I hope you are ahead on your poker game, Big John, because you just lost a buck," Bob said, stretching out his open hand.

"She was there? She met you at the square?" asked Doug.

"Right on time," Bob lied.

"Did you get laid this time, Bob?" asked Herby.

"Of course he got laid, right Bobby boy?"

"No I didn't get laid, it's not like that."

"What the hell are you waiting for, permission from Winston Churchill?" asked Doug.

Bob smiled. "It's not like that, movie star."

"Can't you see the big dumb bastard has gone and fallen in love?" said John. "Look at his face. She must be quite a dish to get him all dreamy-eyed liked that."

"She is quite a dish," Bob smiled as he thought about her butt swishing down the street.

"Doug told me how you met her. I think I'll try that scheme tomorrow night," said Herby.

"I thought you saw that movie tonight. Are you planning on sitting through it again?" asked Bob.

"I will if I can get laid like you," he grinned.

"I didn't get laid."

"Where did you go tonight after you met her?" asked John.

"We went to this little café off the square and ate rabbit and chewed gum."

Herby was just about to ask another question when the air raid siren started to blare again. "Shit," he said. "I was just getting comfortable."

"Look at the bright side, Herbert," said Doug. "If it wasn't for the Krauts, Bob would never have gotten laid tonight."

Bob shook his head, pulled on his helmet, and ran out the door.

It was June 3, 1944. It was three days before D-Day.

Chapter Seventeen

"Battle fatigues?"

"Battle fatigues twenty-four hours a day," Dutch said back to Bob and then looked around at the other nine men currently manning Gun Six. "We have to be ready to go at all times, those are the orders."

The men said nothing at first. They all just nervously looked around at each other. They were set up just out in front of the hotel, with sandbags all around the gun and ammo stacked nearby. They were all wearing helmets and flak jackets and were closely watching the sky when the sergeant returned with the orders.

"In town, as well?" asked Doug. "Everywhere?"

"Twenty-four hours a day means in town and everywhere, you idiot."

Herb chuckled at Dutch's reply, and the Sergeant turned and scowled at him.

"Sorry, Sarge," he said, and dropped his smirk.

"And I wouldn't count on spending too much time in town from now on," Dutch continued. "The Colonel hasn't cancelled leave yet, but I'm sure that will change soon enough."

Oh shit. I've got to see her one more time or I'll never find her again.

"Sounds like the party is about to start," said John, as he gazed out over the channel.

"Well, don't worry," said Dutch. "It won't start without us. Be prepared to break down the gun, and to put a good coat of grease on her."

John nodded and looked over at the big gun. "Keeps the salt off it," he said.

"It's rough out there and I doubt we are going to ride on the Queen Mary this time," said Dutch. "It's probably going to get splashed and I would rather not drag a rusty gun all across France."

"Just say the word, Sarge," said Herby.

Gun Six of "C" Battery would be ready, as would the entire 386th. The Allies were in their last days of preparation for the greatest invasion attempt in world history. The Allies had built up their forces to include over 11,000 ships, over 19,000 aircraft, and nearly two million men.

On the other side of the channel the Germans waited and fortified their beaches and landing grounds. They mined their harbors and turned the ports into fortresses.

They knew that an Allied invasion was imminent, but they didn't know where and they didn't know when. It was a long coastline to defend, but Field Marshall General Erwin Rommel, who had been put in charge of the defenses, was determined to hurl the invaders back into the sea.

The Allied Supreme Commander, General Dwight D. Eisenhower knew that wasn't an option. Failure was not an option. If the force didn't get a foothold on the continent this time then it would be years before they could try again, if ever.

The Allied commanders spent over a year planning "Operation Overlord," and the Germans spent that long and longer to fortify their front lines with billions of tons of concrete and steel bunkers.

"Pais de Calais," Rommel decided, looking down at the map. "It's the shortest way across the channel, and Patton is there. We bring our armor to Pais de Calais."

By using disinformation with subterfuge and decoys they tricked the Germans. They convinced them that Patton's army was amassing on the English side, but it was actually inflatable tanks and fake radio signals about a fake "Operation Bodyguard."

Rommel inspected his fortifications with confidence that Pais de Calais would be the meat grinder he wanted it to be, and was now backed up with the bulk of his armor. Thousands of tanks and artillery pieces, including some of the largest guns ever built, waited and pointed towards England.

It was time for Ike to make his move, but the weather wasn't cooperating. They needed a break in the storm so they could safely cross over without having the whole operation turn into chaos. They postponed it one day and hoped that wouldn't drag to two, or three.

An army will get restless when the waiting drags out. Especially if they don't know what exactly they are waiting to do, or where and when they were to do it. Command decided to start loading the ships. Start getting the men and equipment aboard and ready and move the next waves down right behind them.

Ike knew that if he loaded his landing craft then he had to go soon, the men couldn't be sustained for long when packed in like that, but if his break in the weather was a narrow window, he wanted to be able to pull the trigger.

The crew of Gun Six stayed on watch most of the day. Tanks and artillery and thousands of men filed past them towards Poole Harbor. It was a never-ending parade of military might, the likes of which had never been seen before.

"They are going to stick us on that line pretty soon," said Herby.

"I'm not looking forward to that boat ride," said Doug.

"I just hope I can get into town for one more night," said Bob, regarding his biggest worry. "I don't know her address or anything, and she will think I ditched her."

"You just want to get laid one more time, Bob," said Herb.

"I didn't get laid, Herby, but I'd like to one day so I will need to know how to find her."

"Anytime now, Bobby boy," said Doug, as he put his arm around Bob's shoulder. "You're cutting it kind of close."

"Yeah, just my luck. Just when I fall in love I have to go invade friggin' France."

"I knew it," Doug jumped up and shouted and pointed at Bob. "I knew it, you big dumb bastard. I knew you must have fallen for this broad."

"Yeah, I guess I did," he said, smiling and shaking his head. "But she loves me, too, I can tell."

Doug flipped away his cigarette and put his arm back around Bob's shoulder and said, "Just remember, Bobby boy, she's not the only one that loves you. I got your back in case this little girl breaks your heart."

"Thanks, movie star, I've got your back, too, buddy," he said and glanced down at his watch. "But for now I have to run. Now that my shift is over, I have a date to keep."

As Bob scrambled out of the gun pit Herb yelled, "Hey Bob, I hope you get laid again."

Bob chuckled and shook his head, and left. He wanted to go by the mess hall and pick up some food for their picnic — they had some chicken down there he was sure he could get ahold of. And he traded most of his cigarettes off for more chocolate. If smoking meant no kissing, then there would be no smoking.

On the other side of town at The Grand Hotel, the girls had just finished a long day and were filing back into the room.

"Going out with your yank again tonight, love?" asked Emily.

"Of course she is," said Sarah. "The silly bugger is in love now. She'll be running off every chance she gets."

"Where are you going tonight?" asked Rebecca.

"He's bringing some dinner and we are having a picnic down at the seawall."

"Well, we can't very well let you go down there like that," said Sarah, as she looked up and down Lillian's old RAF uniform. "If it's a date you are going on then you should look like it, not like a bloody soldier."

Sarah took out one of a couple dresses she had left, a polka dot dress that Lillian had seen her wear sometimes. She held it up in front of Lillian and nodded, indicating that it should be a good fit.

"Thank you, love," she said as she hugged Sarah. "What would I do without you? I'll get some extra chocolate for you tonight."

"When he sees you in that he will want to give you a whole truckload of chocolate, but you may have to fight off ten thousand other soldiers before you get to the square. That little dress screams, 'Come get me boys!' "

"I'll make it," she said, smiling and holding up the dress in front of the mirror. "I'll make it just in time."

Despite stopping on the way out of the Grand to talk to Becky and Emily, and then running the gauntlet of soldiers whistling at her, flirting with her, and trying to get her to stop and talk, she made it there a few minutes early.

In those few minutes at least twenty different soldiers approached her and asked her to join them, as though they were in line to take a shot at it, one after the other. She shushed them away, trying hard not to hurt their feelings.

Then Bob's grinning face popped out of the crowd. She immediately noticed he was in battle fatigues, and he saw the dress she was wearing just as quickly. Both of them had gut reactions to what they were seeing . . . different reactions.

Bob knew the dress meant that she liked him, liked him a lot — not that he needed the dress to tell him that, but she wore it especially for him. She wanted to be pretty for him, and she was.

But when "Mickey" saw the battle fatigues she knew what that meant. She had been in this war for a long time, a lot longer than Bob, and there wasn't much that got past her anymore.

"Hey Blondie, do you have the time?" he asked, as he sat down next to her.

In an instant she shook off the shock of seeing him dressed that way and smiled at his question. They could talk about that later.

"For you, Yank, I have all the time in the world," she smiled back and he laughed.

"You are just about the prettiest girl in the whole world. Did you get all dressed up for me?"

"Oh no, I always walk around like this, especially during air raids."

"Is that your lucky dress or something?"

"No, and it's not your lucky dress either, so don't get any ideas."

"I'm already the luckiest guy in Bournemouth so I can't complain," he said, as he hooked his elbow with hers. "Shall we take that stroll down to the sea, Mickey, my darling?"

"We shall, love," she said smiling up at him.

"I brought some grub," he said.

"I beg your pardon?" she asked.

"I got some nice chicken sandwiches with lettuce and tomatoes."

"Oh my God, you may get lucky yet, Yank," she said, and they both laughed.

"Well, I would invite you to my hotel but I have roommates."

"You may invite me anywhere you like, but unless it's the seawall I'm not going, thank you very much."

"Do you like the beach?" he asked, as they walked along hand in hand.

"I never saw the water before I went with Sarah a few years ago. It took my breath away then, and it still does."

"My friends and I would jump on the subway and ride out to Coney Island," he said. "There is a nice beach there and a boardwalk. We would sometimes go there to chase girls."

"How do you take a subway to an island? Is there a bridge or something?"

"No, Mick, it's not an island, it's just called an island."

Mickey blinked her eyes a few times and then said, "And do they have grub there?"

"They have some great grub there," he smiled proudly. "They have the best hot dogs in the world there, for one thing.

And they have cotton candy, and they have a great roller coaster called the Cyclone."

"I have no idea what you just said," she replied.

"When are you going to learn how to speak English?" he asked, grinning.

"Your idea of English is not far above grunting, Yank."

When they got to the seawall, it and the small strip of beach behind it were busier than they normally were. Busier in fact then Mickey had ever seen it before. They managed to find a little spot and settled in.

Bob unwrapped the sandwiches he brought along, and then with a wink he fished around in his big pockets and came up with two bottles of beer.

"I can't believe how fresh all this food is. Do they always feed you like this?"

"Not always this good, but we certainly don't starve. Not here in England, anyway. I'm not sure what it will be like in France, but I'm sure Mr. Hershey and Mr. Wrigley will be coming with us."

She dropped her head down a little bit and then looked back out over the channel. "I guess you will find out soon enough," she said.

Bob wanted to say something to ease her worries, but there was nothing to say. They both knew he was going, that everybody was going. Two British gunboats were going up and down the beach shooting the mines that were tethered in the water offshore.

Each explosion sent a geyser of water skyward and a boom thundered close enough to them that they could feel the shockwave. There were even louder booms and flashes of light coming from the direction of Poole harbor, and the horizon was full of Allied warships.

"It sort of reminds me of Coney Island," he said, as they watched the action in front of them.

"Is that a hot dog?" she asked and he laughed.

"No, Mick, I was talking about the fireworks. They have some great fireworks shows there. We eat hot dogs."

"And you chase girls," she said. "I caught that part."

"I never catch any."

"Why are they doing that?" Mickey asked, nodding out at the gunboats.

"I can only guess," he said. "They don't tell me shit."

"What's your guess, Yank?"

"Well, all that stuff is made to keep the Krauts out, but its damn inconvenient now by keeping a whole bunch of guys in. They can't go on their boat rides while snaking through a minefield."

"You better hope they do a good job blowing them up then, Yank," she elbowed him and said. "I can't believe how good this chicken is."

"Yeah, I got what they call a five finger discount on the chicken," Bob said as he opened the two beers, "but these took a little trading."

He handed her a bottle and took a quick swig off of his.

"It's safe," he said with a grin.

"You are bad for me, love. First my first fag, then my first gum, and now my first American beer."

"Well, what should we drink to, Mickey, my darling?" he asked, and held up his bottle.

"To coming back safe," she said, and clinked bottles.

"I'll drink to that," Bob said, and took another swig.

Mickey hesitated, then put the bottle up to her nose and sampled the smell of the freshly opened beer.

"No thanks," she said, handing it back to him. "I think I can do without that."

"Go ahead, try it. It's good once you get used to it."

"Not good at all," she said after taking a sip. "Not good at all."

Then she took a second sip, then a third, and the two of them sat there on the seawall and drank their beer.

Then Bob took another swig and winced a little. "I don't know why you limeys like it warm like this."

"I don't either," she shuddered as another swallow of beer went down.

216

"Hey, I just remembered," he said as he jumped up. "I want to take a picture of you. Especially now with your polka dot dress. Here, put on my hat."

"Go ahead then, Yank," she said, shaking her head.

"Ok, now say MICKEY!"

"MICKEY!"

"Ok, I got it. I hope it comes out because that's the last of my film for now," he said, looking down at his trusty "Brownie" camera. "I'm hoping to take pictures from here to Berlin with this thing if I can get the film."

They sat there for a while and chatted about little things, nothing important, nothing painful or worrisome, just little things. No hopes for the future or fears of the past were important right now. Living this moment will have to be enough.

Another boom along the shoreline startled her and she snapped her head towards it. Turning back around, she looked into his eyes and then her head dropped down, looking through her dangling feet at the sand just below them.

"Are you okay, doll?" he asked.

She nodded but kept her head looking down.

"Listen, Mick, I don't want you to worry. I'm still here."

"For now."

"I'm not going to lie to you, Mick, you're too smart for that. I'm sure we will all be going, the whole damn army by the looks of it. We just don't know when, nobody does."

She lifted her head back up and looked at him and said, "I don't want you to go."

"I don't want to either, but I don't think Colonel Gibbs is going to let me stick around here."

"You're not coming back," she said.

"Yes, I will. And I will write all the time, and get my mom to send you goodies like she sends me," he said, and smiled broadly.

"Can we meet tomorrow night at our bench?" she asked.

"I promise to meet you every night on that same park bench at the same time for as long as I can," he said, as he helped her to her feet. "Let's walk for a little while."

"And then one night you won't be there," she said, putting her hand in his and walking back towards Bournemouth.

"That's right, and then one night I won't be there. But it won't be because I don't want to be, it's because I can't be, and you already know why."

"I hope the weather calms a bit," she said, as she glanced back over the choppy channel. "I'm sure there are a lot of nervous lads looking out over this stormy sky right now."

"I think we are all nervous, but it could be worse."

"How could it be worse?"

"Well, we could be Germans," he said. "Can you just imagine how nervous they're gonna be when all those ships are coming over the horizon in the middle of breakfast?"

Just as she giggled to his response, three soldiers marched right past them in single file until they were five or six steps ahead of them and then turned left, and left again so they were now facing the couple, and at full attention.

"Oh no," Bob said, and she scooted a little closer to him.

"It's alright, Mick, these are just my idiot friends," he continued, making her smile and scan their faces.

"The ugly one there," he pointed, "is Doug. It was a horrible accident, poor bastard, but don't say anything to him, he's real self-conscious about it."

She giggled as the soldiers stood there statue still.

"That's Herby in the middle, and John on the end," he said, and then asked, "Ok ,what do you guys want?"

That's when all three of them snapped their hands up and gave Bob a salute fit for a general, making Mickey laugh and shake her head. "Sir," Doug shouted out.

Bob casually and playfully returned the salute and asked, "What is it, Private?"

"Well, it's the men, sir," he said, as he gestured towards the other two. "They are worried about you, sir."

"They should worry about themselves, it would give them a lot more to worry about," Bob said as he stood in front of them like a general would have, getting into the role.

"Well they are just worried, sir," Doug continued, "that you didn't get laid yet, sir."

"Why don't you guys take a long walk off a short pier?" asked Bob.

"Anything we could do to help, sir?" Doug asked, while the other two had big grins on their faces.

"Ok, you guys are dismissed. Let's go, go away, get the hell out of here and don't come back." Bob said, as he scooted them away. "If you come back I'm going to rub Herby's socks on your pillows."

He looked back at Mickey and said, "That should scatter them."

"What did they mean that you didn't get laid yet?" she asked.

"Don't pay attention to them — they're just giving me a hard time."

"Well, they seemed awful worried about it."

"It's nothing," he said. "Just an army thing, is all. But it's a secret army thing."

"A secret army thing, eh? Well, I hope you can tell me about it someday," she said.

"I hope so, too," he grinned.

As they walked back they passed a little park with trees around it and fewer people than in the square. A good place for couples to talk, so they made their way over to an open bench under a tree.

They sat very close together in the quiet park and chatted on about nothing in particular. Their conversation ranged from things back then to things right now and to things that are yet to come.

"I feel a little woozy from the beer," she said. "I'm glad I only had one."

"Half of one," he grinned. "You're a cheap date."

She elbowed him. She figured he was going to try and kiss her soon by the way they were both flirting, and she might even let him. She felt her heart flutter and a tingle went down her spine at the thought of it.

"Thank you for the chicken, it was lovely," she said, making small talk.

"Sure, doll. I brought you some more chocolate by the way, so you can bribe your mates into liking me," he said, making more small talk.

"You sure look pretty tonight, Mick," he said, now with a more serious face. "I really like your dress."

She smiled. "And you look like a soldier ready to jump on a ship," she said back. "But I must admit, you do look good."

They turned and looked into the other's eyes and fell silent.

Time stood still as they lingered there, waiting for the next sensation. Bob could feel her warm breath brushing his face as her breathing became heavier, but she couldn't help it.

His heart raced a little and his palms got clammy, and he felt a few drops of sweat trickle down the back of his neck. He leaned in and she tilted her head up as the tips of their noses touched.

Both closed their eyes and he could smell the sweetness of her breath, and their lips were so close to touching, he could feel them. *This is it. Our first kiss.*

"Oh, I don't want to set the world on fire," the soldier stood over them singing as loud as he could, making Bob bolt to his feet.

"I just want to light a flame in your heart," he kept singing, never taking his eyes off Mickey, as though Bob wasn't even there.

Bob looked down at Mickey and she looked up at him, and seeing her predicament, he burst out laughing. When she saw Bob laughing she started to laugh, too, as the soldier sang his heart out.

Being a little giddy from the beer, or half of a beer, made her laughter now uncontrollable, as she rocked back and forth holding her sides, with tears rolling down her face.

Bob was standing over her, nearly doubled over, laughing as loud as he had ever heard himself laugh. Neither one heard exactly when the singing stopped, but as they began to calm down they noticed he was gone.

"What the hell was that?" Bob asked, his face cramping from laughing so hard.

She could hardly get the words out, laughing the whole time. "Some crazy bloody yank like you, but this one sings."

"He sings better than I do, I must admit," Bob chuckled.

"He follows me around because he thinks he's in love. My mates think he's daft," she said.

"Daft? That's funny as hell."

"Did you learn a new word, Yank?"

"Yeah, gives me a new word for Herby," he smiled.

"Oh bloody hell," she said, as she jumped up after glancing at her watch.

"Shit, already?" Bob said, leaping to his feet.

She turned to run off and then stopped and turned back to him, reached up and gave him a quick but nice kiss on the lips.

"Goodnight, love," she whispered to him and smiled, then she turned away and trotted towards the Grand.

I hate watching her leave. I don't want to lose this one.

He watched her for as long as he could see her. Just as she disappeared from sight he whispered, "Goodnight, Mick."

Once again he made curfew just in time, and he knew he needed to be more careful, cutting it close the last few nights. Doug came in at almost the same moment, also cutting it close, as he always did.

"Did we have some fun tonight, Bobby boy?" asked Doug, as he caught up with him and put his arm over his shoulder.

"We did."

"How did we have fun tonight, Bobby boy?"

"We went on a picnic," Bob grinned.

"Did we get laid again?"

"Nope," Bob smiled. "It's not like that, movie star."

"Sure it's not, Bob. You guys just go play bridge and drink tea with your pinky fingers sticking out."

"Not exactly," Bob grinned as they walked down the hall, and he started humming just as they walked into the room with Herby and John already there.

Herby looked up and said, "I see Bob got laid again."

"Yes he did," said Doug as he turned and smiled at Bob, who could only shake his head.

"Lucky bastard," said Herb, as he looked down at the paper. "The Yankees are really bad right now, but at least the Dodgers are doing worse."

"Only right now?" Bob asked and grinned.

"I hope the damn Krauts don't come tonight, I need my beauty sleep," said Doug.

"I could use the shut eye myself," said John. "But we still have to listen to Herb and his snoring."

"Hell, I'm wide awake," said Bob.

"Doesn't anybody want to hear what I did tonight?" asked Doug.

"Don't waste your time, movie star, we won't believe you anyway," said Herb, never looking up from his paper.

"Well in that case, I'm not going to tell you."

"Thank God for that," John said, as he sat on his bunk grinning.

Bob sat on his bunk and started taking off his boots and picked up humming from where he left off. He hummed a few lines and then started singing softly to himself.

"Oh, I don't want to set the world on fire, I just want to start a flame in your heart."

It was June 4th, 1944. It was two days before D-Day.

222

Chapter Eighteen

"Cancelled," said Bionde, as he walked from gun to gun. "We're on full alert, we go any minute."

"You heard the Lieutenant," said Dutch. "No more play time."

They watched as the endless columns of men filed past them towards Poole Harbor, and they watched as the heavy laden transport and landing ships pushed their way out to sea to disappear in the grey mist.

A few dozen Sherman tanks rolled by in a column that shook the ground, their commanders' helmeted heads sticking out directing the war machines towards the water, towards France.

Six Royal Air Force Spitfires roared along the beach on a patrol to protect the vulnerable boarding troops. American and British patrols were flying all up and down the coast providing cover for the massive, gathering wave.

American and British bombers were flying outbound almost non-stop as they took their deadly payloads to soften the enemy defenses. The battleships and cruisers were also pummeling the French beaches to tear some holes for the troops to pour through.

The airborne troops were already boarding their planes. Their mission would be to land behind the lines and destroy bridges and communication lines to confuse the enemy and block reinforcements.

"Showtime," said Doug, as he watched the action. Sitting and watching is what they did best.

Bob shook his head as he gazed back towards town and realized there was no way to make it there, Dutch would skin him alive.

"Hey Bob," asked John. "Did you get to say goodbye to your girl?"

Bob just stared toward Bournemouth and shook his head no.

"Don't worry, Bob," said Herby. "Those French girls are going to love us."

"I can't even understand this one half the time, Herb," said Bob. "And she speaks English."

Another huge squadron of American bombers went overhead, on their way to France.

"Those Nazi bastards are going to shit when they see us coming," said Herb. "They'll run away and leave all those French girls behind for us to rescue."

"I hope so," said John, watching the bombers fade away over the horizon. "I hope they run like hell."

"Hey, Bob," Doug said softly so the others couldn't hear. "It will be ok, you'll see."

Bob nodded his head and looked down briefly and then up again.

"You have her address, right?" he asked. "You can write to her and explain that you had to leave."

"She understands that part, movie star. I just wanted to see her one more time. I figured we had a few more days."

"You poor dumb bastard, you got it bad, don't you? Your brain is turning to mush over this broad."

"Hey, what's Bob sulking about over there?" yelled Herby. "Must have been his first time to fall in love like that."

"The second time is even better," said Doug, and Bob just smiled and shook his head while John rolled his eyes.

"Hey, look at that," said Doug, and he pointed out just past the breakers as a pair of small transport ships came into view. "They're carrying tanks."

"Those are called LST's, and I'm sure that's what we'll go over in," said John. "They'll pack them full with our guns when they're ready for us."

Doug looked nervously at the small ships churning in the rough water and asked, "We have to ride over in that?"

"I think so," said John. "Or swim."

"Higgins boats," said Dutch. "Landing craft. That's what we'll go over in, take my word for it."

"Higgins boats," asked Doug. "Are they smaller than that?"

"About the same, maybe a little smaller," Dutch said, and Doug looked back out to sea.

"I'm not going to like that part," said Doug.

"Me, either," said Herby.

"I'm just worried about what we'll find on the other side," said John. "There'll be a hell of a welcoming party waiting."

"I'm worried about what I'm leaving behind," said Bob. "I just want to get this over with and come back."

"He's got it bad, alright," said Doug, shaking his head.

Lieutenant Bionde came by the gun position and talked to the men. "Today we break down "C" Battery, gentlemen. We're going down to the staging area at Poole. Orders are for this battery and "B" Battery to be ready to deploy from there at 2100 hours."

"We got a boat ride to go on tonight?" asked Dutch.

"I doubt it will be tonight, but it's bound to be soon."

"When do you want us to start packing, sir?"

"Break the gun down at 1600 hours. Get her on a tow ball and grease her down."

"Yes, sir," said Dutch to the young lieutenant.

"We can take four guns and two trucks on each boat, so pack the two trucks down with double everything. They'll take turns pulling the guns once we get there, and the other trucks and the 50 Cal's will be right behind you."

"Sure thing, Lieutenant, we'll be ready," said Dutch, as Bionde headed off to the next gun.

"We're on full alert until go time at 1600," he said to his gun crew. "I hope you boys packed your socks and underwear because you won't have much time when they call the break down order."

Bob looked at him pleadingly and said, "Hey, Sergeant."

"The answer is no, Private."

225

"Aw c'mon Dutch. You don't even know what I want."

"I know exactly what you want, and the answer is no."

"I'll be back before you know it, Sarge, I promise."

"Now, look," said the Sergeant. "You're not gonna go running off chasing after a dame, and neither is anybody else. You should have said goodbye when you had a chance. Now since the Krauts don't send a telegram to let us know they're coming, watch the damn sky or get my boot up your ass."

"Ok, ok," said Bob, but he couldn't help stealing a glance back towards Bournemouth whenever he could.

Gun Six, Battery "C" of the 386th AAA / AW Battalion got their orders at 1620 hours, and so they started to break down the gun for transport and put a layer of grease on the breach and carriage. Some of the men were pulling sandbags out of the way while others were bringing in the trucks.

Any time a soldier had a moment to spare he ran up to the room and packed his pack and grabbed his gun. Every soldier now had to have a full pack, helmet and rifle at all times.

"There goes the next two guns," Doug said, as two of the trucks pulled out and got into the parade towards Poole.

"Looks like that may be a couple of ours coming back up," said Herb, as he pointed down the road at the trucks trying to snake their way back. "Pain in the ass that we have to share trucks."

"You in a hurry?" Bob asked.

"It's boring just sitting here."

"I would think you would be used to boring, being a Yankee fan," said Bob, grinning.

Herby had a biting retort that made everybody laugh, but Bob didn't even hear it. He was once again distracted by the road back to Bournemouth that was right there, but may as well have been a million miles away.

Doug clapped Bob hard on the back making him jump and snapping him back to the conversation.

"Don't take it personal, Bobby boy," said Doug. "The Dodgers aren't quite that bad. Not quite, anyway."

Bob didn't hear the comment so he just smiled and nodded as though he had. Herby won this round, by default, as Bob daydreamed about the park bench he wouldn't make it to tonight.

"There are but two words to sum up the way I feel about your opinion of the Dodgers," said Bob, as he turned and looked at Herb. "Rat's ass."

"Now, now, you boys play nice," said John. "What's that song you keep humming, Bob? It's driving me crazy."

"The Ink Spots," Doug smiled. "1941, I believe. 'I Don't Want to Set the World on Fire,' right Bob? I know more about show business than Herby knows about the Yankees."

"I doubt that," said Herb.

"I doubt that, too," said John.

"Hansen!" yelled Dutch at Doug as he worked on the gun. "Did you get your pack yet?"

"Not yet, Sarge."

"Well, what are you waiting for, the goddamn bellboy? Get your ass up there and get it."

"Ok, ok," said Doug, as he scrambled over the sandbags and trotted off towards the China Hotel.

Lillian looked at her watch and then looked around for him. *I have a bad feeling about this.*

He was twenty-five minutes late by now and she feared the worse. *He's going, dammit. And I didn't even get to say goodbye.*

The thought of not seeing him got her a little panicky so she decided to walk the rest of the way down to the China Hotel. It was about four miles from the Square to the China Hotel, but it would be worth it if she could even see him for a moment. *Maybe they are still there. Maybe they can't leave the hotel but they are still there.*

She drew nearer to the last place she knew where his battalion was. *This is hopeless. I'll never find him in this.*

She finally made it to the China hotel, and when she looked up, the first thing she noticed was that the guns were

227

gone. The 386th had pulled up stakes and moved on, leaving behind nothing but sandbags and a few empty ammo cans.

She turned and looked down the road to Poole and it was a traffic jam of trucks and jeeps and men. Some of the trucks were pulling big guns behind and some of the jeeps were, as well. Tanks lined the road and a haze of diesel fumes hung over the whole place.

The noise was an ever-pounding, earth shaking, clanking and banging and yelling from every direction. It all seemed so chaotic.

She knew that he was somewhere in that line and she felt numb. She went into a daydream and just stared at the departing army as the sound went muffled in her head and her peripheral vision narrowed.

"Hey, ain't you Bob's girl?" came the voice that snapped her out of her hypnotic state. "Mickey, right?"

She just stood there blinking her eyes.

"Don't you remember me?" he asked with a big smile and a pack over his shoulder.

"Yes, of course, you're Doug. The ugly one, right?"

Doug laughed hard and nodded his head. "That's me, the ugly one."

"Where's Bob? Can I see him?"

"Let's see what we can do," said Doug. "Wait at the entrance to the park, maybe you can get a quick look at the battalion pulling out. I'll tell him you're here."

"Thank you, love," she said and kissed his cheek. "And be careful, mind you."

"Thanks, doll," he said, and trotted up the road into the crowd.

The truck pulling Gun Six of "C" Battery was just pulling into the traffic jam when Doug ran up and threw his pack into the back of the truck that all the men and equipment were now moving out on.

"Hey, Bobby boy, I've got a surprise," said Doug, and Bob looked up to figure out what he was up to now. "That dish of yours is up there at the entrance to the park. I figured you can wave to her on the way out or something, so watch for her."

"She's there now? She's up there right now? Is she looking for me?" Bob fired off the questions so fast he didn't wait for an answer.

"I just told you, yeah, she's up there, you dumb bastard. It doesn't matter because you…."

Bob had taken a glance back at Dutch who was looking away, and he rolled over the top of the tailgate and started running towards the park.

"Oh shit," said Herby, as he and Doug looked at each other and back at Dutch who, thankfully, seemed too preoccupied to notice Bob missing.

Bob ran up the hill and grabbed her in his arms and spun her around as he swept her off her feet, and they both giggled.

"Just like a yank," she said, shaking her head. "Run off first chance you get."

"Let's sit down for a minute," he said, as he nodded toward the park bench with an old couple sitting on one end. "I think I can get away with this for a few minutes. My buddies will cover for me."

"I hope I don't get you into trouble."

"What are they going to do, make me invade France or something?"

She felt a sudden sadness come over her at the thought of it. "That's not funny," she said.

He leaned over and pulled her close and kissed her, then he kissed her again. They looked in each other's eyes and then he kissed her again. He held her face in his hands and wiped away a little tear.

"I love you, Mickey, my darling. You must know that by now."

"Damn soldiers," she said. "I swore there would be no more damn soldiers, and I meant it. You're going to leave and I'll never see you again. You're going to leave and every time I think of you it will hurt."

"It's not like that, Mick. I'll be back for you, you'll see. I love you and nothing can keep me from coming back."

"I can't believe I fell in love with a soldier. An American soldier at that."

Bob grinned at her and said, "Sorry about that, Mick."

"No you're not, you big liar," she said, and punched him in the chest on top off his flak jacket. "Don't tell me you're coming back if you're not."

"Hey, wait a minute," Bob said. "You just said you fell in love with me, too. I knew you did, you couldn't help it now, could you?"

"No, you bloody Yank, I couldn't. But don't be so proud of yourself. I have very poor taste when it comes to men."

"Couldn't be that bad, you chose me."

"I rest my case," she smiled, and then her head dropped down and the smile quickly faded.

"Don't worry," he said, lifting her head up by the chin. "I'll write to you all the time, I promise."

"I'd like that," she said. "And please be careful."

Bob heard Doug's whistle in the distance and he knew the battalion was about to roll. He looked up nervously at the park entrance, knowing he was pushing his luck.

"I have to go, Mickey, my darling."

"I know, but I don't want you to," she said as her voice cracked. "I don't want to say goodbye."

"Let's not say goodbye then," he said, and she lifted her head again to look in his eyes.

"Why not?" she asked.

"Saying goodbye is bad luck. Didn't you know that?"

"No, actually I didn't," she said as Doug whistled again.

"This isn't goodbye, my darling. This is so long, so long until we meet again. I will come back, I will always come back."

She nodded and swiped at a tear forming that she didn't want him to see. He had enough to worry about without worrying about her, but she couldn't help it.

"So this is the deal, Mick. Let's promise to never say goodbye. Never ever. For as long as we live we will never say goodbye. We can say see you later, or so long, so long until we meet again, but we will never say goodbye, ok?"

Mickey just nodded.

"Ok, Mick?"

"Alright."

"Good. Now I have to say so long to you. So long until we meet again."

"So long," she said, and he leaned in to kiss her.

He gave her a nice long kiss, and he stood up to leave at the sound of yet another whistle. "I'd know that whistle anywhere," he said.

Wait!" she said and pulled him back down to give him one more kiss, one more big kiss, one he would never forget.

"These girls are going to lose the war for us yet," the old woman said to the old man sitting on the other end of the bench, apparently with the intention of being overheard.

Bob and Mickey broke their kiss with a laugh and a giggle as they took a glance towards the sour faced old couple and back.

"Must be related to the waiter," Bob grinned, making her laugh some more.

"Cover for me, Herb," Doug said as he rolled over the tailgate when Dutch was looking away, leaving Herby speechless and a little panicky. "I have to go get that big dumb bastard before he runs off with that skirt."

When he got to the top of the stairs he could see the two of them kissing. Bob's pack was on the bench with his helmet on top of it, and his gun was leaning up against it.

"Bob, let's go, we're moving out. The trucks are rolling, you have to come now."

Bob stood up and put on his helmet, slung his rifle over his shoulders, and fished out a couple candy bars from his pocket and gave them to her with a smile. "I was going to give these to you tonight."

Then he picked up his pack, ran up the stairs and out the entrance to the park, and disappeared.

The truck pulling Gun Six was starting down the road behind the long parade of equipment lined up in front of them, so it was moving slow, but it was moving. When the two of them reached the road, Doug could see the truck was a good hundred yards further down the road than it was when he left it.

"Run, Bob," he said. "You would have never found it if I hadn't come and got you."

"Thanks, movie star, I owe you one. How do we get back in that truck without Dutch seeing us?"

"We don't," said Doug. "Just leave it up to me, I have a plan."

"Oh shit," said Bob. "We're screwed."

"When we get to the truck, just throw your pack up into the back and jump in like nothing happened. Leave the rest to me."

"I don't have much choice, I have to do that anyway, we both do, the truck is gaining ground," Bob said, as he picked up the speed and started to pant under the heavy load he was carrying and wearing.

When Bob reached the truck he threw his pack up to Herby and jumped on the step bumper and climbed over the tailgate. Doug was right behind him, laughing and slapping Bob on the back. Dutch had been sitting towards the front speaking to a soldier sitting across from him when he saw Bob and then Doug climbing into the truck they should have already been in.

"What the hell is going on?" Dutch screamed and his face turned red as the veins in his forehead started to pop. He lifted his butt out of the seat a little bit but he couldn't get to them unless he climbed over everybody first, lucky for them.

"Did you see what this dumb ass did, Sarge?" asked Doug.

"Enlighten me, Hansen."

"He dropped his pack off the back of the truck, Sarge," said Doug laughing. "If we hadn't jumped off to get it, every truck in the army would have run over it by morning. What a butterfingers."

Dutch looked at Doug and the scowl faded and a little grin formed. He looked at Bob and said, "You idiot."

Bob shrugged his shoulders and grinned a stupid grin. "Sorry, Sergeant," he said, as Doug winked at him.

Lillian walked up the steps, as well, and was able to position herself so she could watch the trucks go by. She hoped for a glimpse of him, but that hardly seemed possible.

Truck after truck rolled by, choking out diesel fumes and digging ruts in the road as they clawed their way towards the coast.

As she stood there watching, two British soldiers walked up next to her and tried to chat her up. She had no desire to be flirted with right now so she tried shushing them away, but they were persistent.

They stood on either side of her talking but she just tuned them out and kept looking for Bob. If she ignored them, maybe they would go away, although that seemed like a strategy that never worked, especially on the singers.

"Hey fellas, look," Bob said as he pointed toward the edge of the park. "There's my girl."

He started waving to her and she started waving back. The two soldiers, seeing what she was doing, also started waving at Bob and had big grins on their faces.

Herby saw the two English soldiers flanking her and, elbowing Bob, said, "Look at that, she's not wasting any time."

The whole truck broke into a fit of laughter. Even Dutch was doubled over at Bob's plight. The truck turned the corner and Mickey disappeared from sight.

"Women, eh, Bob?" said Doug as he clapped him on the back. "You really should leave this kind of thing to the professionals."

"I don't know, pretty boy. Seems like I'm doing pretty fair for an amateur."

"If it wasn't for me you wouldn't have met her," smiled Doug.

"Well, I guess I double owe you then, movie star."

"Well, I guess you do."

"Did you get to say goodbye to your girl, Bob?" asked John.

Bob paused and smiled as he watched Bournemouth fade from sight and he said softly, "No John, I sure didn't."

"What the hell were you doing then?" asked Herb, but Bob didn't respond.

So long, Mickey, my darling. So long until we meet again.

It was June 5, 1944. It was the day before D-Day.

Chapter Nineteen

The Battalion finally made it down to Poole Harbor well after dusk, and were directed to a staging area. The remaining half of their trucks were commandeered with the promise they would be returned within a few hours, so the men didn't even get a chance to pull their packs off before they headed back up the road.

"I guess all we can do is sit here," said Bob, as he watched out to sea at the distant flashes that looked like lightening.

"I'll sit here the whole rest of the war if they want, that would be fine with me," said Herb.

"You won't meet any of those French girls sitting here, Herby," chided Doug.

"At least I'll have an ass to sit on," said Herb. "Nobody here will shoot it off."

"I'm going to try and get some shut eye," said Bob, as he laid down next to Gun Six. "We ain't shooting anything tonight."

"That's a good plan," said John. "We all should."

Bob wanted to sleep, but just lay there listening to the rustling army all around him, and the waves rolling up the beach. He had a thousand thoughts in his head that were all snatching sleep away from him, even though he was on the brink of sheer exhaustion.

I can't stop thinking about Mickey, no matter how hard I try.

He relived every moment he'd spent with her again and again in his head, and he worried that if something happened to him he would break his promise, and her heart.

He imagined how his mom would react if something bad happened to him. *I have to write her again.*

He couldn't stop thinking about what awaited the battalion on the other side of that channel. *I wish they would at least tell us when we're going. And I wish I could get this damn song out of my head.*

It was a restless night with warplanes constantly roaring overhead, tanks clanking down the road, and tens of thousands of men milling around, awaiting their turn. No one could sleep through all this noise.

I have to pee. He lay there trying to convince himself that he didn't, but he wasn't having much luck.

He pushed himself up onto his elbows and looked around a little bit to see the first traces of dawn in the sky. Somewhere through all the noise around them, Bob could hear a familiar sound.

"Dammit, Herby," Bob said, shaking his head as he looked over at Doug, who was also awake. "I thought there was a Sherman tank parked next to us, but it was Herby snoring again."

"Tanks are quieter," said John, with bloodshot eyes. Herby was about the only one getting any sleep. "Somebody throw a bucket of water on those bagpipes he calls a nose. Hey — the trucks aren't back yet."

"Goddamn army," said Bob. "All my crap is in my pack on that truck. I can't even write a letter."

"Don't cry, Bob," said Doug. "We'll get it back for you."

"Kiss my ass, movie star."

"Did the trucks get back yet?" Herby said with a yawn, as he sat himself up.

"Look who's back from the dead," said John, nodding towards Herb.

"Can't we just leave him behind?" asked Doug.

"I got to piss," declared Herb. "You would miss me too much, movie star. You wouldn't have anyone to pick on."

As they stood there in line peeing, an orange light was growing on the horizon. The sun was struggling to poke itself up and chase the dark across the sky. As that orange glow appeared, the first waves of men were landing in France.

"What's today's date, anybody know?" asked Doug.

"Sixth," said Herby. "June sixth."

In the predawn hours that morning, over 5,000 ships left the shores of England for the beaches of France, supported by over 19,000 aircraft. The 82nd Airborne landed behind enemy lines and captured the town of Sainte Mère Église before dawn, making it the first liberated city in France.

Half an hour later, Bob stared into the smoky haze of the channel, staring at the invasion force under way. Not a space on the horizon could be seen without a ship in it. From the shoreline to as far as could be seen, it seemed one could almost walk across the boats to France.

"Where is my goddamn truck?" Dutch grumbled to no one in particular, though everyone heard it.

"There goes breakfast," said Herb.

"I need my toothbrush," said Doug, licking the roof of his mouth.

Dutch just shook his head and muttered, "Goddamn bunch of prima donnas."

Bob turned away from the channel back to join the conversation when he noticed Colonel Gibbs talking to the men of Gun Five, not ten yards away. Lieutenant Bionde was with him, and Dutch had no idea that Gibbs was right behind them.

Out of what seemed to be utter frustration the Sergeant yelled out loud, "Where is my goddamn truck? Goddamn army."

Bob grinned. *This should be good.*

"Lose something, Sergeant?" asked the Colonel from over Dutch's shoulder. Everyone snapped to attention, including the Sergeant who recognized the voice in his ear.

"At ease, men," Gibbs said. "Don't worry about your truck, Sergeant. The army had to borrow it for a bit, but we'll give it back soon."

"Thank you, sir. It's just that my men are itching to get into the fight."

Bob looked around at the other guys' faces with the same, "I didn't say that," look that he had on his. "I can wait," he whispered as he elbowed Herb, and Herb nodded.

"Gather round, gentlemen," the Colonel said, and the men of Gun Six, Battery "C", did just that. "I want to personally visit every gun crew in the battalion and tell you guys how proud I am to lead the 386th.

"I expect great things out of Gun Six," he said, clapping Dutch on the back. "Sergeant Van Holland is one of my best men, and I have all the confidence in the world that you will be one of my best crews."

The men nodded and smiled. Bob felt proud that they were working for Dutch after hearing the Colonel's words, even though he was a hard-ass. Maybe it was worth it, or maybe the Colonel was telling the same thing to every gun crew out there.

"I don't know when we're going, or where we'll go," Colonel Gibbs continued. "I don't know what to expect when we get there, but I do know that whatever it is, the 386th will rise to the challenge. And I want you to know that wherever and whenever we go, I will be with you all the way. Now a short prayer."

All the men pulled off their helmets, and, following the Colonel's lead, bowed their heads, waiting for him to begin.

"Lord, we ask that you watch over us and protect us from our enemies, and grant us the strength to be victorious over the evil empire with whom we battle. Lord, please give comfort to our loved ones as they await our safe return. May God bless the 386th, and the United States of America. Amen."

"Amen," the other men repeated.

Without another word the Colonel ducked under the barrel of Gun Six, and continued on to the next crew. Bionde went with him but not before giving Dutch and his crew a wink and a nod on the way out.

The 386th spent most of that day doing nothing. They had no trucks, they had no packs, they had no food, and no water.

"Hey look at the bright side, we got our rifles!" said Herb sarcastically. "Whose bright idea was it to require every soldier to carry a rifle, even gunners?"

"We drag around the biggest machine guns ever built and they want us to sling those heavy rifles, too," John said, shaking his head.

"Stop being a crybaby, Herb," said Doug, pulling on his boots and still lapping at the roof of his mouth. I need my damn toothbrush, at least some water. Where the hell is our truck?"

"Herb's just mad because now he has two guns he can't hit anything with," Bob said, grinning.

Dutch had wandered off to check on supplies and when he came back he had good news about breakfast. "They have a mess set up over there on the end of this row for truck-deficient gunners such as ourselves."

"Where is it, Sarge?" Bob asked.

"Walk down that row of tanks — just follow the smell of corned beef hash."

"Is it that dog shit we had last time they called it that?"

"God, that was some bad corned beef hash. It must have been left over from WWI."

"Try civil war, more like it."

"Don't worry, boys, this stuff is pretty new, less than ten years old I would bet," said Dutch, smiling.

The boys came back to the gun each carrying a big cup of coffee and a mess plate of corned beef hash piled high.

"Is this the army's idea of a last meal?" said Doug, stirring his gooey blob of so-called hash, pushing and pulling it around the plate trying to find a good side.

"This shit still tastes like dog food, and it smells like it, too," said John, trying to gag it down.

"It would take a damn hungry dog to eat this crap," said Bob, as he struggled with every bite.

This was the first of what would turn out to be a string of bad meals as they waited there at Poole harbor. Another day came and went, and then another, without their trucks or their gear. All they could do was sit there and wait and watch an army march past them and sail into the mist.

Bob would sometimes sit by the gun leaning against one tire, lost in thought as he stared out to sea.

"Why the hell did they have to move us here if we're just going to sit and wait? We could have stayed put and I could have seen Mickey again."

Long after dark on June 8^{th,} the trucks with the packs and gear showed up. Everything was strewn about the truck, including packs, ammo, and spare parts for the gun. It was obvious that it had been unloaded and thrown back in.

Doug and Bob stood staring into the back of the big truck and its jumbled cargo.

"I thought they said they were using the trucks to tow guns and trailers down to the harbor," said Doug.

"It looks more like a giant picked it up and shook it like a martini," said Bob.

Dutch showed up at the back of the truck with the rest of the gun crew. "Let's get to work, boys. You have one hour to make that truck perfect. Everything comes off and then back on again."

"C'mon Dutch, it's the middle of the night. Can't it wait?" asked Herb.

"Do it now," the Sergeant snapped, freezing the men in place. "Do it now and then hit the sack. We go first thing in the morning, I got the word a few hours ago. Do it now."

Dutch walked away leaving the guys speechless and looking back and forth at each other. After a few quiet and shuffling moments, John jumped up into the back of the truck and started passing down the packs. Herby jumped up with him and helped.

The whole crew worked in silence for a few minutes until John said, "Let's get these spare gun barrels out so we can stack the ammo."

The truck carried six extra barrels for the gun and many other spare parts, as well as cases and cases of the big 40mm ammo. It all came off, and it all went back on, and it was done in 52 minutes.

"At least we got our packs," said Doug, as he fished around for his toothbrush. "We movie stars got to have shiny white teeth."

"Hey, Herb," John said. "Why don't you go sleep with the guys at Gun Five and keep them awake all night?"

"Better yet," said Bob, "go sleep with the Krauts so they're too tired to fight."

"I don't think the guys on Gun Five like me," said Herb. "And I'm sure the Germans don't."

"What makes you think we do?" asked Bob, and they all laughed.

"Well, I'll tell you what," said Herby. "Why don't you all just go to hell?"

Everybody laughed and Herb said, "I'm going to snore as loud as I can for the rest of the war, and I'm going to fart all night."

"What else is new?" asked John.

"What is this, the goddamn third grade?" Dutch popped out of nowhere and yelled. "Go to sleep or I will hit you over the head with a pipe, is that clear?"

With only four hours to spare until dawn on June 9th, the crew of Gun Six finally settled in for the night and got some sleep. Doug had clean teeth, Herb was snoring like a bear, and Bob even managed to jot off a V-Mail to his mom.

Bob was dreaming in a shallow sleep. *Mickey is behind me, and France is in front of me. I'll be glad when it's the other way around. She's probably wondering what's going on. The world is probably wondering if it's started yet. I wonder if Mom knows.*

Mickey knew, and so did the whole world by now. The invasion was on in full force. Bob was cut off from the world so he had no access to radio or newspapers. Dutch would only tell them what they needed to know, and he deemed that to be very little.

A few days earlier, on June 6th, President Franklin D. Roosevelt made an announcement to the world that the invasion force was on its way to France. People around the world listened to his words and his prayer, including Archie and Anne, Mickey, William, Joyce and Ted, the Commander and his wife, and even Margaret. And also, all the girls at the Grand hotel.

Archie was trying to dial in the best signal he could on the old radio, and he turned up the volume so he could hear the words over the static:

> "My fellow Americans: Last night, when I spoke with you about the fall of Rome, I knew at that moment that troops of the United States and our allies were crossing the Channel in another and greater operation. It has come to pass with success so far."

The color ran from Anne's face as she heard the news and, almost fainting, dropped down into the chair. Archie sat next to her, taking her trembling hand. She looked up at him as he nodded and gave her the tiniest hint of a smile, then looked back at the radio.

> "And so in this poignant hour, I ask you to join with me in prayer."

The girls at the Grand were sitting around the radio listening to the American President. Sarah extended a hand out to her right and to her left, and following her lead, the girls linked hands in a circle and bowed their heads. Lillian had done a lot of praying in the past with little luck, but she needed all the hope she could get right now.

> "Almighty God: Our sons, pride of our Nation, this day have set upon a mighty endeavor, a struggle to preserve our Republic,

242

our religion, and our civilization, and to set free
a suffering humanity."

William slid his chair closer to Joyce and put his arm around her, as Ted stood in the kitchen doorway shaking his head. Commander Grisham and his family were huddled around the radio in the other room.

"It's about bloody time," said Ted, and Joyce shushed him, but William nodded his agreement. "I need a drink," he said, and walked out.

> "Lead them straight and true; give strength to their arms, stoutness to their hearts, steadfastness in their faith.
>
> "They will need Thy blessings. Their road will be long and hard. For the enemy is strong. He may hurl back our forces. Success may not come with rushing speed, but we will return again and again; and we know that by Thy grace, and by the righteousness of our cause, our sons will triumph."

Anne started to cry so Archie squeezed her hand a little tighter.

> "They will be sore tried, by day and by night, without rest until the victory is won. The darkness will be rent by noise and flame. Men's souls will be shaken with the violences of war.
>
> "For these men are lately drawn from the ways of peace. They fight not for the lust of conquest. They fight to end conquest. They fight to liberate. They fight to let justice arise, and tolerance and good will among all Thy people. They yearn for the end of battle, for their return to the haven of home.

"Some will never return. Embrace these, Father, and receive them, Thy heroic servants, into Thy kingdom."

Anne bent over and put her hands in her face and started sobbing, her body heaving as she gasped for air in an apparent panic attack. Archie leaned over and turned off the radio. "Enough of that for tonight. We can read about it tomorrow."

Meanwhile, the girls at the Grand were gathered around the radio, listening to the entire prayer.

"And for us at home — fathers, mothers, children, wives, sisters, and brothers of brave men overseas, whose thoughts and prayers are ever with them — help us, Almighty God, to rededicate ourselves in renewed faith in Thee in this hour of great sacrifice.

"Many people have urged that I call the nation into a single day of special prayer. But because the road is long and the desire is great, I ask that our people devote themselves in a continuance of prayer. As we rise to each new day, and again when each day is spent, let words of prayer be on our lips, invoking Thy help to our efforts.

"Give us strength, too — strength in our daily tasks, to redouble the contributions we make in the physical and the material support of our armed forces.

"And let our hearts be stout, to wait out the long travail, to bear sorrows that may come, to impart our courage unto our sons, wheresoever they may be.

"And, O Lord, give us Faith. Give us Faith in Thee; Faith in our sons; Faith in each other; Faith in our united crusade. Let not the

244

keenness of our spirit ever be dulled. Let not the impacts of temporary events, of temporal matters of but fleeting moment — let not these deter us in our unconquerable purpose.

"With Thy blessing, we shall prevail over the unholy forces of our enemy. Help us conquer the apostles of greed and racial arrogances. Lead us to the saving of our country, and with our sister nations, into a world unity that will spell a sure peace, a peace invulnerable to the schemings of unworthy men. And a peace that will let all of men live in freedom, reaping the just rewards of their honest toil.

"Thy will be done, Almighty God. Amen."

Moments after the speech the radio in the girls' room started becoming overwhelmed with static, and as hard as Sarah tried, she couldn't tune it back in.

"Just turn the bloody thing off," barked Lillian. "I don't want to hear anymore anyway."

"At least it's no secret anymore. We know the lads are on their way," said Becky.

"A lot of our lads are already there," said Lillian wistfully, as she drifted between anger and profound sadness. "You heard the American President, many will never return. Never return, like Jim and like Jake."

Sarah scooted up close and said, "You're right, Lily, many won't come back. All you can do now is believe with all your heart that your yank will be safe and this awful war will end soon."

Lillian nodded and pushed a tear off her cheek.

"Every bloody one of them will tell you they don't want to go," Sarah continued. "They will give every reason in the world, but they don't really mean it. They don't really believe it."

"I don't understand."

245

"Listen love, do you think for one bloody minute that this yank would stay behind, even if he could? Do you think he would watch his comrades sail off without him?"

"They're young. They think they are bullet proof."

"They have faith, Lily. Unshakable, unbreakable faith. We need to have faith that they will come home, and that they will come home victorious, and this terrible war will be over once and for all."

"Thank you, Sarah. You're right. He'll be back, safe and sound," she said, trying to convince herself.

"And get this bloody war over with so we can get back to our normal lives," said Sarah, shaking her head.

Lillian nodded and smiled. *What is normal? This is the most normal part of my life so far. Being with these girls in this place makes me feel like I'm part of something important.*

"Did you have a chance to say goodbye to your yank, Lily?" asked Becky, also trying to comfort her friend.

"No, I didn't," Lillian said, dropping her head down and closing her eyes.

Becky looked at Sarah and then at Emily. They all knew how upset she was at not saying goodbye to Jim, or for that matter, her sisters.

Before Becky could say another word, Lillian lifted her head up smiling and said, "We never said goodbye, and we never, ever will."

Nobody had a response to her odd reaction except Sarah. Sarah always had something to say. "Don't pay any more attention to her, she's daft. Too much time with that yank, I would say."

"Well, if you're not going to pay any more attention to me then I suppose you don't want any of these," Lillian said, as she held up the two Hershey bars.

They all squealed with delight as they divided up the candy, and the room fell silent as they savored the rare treat.

"I don't care what anybody thinks," said Emily. "I'm really getting to like this yank of yours, love."

Lillian nodded and went into a little daydream as the chocolate melted slowly away. *I remember how he ate half of his in one bite.* She smiled. *And how he stuck his gum to the table, the cheeky bugger.*

She would think about him all day, and dream about him all night. Now she had faith that he was somewhere thinking about her, dreaming about her. And she was right.

In the early morning hours of June 9th, the 386th was given the green light to get the guns hitched and be ready to muster up for the boat ride over. They had one more awful breakfast, and then Gun Five and Gun Six and their crews met the loadmasters at the dock to squeeze everything and everyone they could on board.

Gun Seven and Gun Eight were already loaded, their tow bars facing forward so the truck could hook up and pull them straight out. Gun Five and Gun Six were backed in the same way, while the two trucks shared by the four guns were backed in last.

The four gun crews packed themselves into every spare space on the boat, standing room only — no bathroom, no food, and only the water in their canteens. Bob didn't even have any candy bars, but he smiled when he thought about why.

Suddenly reality reached up and slapped him in the face as the huge ramp door pulled up and the big diesel engines on the boat roared to life. Bob looked over to see a very pale Doug darting his eyes around, and then at John, who seemed to be looking at the sky to assess the weather conditions.

If John ever gets rattled, he sure hides it well. The always calm and cool John. He's a rock.

"Holy shit," said Herby, the opposite of John. "Holy shit."

"Relax, Herby," said Bob. "We'll be there before you know it."

"To hell with that, I don't want to be there before I know it. I don't want to be there at all."

"Shut the hell up, all of you, or I will use you as an anchor," Dutch said, trying to keep any panic from spreading throughout the boat.

As they pulled out of Poole the boat got into the breakwaters, making the bow pitch high into the air before crashing and splashing back down as they went headlong into the waves, lurching the crowded men forward and then throwing them back again. With each up and then down motion, the cold sea water came splashing down on the men and on the guns, making Dutch scowl at the salt that would soon attack his gun if he didn't get it wiped down as soon as possible.

Once they cleared the harbor, the rolling and pitching of the boat got even worse. Besides the up and down of the bow as it clawed past the waves, in the trough of the waves there also came a slamming side to side rocking motion, pushing the shoulder-to-shoulder men left and right before again crashing into the spraying wave in front. Up and down and side to side and up and down and side to side and up and down, over and over and over again.

Bob was holding on to everything and anyone he could as he was banged sideways and forward and backward and then sideways again. Even worse was that he couldn't see over the sides. They were too high and they were armored to protect the crews.

"I feel like we are in a giant floating bathtub," said Bob, and Doug nodded.

Bob could hear the pitch of the engines change when the boat topped the waves as the stern lifted out of the water and the props had nothing but air to bite into for a few moments. He felt queasy and claustrophobic. *This is as close to hell as I ever want to be.*

"You're looking a little gray in the gills, movie star," chided Herb. Herb was still cracking jokes but the rest of the boat got quieter and quieter as the effects of the sea started getting to them. "Not exactly the Queen Mary, is it?"

"Shut up, Herb," said Bob, and John nodded.

The four guns, two trucks, and sixty-eight men with all their gear on the big landing boat pushed ahead into the wind and rough sea. Two steps forward and one step back.

The constant spray of cold, salty water, and the smell of the diesel fumes had all the men getting a little shaky. Even Dutch was struggling with holding down breakfast. "That shit tasted bad enough the first time," he said, making some of the men in earshot gag, cover their mouths, and close their eyes tight.

Seagulls glided by overhead in the slate gray sky, and somewhere high above them, the humming of warplanes was constant. The convoy of ships they were part of seemed endless, as was the convoy of empty vessels returning for more cargo.

These boats and ships had ferried men across the rough channel for days. On June sixth, just days earlier, 57,000 American soldiers landed on the beaches of France, as well as 75,000 British troops. Of those, 2,500 were killed and 8,500 were wounded. That was just the first day.

The casualties were still piling up as more waves of allies landed and met heavy resistance by a dug-in German army. In preparing for the invasion, the Germans built thousands of obstacles to tangle up the boats, with gun emplacements above to stall the landings and then kill them on the beaches.

Now it was June 9th, or "D plus three," and the AAA gunners were being brought in to protect the grounds that had been, inch by inch, purchased in blood. Over the next few weeks, 53,000 AAA gunners and their guns would be brought in, as well as light tanks and artillery.

The eight hundred men of the 386th "Skywatchers" and their thirty-two big 40mm cannons were to be among them, if they could just make it there.

By now most of the men were quiet or talking in a whisper. Everyone was pale and holding onto something or leaning against something. A few took little sips of water, and while it helped some of them, it made others feel worse. Almost everyone on the boat was on the very edge of losing it.

"Where is that goddamned beach?" Dutch grumbled, but no one answered.

Bob wondered the same thing as he began thinking about his father, the fisherman. *Close, I hope. If I get seasick, Pop will disown me. That will be one war story he will never hear.*

He tried to keep his mind off the rocking motion of the sea as the waves battered the boat and the gulls squealed above them. *I wonder what Mickey is doing right now.*

Herby and Bob were shoulder to shoulder while facing Doug and John, only inches apart in this cramped quarters. John and Doug were against the port side wall of the boat while Herb and Bob had their backs to Gun Six. Every time the boat rolled left Herb and Bob were pushed into the other two before being jerked back into the gun with John and Doug almost pinning them there.

Herb elbowed Bob and with a grin he said, "Watch this."

"Hey, Doug," said Herby.

Doug just looked down at his feet and didn't answer.

"Hey, Doug," Herby said, grinning and a little louder this time.

"Don't you do it, Herb," said John.

"Yeah, shut the hell up," said Bob, as a gush of seawater rolled over the edge of the boat, nearly cutting him off in midsentence.

"Hey, Doug," Herb said again, even louder and with a broader grin.

"C'mon Herb. Don't," said John, almost pleading.

"Don't you fucking do it, Herb! Shut the hell up!" Bob yelled.

"You guys have no sense of humor," said Herby. "I just want to ask the movie star a question is all. Hey, Doug."

"Please, Herby," pleaded Bob. "For God's sake, for the New York Yankees, and for French girls everywhere, just put a sock in it."

"Well, Bob, if you were Jewish, if you were a Yankee fan, and if you hadn't just got laid by an English dish, then I might listen to you."

"I didn't get laid."

"You should have, you dumb bastard. Hey, Doug."

Doug just shook his hanging head as his face went from gray to white, trembling as though he were cold. Up and down and side to side the merciless and unrelenting English Channel battered the helpless boat.

"Just leave him alone," said John, but a corned beef hash tasting burp took the fight out of him.

"Just one question, movie star. Just one, I promise."

Doug lifted his head up slowly and looked into Herb's grinning face and said with a scowl, "What?"

"Do you want some oatmeal?"

The last word barely left Herb's mouth when the chain reaction started. Doug dropped his head back down and vomited, hitting Bob at waist level and all down his leg and on one of his hands.

Bob was next, blasting corned beef hash all over John, causing him and Herby to lose it, as well. It only took seconds for the domino effect to go through the boat. There is nothing like the smell of vomit to push one over the edge when being so close to losing their lunch already.

Dutch was in a corner of the boat with the other three sergeants and the Lieutenant, now wearing each other's breakfast. It seemed to be everywhere — on the guns and on the trucks, on the walls of the boat, on each other, and on the deck, making it a slippery mess.

Doug managed to lift his head up again to look at Herb and said, "I'm gonna get you for that, you bastard."

Herby started to laugh, but then puked again in the middle of it, making it come out of his nose and down the front of his jacket.

"I hope you drown on it, you son of a bitch," said Bob, trying not to lose it again.

Private Tucker from Gun Five had been clamping his hand over his mouth with his eyes shut tight, and when he heard Bob say that he exploded, shooting out his nose and from between his fingers.

251

"Speaking of drowning," said John, as he looked over at Herb, "Let's just throw that bastard off the boat and be done with him."

Bob thought he was getting past the worst of the nausea so he took a deep breath to steady himself. It might have worked but for the gagging smell in the air. He wiped at his face and then realized he had Doug's last meal on his hand, which was now on his forehead, and he lost it again.

An agonizingly long twenty minutes later, the men on the boat began to quiet down, they simply had no more to give. They were weak and drained and they stunk.

"I'd rather face the damn Germans than spend one more minute on this boat," said Doug, and everyone nodded.

"Why not," said John. "It's not like this day could get any worse."

That's when Bob noticed the little "tink tink" coming from above. It was raindrops hitting his helmet. Suddenly a huge clap of thunder exploded overhead and the sky burst open, turning their boat into an ark.

As if the sea hadn't been violent enough already, it now became a cauldron, battering the boat and its miserable passengers even more.

I hope those damn guns are tied down good. Bob imagined himself being crushed against the wall of the boat by the five-thousand pound weapon.

"I guess you won't be playing a pirate in any of your movies, eh, Doug?" Herby asked.

"No pirates. No boats at all, unless maybe the Queen Mary again, that wasn't so bad," said Doug. "I'll be playing the romantic leading man that all the girls want to kiss."

"Might want to wipe the puke of you face first," said Bob.

"You might want to wipe his puke off of your face, too, Bob," and everybody laughed, even Bob.

It was now raining so hard that they had to yell just to hear each other. At least everything was getting a good cleaning, and the two trucks, four guns, and sixty-eight men, sixty-eight miserable men, inched ever closer to France.

Two hours later when the sea calmed down a little bit and the skies cleared a little bit, a crewman on the boat made an announcement.

"Omaha beach, easy red section, dead ahead. We'll be on the sand in less than thirty minutes. We hope you have enjoyed the ride, don't forget to tip the crew."

"Holy shit," said Herb.

They all got quiet for a few moments, just looking at each other's faces, trying to gauge each other's fear while showing none of their own.

"You know," Bob started, "I'm beginning to like this boat. Maybe I'll just stay on board and go back and forth a few times."

Everybody grinned nervously at that remark. There was more than a grain of truth in it.

"Weapons check," yelled the Lieutenant. "Load your rifles and point them skyward. There are no Nazis on this boat, so don't shoot until we get off."

"Shit," said Herby. "Shit, shit!"

Jesus! Bob looked over at Doug who was still pale and shaky but now his wide-open eyes were fixed forward. *I hope he's okay.*

Suddenly the boat crunched onto the beach and lurched forward, slamming all the men towards the front just as the big door dropped down. Welcome to France.

Bob didn't know what to expect as he charged off the boat, along with half the other men. The two trucks that had been started just before impact were running. As the men pulled the first two guns out onto the beach, the next two were made ready for the trucks to come get them, as well.

Guns Five and Six were halfway across the beach on their way to the tree line and apple orchards when Bob realized something. *There's nobody shooting at us.* He was trying to get his weakened legs working again but he was still unsteady.

Planes were screaming up and down the shoreline right overhead, most of them Allied fighters, but the German marauders were doing their best to disrupt the landings and advancing waves of troops. Two Spitfires roared by blasting away at an FW-190, the empty casings raining down on the men, one even bouncing off Herb's helmet.

Bob couldn't help but grin when Herby glanced up in confusion at the ding sound his helmet made before he kept on running, a little faster than before.

"Here, goddammit, here," yelled Dutch, as the truck swung around and stopped, followed by the men swarming to get it unhitched and set up. Some of the men were pulling ammo down off the truck and stacking it while others were swinging out the levelers and unlocking the barrel.

Within two minutes Gun Six was loaded, leveled, and pointing skyward with a full crew manning it and scanning the sky, then the truck was on its way back to the boat to grab onto the next gun.

Bob was crouched down next to Herb, John was on the gun looking down his sight, while Doug was standing on the gun platform with a clip of ammo ready to push down into the breach as soon as it needed a reload.

"Shit, we're still alive!" said Herb, as though he were surprised.

"Shut up," yelled Dutch.

Bob blinked his eyes and began to take it all in. The fight for this beach was pretty much over with, and the Allies now owned this real estate. The 386th was there to help them keep it. The evidence of the brutal fighting that happened here in the last few days was all around them.

An acrid, burning smell filled the air, making his eyes water and his throat burn. The sand was pock-marked with blackened craters. A layer of smoke hung over the beach as it filtered its way down through the trees above them.

Sections of minefields and barbed wire were blasted open for the assault, with burning and destroyed landing vessels left scattered up and down the mist shrouded beach. Some of the men on board those boats never made it to dry land, either cut down getting off, or drowning in the rough surf.

Bob flinched as an earth shaking explosion somewhere inland vibrated up through his boots, followed by four more and then bursts of machine gun fire. *Is that us or them? This is chaos. What the hell do we do?*

This is not how Bob expected it to be. He really didn't know what to expect, but he didn't imagine it to be so overwhelming. The sight and sounds and smells were too much to process all at once, and as he looked around at his crewmates he saw the shock and fear in their faces that he was feeling.

"Aw shit, Bob," said Herb, as he nodded down the beach. "Look at that. Poor bastards."

"Jesus," said Bob, as he and the others gazed upon the corpses of their comrades lain out on the beach waiting to be taken away.

"Jesus Christ," Doug said softly, as he shook his head. "Look at all of them."

Lieutenant Bionde came running up to Gun Six with two privates and yelled over the noise to Dutch, "What's your status?"

"Gun Six is one hundred percent, sir. We still need our truck, but we are up and ready with no casualties."

"All the trucks and the rest of the guns should be ashore in the next few hours. They are bringing in the fifty calibers, as well."

"That's good, sir," Dutch replied, and the other men nodded.

"You boys be careful," Bionde said. "Sergeant Bennings from "A" Battery stepped on a mine and was killed, and a couple of his men were hurt pretty bad in the blast."

"Shit," said Dutch.

"And a lucky bomb in the tree line took out three officers from headquarters battery, including Major Parker."

"Major Parker?" said Bob, scooting around near Dutch and Bionde.

"Afraid so, Private. Would have gotten the Colonel, too, if it had hit a minute earlier."

"But he's ok?" asked Dutch. Before he got an answer a shell exploded on the beach not thirty yards away, shaking the ground and sprinkling them with sand.

"I have to go," said the Lieutenant, "Gibbs is fine. You should have your own truck here soon. Once "B" and "C" Batteries are formed up, we are heading for Sainte Mère Église. You men be careful. I don't want any more men lost if we can help it."

"Where the fuck is that?" asked Herb as Bionde trotted off, and the Sergeant shrugged his shoulders.

"I can't believe the Major was killed," said Bob. "He was a good guy."

Nobody knew what to say, so nothing was said. The 386th had its first casualties. Bob licked his dry lips and tasted the salt that the channel deposited there, and realized how wet, and suddenly, how hungry he was. Dry land had calmed his nausea, and the run up the beach made him forget about anything else, but now he was starved.

Doug was still up on the gun platform, but was now crouching. He still looked pale and shaky and his eyes were darting around. A swarm of about two hundred Allied bombers flew high overhead going inland to discourage German reinforcements, adding to the over three million tons of bombs dropped on Germany.

"Goddamn I'm hungry," said Herb, and everyone else nodded.

"Me, too," said Dutch. "Everybody grab a quick bite out of your rations, we'll be on the move PDQ."

A few minutes later, two trucks came slipping and sliding up the beach to reach them, one carrying the big 40mm, and the other dragging the quad 50cal behind it. Two hours later, both "B" and "C" Batteries were complete and ready to move.

Cherbourg was a city on the tip of a peninsula jutting out into the channel, and was the deep water port the Allies needed to resupply the landing force with large freighters and troop ships. Hitler ordered the German garrison there to fight to the last man.

Sainte Mère Église was on the way to Cherbourg, and there was a vital airfield there, an airfield that would be protected by the Skywatchers. Gun Six was swung around and once again hooked on the truck, and then pulled in line as half the Battalion headed off, wet and dirty, and still a little shaky, towards Sainte Mère Église.

Mickey stood at the seawall staring out over the crowded channel. There was a strong wind blowing and a mist in the air that was enough to make her damp and shiver, even on this summer evening.

I knew I shouldn't have fallen in love with you, you bloody yank. I should have listened to Sarah.

The channel was rolling and churning as though it was angry at the crowd of vessels that covered it and it was trying to flick them off. *I hope they made it alright. I hope they're safe and dry.*

With a clap of thunder overhead, the rain started coming down heavily. She opened her umbrella, took one more glance out to sea, and turned to make her way back to the Grand.

Chapter Twenty

Battery "B" and Battery "C" fell in line behind a column of light tanks and trucks packed with troops, all on their way to Cherbourg. It took two days of starting and stopping and waiting for the roads to clear before they made it to Sainte Mère Église and they immediately set up the guns around the airfield.

"A" Battery and "D" Battery were a day behind and were diverted to the airfield at Pointe du Hoc, which was seeing more attacks from the sky than was expected. On the way there the Germans nearly made a breakthrough, and so for half a day the guns were leveled and hidden in a tree line to be used as antitank guns, a role they were well suited for.

No such breakthrough succeeded, so they moved on to their new assignment. Over the next few weeks the fighting in Cherbourg raged on, making the two protected airfields that much more important.

Pointe du Hoc was attacked by two ME-109's and both were shot down. They made the fatal mistake of lingering too long over the field, giving "A" Battery a few extra seconds to get a line on them. Both pilots were killed.

Five FW-190's appeared over Sainte Mère Église. One was shot down and one limped away smoking. The pilot of the one shot down bailed out and was captured.

No forward observer was needed at Sainte Mère Église so Bob stayed with the gun crew for the next six weeks that they were stationed there. They took over the headquarters and barracks buildings around the airfield, the same ones Germans took from the French.

It was summer now, and it seemed like it was raining all the time, or balmy and muddy with a fog thick over the field every morning. Everything was muddy, and Bob was constantly banging or scraping his boots on something to keep from walking around with an extra five pounds on each foot.

The mud would get up on the gun platforms, on the foot pedals, and in the trucks. It was walked into the barracks building and the mess hall, and seemed to have everything caked with the dry, hardened clay-like residue.

The gun had to be cleaned two or three times a day to keep the mud off, and the barrel and breech had to be wiped down and oiled due to the mist and fog.

The locals were thrilled to have the Americans liberate their town, and the American and French flags waved as they rolled in. Gun Six was set up on the very farthest end of the field, so the French civilians would often bring the guys snacks and goodies and gifts, even though the Americans had far more supplies than the civilians did.

Some of the local girls would come out to the gun and flirt with the guys, but only when Dutch was not around because he would run them off. Herby took to one right away, and would smile and blush when he would see her coming.

"God, I dream about that girl," Herb proclaimed.

"Oh no, not you, too," said Doug.

"I know just how you feel," said Bob, smiling.

"Don't you get all love struck on us here, Herb. It's hard enough listening to Bob crying himself to sleep."

"Only crying I do at night is because of Herby snoring. You better give that girl fair warning, Herb."

"I'm gonna smother him one of these nights," said John, and they all laughed.

"I think she's coming around again today," said Herb. "I think she likes me."

"Well, since we are only over there when we are on the gun, I don't see much chance for romance blossoming anytime soon," said Doug.

"I can dream, can't I?"

The 386th fell into a routine, and while there was a lot of air traffic in the busy sky above them, there were only a few alerts and no more engagements just yet, which was fine with Bob.

Weeks later, with savage battles that even went house to house at times, Cherbourg fell. Hitler had ordered the garrison there to fight to the last man, but surrounded, outnumbered, hungry and exhausted, the remaining 27,000 German soldiers surrendered to the Allies.

Many of the captured soldiers were shuttled across the channel and loaded onto open trucks for their journey inland.

Lillian and the girls and most of the people in town watched as truck after truck of Germans, their heads hanging and expressions blank, were rolling past the square.

Lillian looked at the men, many mere boys. *I almost feel sorry for them.* Many people jeered at them and some stared wide-eyed like Lillian at the enemy they had never seen before.

"War's over for them, lucky bastards," Sarah said, shaking her head. "They should take them all out and shoot them."

Lillian looked over at Sarah and then away again. She had mixed feelings about that kind of thing. "I hate this war," was all she could manage to say. "Let's go down to the seawall."

"So I can bloody well stand there and watch you stare out over the sea missing your yank? No thanks."

"Come on, Sarah, come with me. I don't want to go down there alone. Besides, it's always more fun when you come," Lillian smiled, trying to flatter Sarah into it.

When they got there, Sarah was glad she gave in. Both girls stared out towards the channel and were elated at what they saw. For the first time in six years, the razor wire had been rolled back, the minefields cleared, and the obstacles were gone.

Other than the clusters here and there of military vehicles and soldiers, the beach was a beach again. There were even people walking up and down the sand, some couples holding hands, and a couple of dogs.

Sarah made a squealing sound and bolted toward the beach with Lillian half a second behind her. As soon as they hit the sand they kicked off their shoes and ran down to the water.

"I wondered if I would ever feel this again," Sarah said, grinning as she stood in the ankle deep cold water. She could feel the outgoing rush of the waves pull at the sand between her toes and then bury them again when the sea surged back in.

Even though they were still in uniform, they splashed and played and giggled at the simple joy of putting their feet in the water. Lillian had spent years lost in thought staring out over this beach, and now for the first time, she could touch it.

"Everything is going to be alright, love," said Sarah reassuringly. "See how far our lads have come? It's all but over now, just a bit longer."

"We'd better get back," Lillian said. "We need to tell the girls the beach is open. We need to tell them the good news."

Sarah and Lillian made their way off the beach, found their shoes, and with one last glance out over the gray mist, headed back to the Grand.

By mid-August, the Battalion was once again put on standby to leave at any moment. Trucks were packed and ready and all the men's personal gear stayed ready and close by at all times.

"Operation Overlord" officially ended on August 21, 1944 with the Allies landing 2,052,299 soldiers in the invasion of France. Killed in action were 36,976 men, with 153,475 wounded and 19,221 missing in action. In addition, 4,101 aircraft were destroyed, killing 16,174 airmen.

Knowing they would be leaving soon had Herb looking like he was about to have a panic attack. Every time he was out at the gun pit he would look for her. When she would show up he would get this big, goofy smile on his face. One afternoon Bob saw the pretty brunette give Herb a scrap of paper, which he folded and put in his pocket.

Then she leaned close and whispered something in his ear, making him laugh. She kissed him on the cheek before scurrying away, leaving him standing there watching her as she disappeared from sight.

"I only have one question, Herb," said Bob, as he walked up next to Herb who was still staring at where she used to be.

"What's that, Bob?"

"Did you get laid?"

The 386th were transferred over to the 3rd Army, also known as "Patton's Army." General George was a strict soldier's soldier. The men had to wear their ties and have shined boots and a tucked in shirt even in the midst of battle, but they loved him, and they loved serving under him, even if only for the privilege of saying they did.

The Americans and the British were bearing down on the French capital as the French resistance staged a desperate and savage uprising in the city. Hitler, seeing the writing on the wall, ordered it burned to the ground, but once again his orders were disobeyed.

Paris was liberated on August 25, 1944, and the world danced in the streets. Every freedom-loving person in the world was a Frenchman that day, and every Frenchman was free. Bob smiled when he heard the news. *Just a little bit longer, and it will all be over and I can go back to Mickey.*

Bob wrote to Mickey and to his mom as often as he could. Sometimes he would get three or four letters at once as they caught up with him. He told his mom about the girl he met and fell in love with and asked if she would send her some of her famous goodie boxes.

His friends all enjoyed it when Bob got one with some extra snacks and some magazines to pass around. He smiled to himself when he thought of the surprise Mickey would have when she got the first box.

He told his mom not to worry, that there was nothing really going on and they were spending most of their time playing blackjack and throwing a baseball around. That wasn't entirely true, nor was it entirely false. They had a lot more down time now as the Allies had gained air superiority. Enemy aircraft were few and far between, at least where the battalion was stationed.

Bob also asked his mom to start holding some money out of his pay to buy Mickey a ring. He wasn't really sure how much of his pay Pop was going to let him keep. *Old bastard is probably going to charge me for having raised me.* He smiled to himself.

The battalion skirted their way around Paris, and by the fall they were near Verdun, going from airfield to airfield occupying buildings that the Germans once took from the French. Bob had been sitting in a chair leaning against the wall in a half bombed out building as he daydreamed of Mickey with his eyes closed and his toes barely touching the ground, when suddenly the crash of an empty bucket kicked across the room jolted him into reality.

Bob's chair clunked as the two front legs dropped down to the ground, and John jumped to his feet, surprised by the sudden clatter in the quiet room. Doug didn't even look up. He just sat there slightly shaking his head and then went back to whatever it was he was thinking.

"Goddamn Nazis," Herb said, red faced. He slapped a newspaper down on the table and pointed at it like a prosecutor pointing at a smoking gun. "Bastards are ruining baseball, Bob."

"Those bastards," John said smiling, as Bob shook his head.

"Well, you ruined a damn good dream I was having, Herb. Thanks a lot," Bob said, with a fake scowl.

"I think its Herb's mission in life to deprive us of sleep," Doug mumbled, still resting his head.

"I'm not kidding here, damn it," said Herb, getting louder and redder. "The Yankees would have never finished in only third place if half the team wasn't over here fighting Germans."

"Shit, Herb, the Dodgers lost lots of players. They all did," Bob shot back. The last thing he wanted right now was to get in a baseball debate with Herby.

"I hear the girls' teams are doing pretty good," said John.

"Girl teams! Are you friggin' kidding me? You must be a Dodger fan if you like watching girls play baseball," Herb said, grinning.

"Go to hell, Herb," said Bob, then shook his head as he realized he was getting sucked in.

"I like watching girls do just about anything," said Doug, finally lifting his head. "I like watching them do nothing, too."

"Girls can't play baseball, they just can't," Herb ranted. "Show me a girl that can hit like Babe Ruth and I'll marry her."

"You would marry a girl that looks like babe Ruth?" asked John, causing Bob and Doug to burst into laughter.

"I said hit, goddammit. Hit like Babe Ruth. You know what the hell I mean. Damn Nazis must hate baseball like they hate everything else."

"You know why they don't like baseball, Herb?" asked Bob.

"Enlighten me," said Herb.

"Because they know that it's three Reichs and you're out," said Bob, causing another bout of laughter.

The 1944 World Series was played despite the Nazis, or the Japanese. The series was an all St. Louis event — the Cardinals against the Browns. Both teams had lost players to service, especially the Browns. The Browns were now a team of misfits, drunks, and unfit for duty 4-Fer's, and they even had a one-armed player named Pete Gray.

The Cardinals took it four games to two, another season in the history books. Everybody hoped, no matter who their favorite team was, that soon the players could turn in their army greens for pinstripes, and their guns for bats.

In early December of 1944, all four gun batteries and the headquarters battery moved into Verdun and set up around the airfield and a few other strategic places around the city. Bob found a quiet place and jotted off a letter to his mom, actually a picture he drew for her, and then wrote a long, heartfelt letter to Mickey.

He had trouble finding paper, so the letter to Mickey was written on a brown piece of scrap paper, similar to that of a paper bag. It didn't matter, she would understand, and it was the words that mattered. He had to tell her how he felt and how he missed her so very much.

On December 20th the word came down that "B" and "C" batteries would be moving to Metz where a key airfield had been taken. The headquarters battery would also move to Metz, with the Colonel and the intelligence division.

On December 24, 1944, "B" and "C" batteries rolled into Metz and joined the headquarters battery that had gotten there the day before. Intelligence had mapped out all the gun positions, so the men got to work setting up the sixteen big guns around the airfield. Even though it was Christmas Eve, and even though bad weather had everything grounded, the Colonel ordered the battalion on high alert around the clock.

The Germans were conducting a major surprise offensive in an attempt to spearhead a "bulge" in the Allied line and split the forces in two, so the Colonel wanted to be ready in the unlikely event they would attack here.

Communication lines had to be run to the outposts, guns had to be dug in and supplies stacked near them, quarters and the mess hall had to be set up, so even though it was Christmas, there was a lot of work to be done.

Back at the Grand hotel, on December 22nd, Mickey received a Christmas goodie box from Bob's mom, filled with cookies, candies and nuts. Two days later she got the best present she ever had, the letter from Bob.

Lillian found a quiet little corner and carefully opened the makeshift letter and smiled at the extra effort he put in just to write to her. The letter was dated December 10, 1944. With shaking hands, she began to read:

266

Hello Mickey Darling,

I've been neglecting you something awful lately, but please believe me I couldn't help it. I can't explain due to military regulations but I'm sure you would understand if you knew the circumstances.

Say, you sweet wonderful creature, it looks like you're getting worried because I didn't write. It seems you're afraid that I don't love you anymore. Well, get that foolish idea out of your cute little blonde head. Ever hear that saying about how absence makes the heart grow fonder? Well, if it's at all possible I not only love you but I'm falling harder in love with you every day. In fact, I'm not only hoping to go to England after the war but I'm going to see to it that I get there even if I have to swim the channel. The reason I want to get to England so bad is to see you and ask you to marry me. With all the inconveniences that a war offers I'll be damned if I'm going to propose by mail. I want to be right there looking straight at you and say, "Mickey, my sweet, my love, lets haul off and get married." And I want you to tell me right there either yes

267

or to go to hell, whichever you wish. Thanks to your landlady I had to tell you that I love you on a street corner. I hope this time I can come in the house and propose.

Of course there's a few drawbacks to this whole deal. I've only been with you a week, but hell that's long enough. A guy doesn't really love a girl if he has to have more time to think things over before he marries her. Another thing, I don't know how you'd compare Brooklyn with Bournemouth for the rest of your life if you did marry me. By the way, just how would you like to live in the states? Write me a nice long letter and let me know how you feel about this whole thing.

Before you write, however, I want you to take plenty of time out to think this over. Marrying me might mean that you never see England again. That's really a pretty drastic step in itself. Then there is the character that you would attach yourself to. But of course you have your own opinion of me and the answer you give would be entirely up to just how much you do love me.

Well, it's now five o'clock in the morning and I've been on and off this letter since twelve last night. I think I said what I really intended to say, that is I love you so much that I want to marry you. I'm not kidding about this, honestly I'm not. It's no laughing matter. Don't forget now we have a date after the war so I can propose to you.

All My Love,
Bob

Tears of joy welled up in her eyes, relieved to hear that he did love her and was coming back. If a long time went between letters she worried either something had happened to him or that he didn't really love her.

Every letter from him validated her hopes and dreams, and every span of time between letters served to build up her anguish and doubts again. Her life seemed like a constant series of ups and downs.

As Lillian walked into the room rubbing away the tear in the corner of her eye, the happy tear, lest someone see it, Sarah squealed and jumped up and down waving the letter she got from her Canadian. "Trade, trade, trade," she yelled to her when she saw that Lillian also got a letter from her soldier.

Both letters were passed around to all four girls and the giggling and teasing went on half the night. The goodie box was pulled out, cookies from Bob's mom were shared, and small gifts were passed around.

Lillian sat back and listened to her friend's laughter, felt the wonderful cookie melting in her mouth, and thought about the man she loved and hoped he was thinking of her at that same moment.

After both letters were passed around and back again, Sarah said, "Your yank is a little rough around the edges but I must admit, his mum makes good cookies."

"I think he is very romantic," said Becky, with cookie crumbs in the corner of her mouth. "Does he have a brother?"

"He's funny," said Emily. "I think your Canadian is a little stiff."

"You can be sure of that, love," Sarah winked and they all giggled.

Night fell and the girls sat around talking and laughing and eating cookies, and telling Christmas stories from days gone by. Lillian sat and listened as the stories came to life in her mind's eye, filling in the empty places where her memories should be.

But it didn't make her sad because she was done looking back, her life was ahead of her now. She was here with her best friends, she was happy, and she was in love. *This is the best Christmas I've ever had.*

Back at Metz, Bob and Herb with Doug and John got the two big spools of cable off the truck and were getting ready to run it out. Lt. Bionde was showing Bob on the map where they wanted the observation post set up. As he talked, snowflakes fell and made little blotters on the hand drawn sketch

The airfield was in a bowl shaped valley, with a tree lined ridge all the way around. An observer on either end in the tree line would provide a large projection of the line of sight the battalion needed to maintain awareness.

The snow was falling a little heavier now, muffling the sound and dusting everything white. The four men with heavy coats, helmets, and their M1 carbines slung over their shoulders, hoisted the two rolls of cable and began the mile plus trek to the outpost.

They had to work their way through thick woods until they found the goat path Bionde told them about, and follow that up to the ridge, rolling out cable the entire way. The constantly falling snow was enough to keep them wet, so even colder.

They had been talking and laughing as usual for awhile but the uphill trek through the rough terrain carrying the cable and their rifles had them winded. "Where the hell is the top of this mountain?" Herb snapped.

"I think Bob got us lost," said Doug, smiling his big grin. "This was supposed to be a hill, not Mount Everest."

Doug barely got the last word out when he stepped on a patch of ice hidden just below the new snow and his boots went out from under him. His gun clattered across the ground and his helmet tipped forward almost to his eyes as he fell hard on his rump.

Bob and John glanced at him to be sure he was okay, and Herby broke into laughter. When Doug tried to get up, he slipped and slid and fell again. Herby nearly doubled over laughing at him.

"Good thing you're gonna be a movie star and not a ballet dancer, eh, buddy?" said Bob, grinning as he pulled him to his feet. "Hurt anything important?"

"Just my pride, and my ass is all wet."

"Well, you were always good at breaking the ice," said Herb, still laughing and pointing at his damaged friend. "Better go get your gun, movie star."

"Oh shit," said John when he saw them. "Goddamn German soldiers."

"Jesus Christ," said Herby as he ducked down. "Do they see us?"

"Looks like they are coming right at us," said Bob.

"Looks like they saw us before we saw them," said John. "Or they heard Herby laughing from the next valley."

"Jesus Christ," said Herb.

Doug had retrieved his rifle and crawled up alongside the other three and peered off, down the far slope. There were five of them, and they were crossing the field walking towards the bottom of the hill. It was evident by their footprints in the snow behind them that they were headed straight for the four Americans.

It was hard to make out their features in the falling snow, but they clearly had on the long gray winter coats of the German army, rifles slung over their shoulders, and snow covered helmets on their heads.

"We need to get the hell out of here," said Doug, as he pulled his head back down.

"No," John barked. "We have good cover here, we move and we will be out in the open."

"He's right," said Bob. "Better they are the sitting ducks and not us. We should hunker down."

"We should send someone back to the Battalion to get help," said Doug, with the sounds of panic cracking his voice. "Their rifles out range our pop guns."

"We don't have time, and we are already outnumbered," said John.

"We stay together," Bob agreed, worrying that it might not be him that gets sent for help. "Nobody leaves."

As the four men debated their predicament, the Germans moved ever closer until they got to the bottom of the tree covered slope. The four panic-stricken Americans watched from the ridge as the enemy began working their up way towards them.

"Jesus Christ," said Herb. "We're gonna have to fight the bastards."

"Shit, I don't want to get my ass killed on Christmas," said Bob, as he trembled with a combination of fear and cold.

By this time the four of them were crouched down side by side, guns up and fingers on triggers. "Shoot them," yelled Doug.

"Wait," John shouted back.

"Shoot the bastards," Doug yelled again. "Shoot them before they shoot us."

"Wait," John said again, stealing glances at the group of soldiers making their way up the slope.

"We're gonna have to shoot the bastards, John," said Bob, trying to stay calm but having a hard time. He was shaking and his hands were clammy like they were back in that alley with the slingshot when he was a kid.

"Not yet," John said, almost in a whisper. "Not yet."

"Shoot them goddammit." Doug was trembling so bad his rifle was shaking. His face was pale, his eyes were like saucers, and his finger was on the trigger. "Shoot them now."

"Jesus Christ," said Herby.

"Just hold on a second," John said.

"We have to kill the bastards, John," said Bob. He could feel his heart pounding in his chest, his ears ringing and his vision narrowed as the fear threatened to overwhelm him. He heard his voice getting louder, "Shoot, goddamn it."

"Shoot them," Doug was screaming now. He stood up and held his rifle to his shoulder. "Shoot them now, goddamn it."

"Stop!" John yelled at the Germans. "Stop or we'll shoot."

"Jesus Christ," yelled Herby, as he pointed his rifle at the Germans and put his finger on the trigger. "Jesus fucking Christ."

"Shoot! Shoot!" Doug was screaming.

"Stop!" John shouted again down the hill. "Stop or we'll shoot."

"Shoot, goddamn it. I'm shooting," said Doug, and he tried to site in on one of the targets, but the gun was shaking so bad he couldn't line up a shot.

"We have to shoot, John!" Bob was screaming now, too. "I'm shooting now, goddamn it."

"Stop, goddamn it. Stop!" John was on his feet now and with his hands cupped around his mouth he shouted as loud as he could at the Germans, who were by now more than halfway up the slope. "Halt! Halt or we'll shoot!"

"Oh shit," said Herb. He lined up on one of the silhouettes and tears formed in the corners of his eyes as he started to put pressure on the trigger. "Jesus Christ," he whispered.

Bob, seeing Herb follow Doug's lead, also put one of the Germans in his sights and got ready to fire.

"Wait," said John. "Just wait a second. What is that? Listen."

"What the hell is that?" Bob asked. "Is that music?"

"I don't hear any goddamn music," said Doug. "It's a trick, shoot the bastards."

"Quiet, just listen," John said.

"What is that?" Bob asked. "Is that singing?"

"Yeah, I hear it, too," said Herb. "I hear singing."

"Singing?" asked Doug. "What the hell are they singing?"

"Christmas carols," John said, astonished. "I think they're singing Christmas carols."

"They are singing Christmas carols," said Bob. "They're singing goddamn Christmas carols."

"Jesus Christ," said Herb. "Why are the Krauts singing us Christmas carols?"

"Put down your guns, fellas. They're not Germans," John said.

They were now close enough to see that they were not German soldiers, though they all wore long German winter coats, probably taken off a battlefield from an enemy that no longer needed it. Their hats were big furry hats like the Russians wore, but coated with snow they had been mistaken for helmets.

As for the weapons they carried over their soldier, only one was a rifle, an old German Mauser. One guy had an old musket, and the other three had shotguns. One of them was carrying something all wrapped up in a bundle.

"Holy shit, I almost shot them," said Herb.

"Put down the gun, Doug," said Bob. "It's ok."

"Americans!" the closest of the advancing party shouted out.

Doug was still shaking and holding his gun to his shoulder with his finger on the trigger.

"Put down your gun, Doug," John said calmly. "Don't shoot, movie star, it's ok."

Doug looked over at John with beads of nervous sweat running down his cold face, then darted his eyes at Bob, who nodded and managed a small reassuring smile.

"It's ok, Doug," John said again. "Put the gun down."

It was as if Doug was frozen in that position, as if he couldn't accept that he was safe now. Herb stood up next to him and softly touched the top of his rifle and pushed it down until it pointed at the ground.

"It's ok now, movie star," Herb said, as he helped him lower the weapon. "Everything's ok now, my friend."

Doug dropped to his knees and put his hands to his face and wept, shaking as the burst of adrenaline left his body. At the same time the group of five crested the hill and walked towards the Americans.

"Americans!" the lead person in the group shouted, and they realized for the first time it was a woman. "Americans!" she shouted again.

She looked to be around forty, but it was hard to tell. A few years of war had a way of aging a person. She had a big smile on her face, and a double barrel shotgun slung over her shoulder.

With her were four men. One was a teenager, sixteen at most. Two were about the same age as the woman, and one had to be over seventy, but even though his broad smile revealed a mouth without teeth, he seemed to be pretty good for his age.

He had trekked through the snow with the others, up the hill, and with the heavy old musket over his shoulder; he also carried the bundle.

The group walked up to the four soldiers, and as if by a mother's instinct, the woman walked straight to Doug and pulled him up off his knees. She put her hands on both sides of his face and with a big smile, she said, "Americans, we love you."

She wrapped her arms around him and held him tight and Doug trembled and wept. She whispered in his ear, "Americans, we love you," and his knees almost buckled, but he somehow managed to stay on his feet.

The other men were hugging the American soldiers and kissing their cheeks. One of the men made the sign of the cross before hugging each soldier. Herb grinned at that and glanced over to see Bob grinning back.

"I guess he heard you yelling out for Jesus Christ about ten times, eh, Herb?"

The man, hearing the only words he understood so far, Jesus Christ, smiled broadly and made the sign of the cross again, and the men nodded a thank you.

The woman released her hold on Doug and gave warm hugs to the other three soldiers. "Americans, we bring you Christmas," she said in broken English. She then nodded to the old man, and he stepped forward with the bundle and smiled his toothless smile again.

"We have little," she said, "but we share. We share Christmas with you."

The old man proudly picked open the bundle to reveal a cooked rabbit, still hot because it was still covered in fur and wrapped up so well.

"We share Christmas, yes?" she asked.

Bob looked at the other three guys and they all seemed as flabbergasted by the whole experience as he was. The last few minutes had been a roller coaster ride of emotions and his guts were not untangled yet.

"Merry Christmas, yes?" she asked with the same smile and looked around at the soldiers as the other men in her group smiled and nodded.

"Merry Christmas, yes," said John. "Hey fellas, everybody empty your pockets, I don't think a rabbit is going to feed nine of us," he chuckled.

"We can't take their food," Doug stuttered out. "It's all they have."

"It's not about that, movie star," said Bob. "This is about Christmas. They shot and cooked that rabbit, walked all the way up here, to share Christmas with us. We can't say no. It wouldn't be Christian of us, would it, Herb?"

Herb nodded and smiled and said, "Not to mention they risked their lives."

"Christ, I can't believe I nearly shot them," said Doug, as he looked down at the ground and shook his head.

In the next few minutes every pocket was emptied in a circle. There were chocolate bars and gum, beef jerky, crackers, some odd pieces of candy, and a loaf of bread the woman pulled from under her coat. With his big hollow smile, the old man pulled out a flask of brandy and winked at the soldiers.

The group gathered in a tight circle, and following the men's lead, the soldiers pulled off their helmets and bowed their heads. One of the men spoke a prayer, but none of the soldiers understood a word until the Amen at the end, which they all repeated.

As they all stood in a circle and shared the meager meal, through the language barrier, they figured out that the group were Belgians. They were displaced by the Nazis, and had been hiding in the woods for years.

The woman said, "Thank you, Americans. You free us," she said, and started to cry. "We go home soon."

She turned and said something to her group and they all nodded and smiled, and the teenage boy began to cry softly, but though his lip trembled, he kept smiling.

"Bless you, Americans," she said. "Bless you, and Merry Christmas, yes?"

"Merry Christmas, yes," said John.

The lump in Bob's throat was making him have a hard time swallowing, as he wiped at the tears forming in his eyes. *The poorest people I've ever met, just gave me the best present I've ever had.* He shook his head at the wonder of it.

Doug was openly weeping, the tears running down his face and dripping off his chin.

The old man took the tarnished silver flask and stepped in front of Doug. He held it high in the air and said, "America!" Then he handed it to Doug. Doug took a little pull on it, and passed it to Herb, and around it went until the old man took the last gulp and smiled.

Once again everyone hugged everyone else, and with kisses goodbye for all, the group headed down over the crest of the hill to soon disappear in the swirling snow. The soldiers silently watched their new friends as though the whole thing was just a dream.

"Snow is picking up, fellas," Bob said, clearing his throat halfway, though still feeling the lump. "We better finish up and get back."

Without saying a word, they slung their rifles and, hoisting the wire spools once again, started towards the outpost.

"You know, fellas," John said, breaking the silence. "I think that was the best Christmas I've ever had."

"Yeah, me, too," Herby said, grinning. "Me, too."

Chapter Twenty-One

It was a crystal clear night, and the sky was full of stars as Bob stepped into the frigid morning wind an hour before dawn. The ice crunched beneath his boots and the wind bit into his face as he gathered his gear for the lonely walk to the outpost.

With him he carried the bulky radio, his binoculars, a few pockets full of rations, and his rifle slung over his shoulder. It was New Year's morning, and he was to watch the first dawn of 1945, alone and cold, at what was sure to be another empty sky.

He found the spot under the tree line where the cable ended and connected the radio, called in a radio check, laid out his rifle and binoculars and had a quick snack as a familiar orange glow started to appear in the distant sky.

Over the last week, thirty of the big P-47 Thunderbolt fighters were brought into the Metz airfield, along with their flight crews and ground support. Metz was an ideal base for the fighters, putting them within striking distance of strategic enemy targets.

Bad weather had kept them grounded for the most part, but the clear night, though it made for a cold morning, had all the pilots optimistic about flying on New Year's Day.

As dawn started to break, the ground crews started to clear the ice off the planes and load them with fuel and munitions for a day of patrol. The 386th were already on their guns, set up and dug in, at sixteen positions around the field.

John, Doug and Herb were among the eleven other men that now made up Gun Six of "C" Battery, and though they were able to stay inside for over an hour longer than Bob, the cold was cutting at them as they stomped their feet and rubbed their hands.

"Shit," said Herb, scratching his ass and blinking his sleepy eyes. "I feel like I just went to bed."

"What are you bitching about?" asked Doug. "You slept two days ago. Besides, I thought you were a morning person."

"I am a morning guy, but I think it is still last night. Goddamn baseball hating Nazi bastards," said Herb. "I should be home sleeping off a hangover. It's New Year's day for God's sake."

"Shut up!" bellowed Dutch. "Shut the hell up. You're like a bunch of little kids cry babying like your mama forgot you at the grocery store. Now get to work and shut the hell up."

"My mom did that to me once," Herb whispered, making Doug giggle.

"You want a boot up your ass, Hansen?" the now red-faced Sergeant asked as Doug shook his head. "Then shut up, and keep shutting up."

"I bet the Germans are drinking beer for New Year's, not sitting their asses on cold guns in the snow," whispered John. "Hell, I think they even invented it."

"You would think the last people that would want to take over the world would be the people that invented beer," said Doug, careful not to let Dutch hear.

"Happy friggin' New Year," Herby said, shaking his head.

Bob lay in the snow under a tree and looked out into the dawn now breaking on the horizon. He didn't dare use the binoculars unless he absolutely needed to, because the glint reflected off them could give away his position to any potential snipers. The front was far enough away that a sniper was unlikely, but there was no reason to chance it.

He popped a lump of fresh snow in his mouth and swallowed as it melted, then sucked in some more to quench the thirst he had built up on the long walk to the outpost. Though it was so bitter cold out, he could feel the sweat under his clothes that now threatened to make him even colder, especially his feet.

He pulled out a candy bar and tore off a bite, and followed it with another gulp of snow. He couldn't see the airfield from where he was on the far side of the valley, as it was just beyond the tree line. This had been cold and boring duty over the last week, seeing only a few reconnaissance aircraft in the distance, when he could see at all through the snowfall.

His teeth bit again into the cold, hard candy bar and as he tore it away and began to chew he saw them — nothing but little black dots on the horizon, low to the ground and coming this way.

Oh shit! He spit out the chocolate and grabbed for the radio.

"Wake up, you mutts," he yelled into the radio, and then took a breath as he realized he needed to stay calm. "Looks like about twenty Kraut fighters out of the east northeast, standby for a bearing."

"Jesus H. Christ, twenty fighters! Where the hell did they come from?" said Bionde, and then turned and started barking orders. "Send a runner to warn the Air Corp. Turn ten of the guns northeast up the valley and prepare for attack."

Men ran from the Lieutenant in every direction taking his orders to the gun crews and the fighter squadron. The Colonel heard the warning come over the radio, and with his helmet on and cigar in his mouth, he stepped out of the headquarters building onto the edge of the field.

An aide handed him a pair of binoculars which he immediately trained on the American fighters as they tried to start their engines to get off the ground. Gibbs could see they would take another two or three minutes before they could start rolling down the runway.

"I've got a bearing," Bob said calmly into the radio. "They are coming in balls to the walls and maybe a hundred feet off the deck. North, northeast, 020 degrees, maybe 25 seconds out."

"020 Degrees, one hundred feet, twenty-five seconds," Bionde repeated back for clarity.

He turned to his other runners and yelled, "Set main battery at 020 degrees, 100 feet and prepare to fire on my command."

Ten of the big guns turned their barrels to 020 degrees and set them at 100 feet, aiming along the tree line in front of them. Colonel Gibbs stood there watching as his crews swung into action and, with a burst of smoke, a few of the Thunderbolts started roaring to life.

The other six guns swung away in the opposite direction, hoping to catch the attackers after they flew over and were outbound of the field. Herb grabbed a couple cans of ammo and jumped behind the quad 50 machine gun, ready to feed the long belts of bullets into the breach.

Doug stood on the gun platform of the Bofors with the big four round clip and spun around with the gun as it made its 90 degree turn to face up the valley at the incoming threat, and John leveled it off at 100 feet.

Dutch put his foot on the pedal to fire the big gun, glanced at his crew, and then looked over at Bionde and awaited his next order. The entire field fell eerily silent for a few seconds, until one of the engines on the fighters spit to life, belching black smoke, followed quickly by two more.

As the dots in the sky grew closer, Bob could now make out their ominous silhouettes. He felt a chill down his spine as he stared at the sight for which he had trained but hoped he would never see.

"ME-109's," he yelled into the radio. "Maybe twenty, about ten seconds out."

Actually there were twenty-five — twenty-four ME-109's and a Royal Air Force Spitfire that had been captured and repainted with a Swastika. Bob was on his feet now, and as they came in low past him, he could even see their heads in the cockpits.

"Five seconds out," Bob screamed into the radio as the enemy planes roared past, shaking the ground with their deafening engines, leaving behind the smell of burning fuel as they shot past at full throttle.

"3...2...1...Fire!" Bionde screamed, and a hand signal went to the gun crews as Dutch stepped down on the pedal.

Major Ernst Richter was a seasoned fighter pilot and was in command of this squadron of marauders, hoping to catch the Americans by surprise with this New Year's dawn raid.

Of the twenty-five planes he now led, eighteen of the pilots were under twenty years old. Of those, five were only sixteen. He had six experienced pilots besides himself, but his squadron was suffering from the Luftwaffe's extraordinary losses, so he had to make do.

He had carefully planned every detail of this raid and went over it with his squadron again and again and again. They had pictures of the airfield from the reconnaissance planes, they knew where the P-47's were lined up, and they knew where the guns were.

The plan was to come in fast and low out of the rising sun, hit them hard, and be out of there in under two minutes, causing as much destruction as possible. The American planes — sitting ducks on the ground — were the primary target.

Richter was the lead plane in the squadron as he pushed his ME-109 to full power just off the treetops. Now he pulled back the throttle just a little bit as he saw the tree line approaching, knowing the airfield was just beyond it, so he would have a an extra second to aim his 20mm machine guns into his sleepy targets.

He flipped the safety off the trigger and replaced it with his finger and grinned like a hawk swooping down on his prey. "Happy New Year, you drunken bastards," he said aloud.

Less than half a second later, he exploded in a fireball.

Bionde had the guns fire before the Germans reached the field over the tree line, a second before. The twenty-five enemy fighters flew right into a hail storm of exploding shells that ripped through their ranks.

Besides Richter, three other planes exploded over the tree line as they took direct hits from the big 40mm cannons and their relentless fire. Stabs of flame two feet long were blasting from the barrels with every shot, and the ground shook as the smell of gunfire drifted away from the guns and across the field.

In the second row of German attackers, just behind the leader, one of the sixteen-year old pilots banked hard to the left to avoid the Major's plane, which had just exploded in front of him. He crashed into his wingman, one of the few experienced pilots, sending them both tumbling to the ground, rolling end over end and exploding into flames.

Six of the German planes were taken out in the first few seconds of this fight, but there were still nineteen left.

As the squadron roared overhead, the guns facing away started spitting shells into the sky, exploding all around and behind the attackers. Eighteen-year old Gerhard Hess's fighter had its tail section blown off, veering him into the trees and breaking the plane into pieces, killing him.

Two of the German planes managed to hone in on the runway as a few of the P-47's were trying to get off the ground while the other pilots raced out to start their cold engines. The 20mm machine guns raked across the back row of parked fighters, tearing them in half and setting them on fire.

A bomb that had been loaded onto one of the planes exploded, and twelve of the Thunderbolts were destroyed in an instant, killing eight pilots and eleven members of the ground crews. Undaunted, men scrambled to the remaining fighters to desperately get them aloft and into the fight.

The two German planes that strafed them banked hard to the left to come around for another run, but inexperienced, they banked too quickly and became perfect targets as two of the guns from "B" Battery tore them to shreds with direct hits from the Bofors.

The captured Spitfire had swung around to the west and, flying right over the runway as the first two Thunderbolts were rolling, dropped a bomb intending to disable the runway and strand the Americans on the ground.

The sixteen-year old pilot on his first mission scored a remarkable hit right on the end of the runway, better than anything he'd ever done in practice — a perfect bull's eye.

It would have been a devastating blow to the American squadron, but the young pilot forgot to arm the bomb, and it bounced off the runway, went end over end for about a hundred yards, and came to a harmless stop in a snowbank.

After the ex-British warbird dropped its "paperweight," one of the quad 50 machine guns clipped its tail, shooting off half his rudder. The pilot lost the ability to turn, so he nosed down, flared out and did a belly slide through a lucky-for-him gap in the trees. The little Spitfire, while beat to hell, was back with the Allies.

Another German pilot coming in from the back row of the attacking squadron could see the carnage at the tree line just ahead of him. In a desperate move to avoid the incoming fire, he pushed his nose down as soon as he cleared the trees and dropped down, flying just feet off the ground.

Directly in his path was Gun Six of "C" Battery, and he started spitting flames at the gun, tearing up the ground as it carved a deadly path straight for it. The distance closed quickly, and the gunners would only have time to get off a few shots at their attackers, so they leveled the glowing hot barrel at the murderous, merciless devil.

The death from his 20mm guns raked through the gun pit, ripping four of the men apart, but Dutch's last act on earth was to hold down that foot pedal, slamming a 40mm shell into the nose of the incoming fighter, just inches left of the red spinner on the prop.

The shell went through the engine, through the pilot, and exploded just behind the cockpit, sending pieces of flaming debris and body parts raining down on the field.

Two more of the German fighters were hit with rounds from the big 40mm cannons. One exploded in the sky, the other caught fire, burning the pilot alive before he could regain control. Barely a minute into this attack and the Germans had lost 13 planes, over half their squadron.

Two of the German fighters were smoking and limping away from the fight. They flew right past Bob on their getaway, and he could clearly see flames licking out from around one of their engines.

The first two of the American P-47's roared down the runway, clawing at the sky as the Nazi-killing-fire-breathing dragons that they were set out on the hunt.

Two of the German planes made one more run at the airfield. One was blasted out of the sky with one of the big guns, the other was riddled with rounds from one of the 50's. It crashed into a row of trucks that the 386th had parked just off the field, and five of them burst into flames, ammo exploding, and setting off the fuel tanks, the black diesel smoke pouring across the field.

The German squadron went into retreat and turned their remaining planes back toward Germany, but two were cut off from the rest of the group and became easy pickings for the Thunderbolts. With their eight 50cal machine guns chattering away, the two errant attackers were destroyed by the powerful American fighters.

Bob couldn't see anything from where he was, the forest between him and the field was too thick. He could hear explosions, and he could see black smoke boiling up into the air. He could see the German planes make several passes, and he could hear the strafing runs they were making. *Goddamn it, what the hell is going on down there? This looks bad.*

Most of all he could hear the guns. The ever-pounding, relentless, banging away of the guns. He witnessed a smoking German plane pass overhead. *At least I know they are fighting back.*

Then, as suddenly as it began, the German planes blasted past Bob at full throttle into the direction they had come from.

"I got outbound targets," Bob yelled into the radio. "Maybe eight."

He barely got the words out when two of the P-47's blasted past him in an earth-shaking, deafening roar. They were followed by two more, who were then followed by three more as they gave chase, turning the predators into the prey.

One of the fuel trucks exploded near the runway, sending a small mushroom cloud up over the field, shaking the ground, and adding another plume of thick black smoke to the horizon.

Holy shit! Bob turned to see the ball of flame rise over the trees and the column of smoke that seemed to push it skyward. "Holy shit," he said out loud this time.

Bob kept glancing out in the direction the planes flew to watch them disappear into the distant sky. He wanted to make sure there was nothing else coming in, a second wave perhaps, but the sky seemed empty and safe as two more Thunderbolts muscled their way out of the valley and into the pursuit.

Though he was supposed to be keeping his attention on the skyline, he couldn't help but look in awe at the smoke rising up from different places, smoke so thick it was leaving behind dots of black soot and oil on the white snow.

"What's going on down there?" Bob finally asked into the radio, not being able to stand it any longer. He had to know what was happening.

"Maintain full alert," came the immediate reply. "Standby for further orders."

Shit. He trained his eyes back towards the horizon. *Shit.*

Colonel Gibbs stood on the side of the field and watched as the enemy planes flew off with the Allied squadron right behind them. He pulled his old, bent up Zippo lighter from his pocket, and puffed the stubby cigar to life.

After clicking it closed, he looked at the lighter and rolled it around in his hand a little before returning it to his pocket. It was a present from his wife, and he thought about her every time he touched it.

"Get my hat," he said to one of his aides as he started walking towards the guns. "Happy friggin' New Year."

Similar reports were coming in from all up and down the Allied line. Some 800 German planes attacked multiple targets in this daring New Year's dawn raid, but their casualties were high and the damage done was minimal compared to their losses. They lost over half of the planes and many experienced pilots.

The Colonel could see that his well-trained crews were already changing barrels on the big guns, and restocking ammo while they threw the empty shells out of the pit and out from underfoot. They were getting ready for another attack, should there be one.

As the Colonel approached Lieutenant Bionde, he saw him grab a private and say something to him and then give him a shove. The private turned and started to trot away, stopping briefly to salute the Colonel.

"What's it look like, Lieutenant?" asked the Colonel.

"Looks like at least fifteen unconfirmed kills for the battalion, sir."

"Casualties?"

"Gun Six on "C" Battery got hit hard, took out four men and damaged the gun, but it's being repaired right now."

As Bionde spoke, he could see Private Mike Jackson running into the tree line and through the brush, heading towards the goat path before disappearing from sight.

"Looks like the Air Corp boys got hit pretty hard. Send them a few dozen men to help with the fires."

"Yes, sir."

"Carry on, Lieutenant, I'm going to walk over to Gun Six and talk to our boys."

"Thank you, sir," Bionde said, and turned to check on his other guns.

Sergeant Wes Waltrip had been on Gun Five of "C" Battery when it clipped the tail of the Spitfire, and he watched as it went down into the woods, leaving a scar on the ground where it slid in between two trees, breaking off its wings and bending the prop back, as snow covered branches fell all over the downed plane.

He could see the pilot trying to push open the canopy and push aside some of the debris that now had him all but pinned. He also saw about a dozen of the Air Corp guys running towards the plane, and by the looks on their faces, they were not here to welcome him to Metz.

"This is going to be trouble," he said. "You guys come with me."

Wes grabbed the three privates standing with him and they took off running toward the plane. By the time they got there, the Air Corp guys had pulled the pilot out and they had him on the ground and were kicking and punching him.

Among the fliers were a major and two captains. One of the captains had pulled his 45 from his holster and racked it as he walked over to the circle of men surrounding the German.

"What the hell are we doing, Sarge?" Private Crocker asked Wes with a twinge of fear in his voice. The other two wide-eyed privates looked at Crocker and then back at Wes.

"I'm not sure yet, just play along," said Wes. "Act like you're supposed to be here."

"Wait, wait!" Wes was yelling as he reached the group, gulping down air from the long run out to the crash site. The three privates, panting and sweating were moments behind him.

The Major turned and looked at Wes and said, "We got this, Sergeant. Go back to your unit."

"I'm sorry, Major, I can't do that. Colonel Gibb's orders, sir."

The Major looked past Wes at the three privates who, although they had no idea what Wes was talking about, kept their poker faces and acted like they "were supposed to be there."

"What orders are those, Sergeant?" asked the stone-faced major.

"He wants him taken prisoner," Wes said with all the confidence in the world. "Colonel says we shot him down so he figures he belongs to us. Might want to have them stop kicking him, sir. I'm not sure how to explain that to the Colonel."

After staring at Wes with a scowl, the Major turned and yelled, "Leave him be."

The airmen looked up at the Major with angry and now confused looks on their faces. "I said that's enough, let's go."

As the airmen shuffled away, Wes and his men walked to the spot where the battered German lay amongst the boot prints all around him in the snow, drops of blood everywhere from the beating he took.

"Danka," said the pilot, as Wes pulled him to his feet. "Thank you," he then said in English.

Wes had him by the collar and pulled him in so he was face to face. "Shut up, you Nazi bastard. Shut the hell up and walk." Wes then flung him forward back towards the field, and the four Americans walked just behind him.

"I don't get it, Sarge. Why?" asked Crocker.

"Like I said, he's our prisoner."

"The Colonel is okay with this?"

"He will be," Wes grinned. "Especially when I remind him that this young Kraut is going to spend the rest of his long life telling people how the 386th shot his plane out from underneath him."

"I still think we risked our asses for this piece of shit."

"Let's not forget who the good guys are, fellas. I have no problem shooting their ass out of the sky, but we don't beat teenagers to death while they're lying on the ground."

The three privates nodded their heads.

"We are not only bringing the Colonel a prisoner, but we stopped something that those fellas would have regretted their whole lives. Tomorrow when they calm down they'll be thanking us. Now let's bring the Colonel his Christmas present."

"I've got incoming," Bob said into the radio. After a few seconds of silence his voice cracked over the radio again. "Friendlies. Our boys are coming back. Don't shoot."

He wasn't sure what happened down there, but from what he could see and hear, he figured the 386th was sure to be wide-eyed with fingers on the trigger.

Four of the P-47's came roaring past him as they approached the field and lined up for landing, followed close behind by five more.

"All nine of ours are coming in, nothing smoking or burning that I can see."

"Roger that," came a voice over the radio. "Air Corp reports three unconfirmed kills."

Just then Bob jumped to his feet and grabbed for his gun as his heart pounded in his chest. He heard the unmistakable sound of the ice and snow crunching under someone's feet as they approached.

"Bob, don't shoot," came the voice through the brush, just louder than a whisper. "Bob, it's me, Mike Jackson."

"Jax! What the hell are you doing here?"

"Hey, Bob," he said and plopped down. He was winded and sweaty from the fast walk up. "Bionde sent me to relieve you."

"Relieve me?" asked Bob. "Why so soon? What happened down there, Jax?"

"It was a real turkey shoot, Bob. We knocked down a bunch of them. They beat us up a little, but's there's a whole lot of Kraut planes we turned into scrap metal."

"Why does Bionde want me back now?"

Jackson looked at the ground and then looked off in the distance at nothing in particular. Then he looked back at Bob and said, "You better get going, Bob. He's going to be looking for you. Just leave the radio, I got it."

Without another word, Bob grabbed his gun and started off towards the field.

Chapter Twenty-Two

Bob ducked and dodged through the brush as he hurried his way down the goat path. White covered branches parted in front of him as he muscled his way through, knocking the snow off them as they sprang back. It started to snow again, but he could still see the black smoke trails, rising up into the whitened sky.

He finally burst through the edge of the tree line and topped the valley rim to look down at the shocking carnage that just a few hours ago was a peaceful, snow covered landscape.

The first thing he noticed was the smoking, burning hulks that once was a row of American fighter planes. Several buildings and trucks were on fire, and men were desperately trying to get them under control.

There was activity all over the field as the gun crews raced out to replace barrels and restock ammo for any other threats. They needed to be ready.

His eye caught a glimpse of the Colonel's hat walking across the field just as he was meeting up with Lieutenant Bionde. He could see they were talking and pointing around the field, then they both turned and looked at something, so Bob looked in the same direction to see what it was.

They were looking at Gun Six, "C" Battery Gun Six, his gun. There was a group of men around the gun in a circle, some on their knees, so he couldn't see what was going on, but he knew right away it was bad.

Oh shit. No, no, no.

He took off running down the hill towards the gun and it was all he could do to keep his footing. He leaned forward to let the momentum take him and hoped his feet would be able to keep up.

As time seemed to slow it was like being in a bubble, cut off from all but the sound of his own panting and the crunch of his boots, desperately trying to gain traction in the snow. He became vaguely aware of the items in his pockets and on his belt chattering and his helmet bouncing up and down on his head as he ran.

He finally reached the bottom of the hill and took off in a full sprint towards Gun Six, running right past the Lieutenant summoning him. A private left Bionde's side and trotted to intercept Bob.

"Hold on, Bob," he said as he grabbed Bob's arm and pulled him to a stop. "It's pretty bad, you need to take a few breaths, buddy."

"I have to get to my crew," he said back, all the while looking over at the gun. "I'd rather be over there than standing here taking breaths."

"Shit, I understand, pal. You want me to take your stuff? I'll hold onto it for you."

"Yeah, yeah, ok," he said, as he handed off his rifle and helmet. Then, pulling off the binoculars from around his neck and almost tossing them, he bolted off for the gun.

He ran up behind John, who was standing facing the gun with his head hanging down and his helmet in his hand on his side. When he heard Bob run up, he looked back at him with a blank and ashen face, and watery eyes. He just shook his head and looked back down.

Bob elbowed his way in next to John. *Oh shit, four bodies.*

He saw Dutch laying on the far side of the gun with a few guys kneeling in front of him getting ready to wrap him in a blanket. He was nearly blown in half, no doubt from a direct hit from the strafing run.

On the other side were two men he couldn't make out because the guys kneeling around them blocked their faces from his angle. He was about to go and see who the two men were when he noticed another man down just behind the breech of the gun.

Bent over the body, holding it in his arms, was Herby, and he was weeping so hard he was shaking. Bob felt his stomach get queasy, and he felt light headed, so much so that he had to lean on the gun for a moment to steady himself.

He turned back to John, hoping he could make it better, hoping that he could fix it, but John just shook his head, and as tears began to fall, he dropped his head down again.

Bob dropped down next to Herb and put his arm over his shoulder, not just to comfort him, but to steady himself, as well. Herb looked up into Bob's face and his expression was that of sheer pain and agony. Tears dripped off his chin and he gulped for breath in the cold morning air.

Bob looked down to see Doug's face, peacefully lying there as though sleeping. Little crystals of snow were beginning to stick to his eyelashes and his face, and he had a slight blue tint to his skin, giving him an almost angelic appearance.

Bob felt himself getting sick and he crawled away quickly on his hands and knees a few feet and vomited. He came back and looked down at Doug, still in such a peaceful state. He just couldn't believe he was dead.

Lieutenant Bionde had walked up behind them by then and was standing next to John. The Colonel had been walking around the field, but he was on his way over to Gun Six now.

"He doesn't even look hurt," Bob said to Herb with his voice cracking. Doug was intact with no obvious wounds, and not even any blood. "What happened to him?"

John knelt down next to Herb, and they rolled Doug on his side. Just below his armpit was a small hole in his coat and just a spot of blood. "It had to be shrapnel, Bob. I don't even see an exit wound."

"Jesus Christ, I can't believe this," said Bob, barely able to speak.

"He was the best of us," said Herb. "This can't be happening. This fucking can't be happening."

The Colonel walked up and stood next to Bionde, who was also trying to hold back the tears. Some of the men came to attention but most kept kneeling around the bodies of their comrades as if he wasn't there.

"At ease, men," he said to the few men that stood as he looked around at the carnage in the gun pit. "Dutch was a good man, Lieutenant. I hate to lose him."

"Yes sir, he was, sir," Bionde answered while swiping at a tear.

"I see Pete Miller there, too, and is that Pearson?"

"Yes it is, sir."

The Colonel walked up to the fourth body with the three soldiers crouched around it. He could see it was Doug Hansen and he stopped momentarily and shook his head before taking the last step and kneeling down next to the men.

Herby looked up from Doug and found himself eye to eye with Colonel Gibbs. "Why Colonel? Why him?" he asked as the other two men shook their heads and sobbed.

"I don't know, son," Colonel Gibbs replied softly. "We will never know why, and it will never make sense. Only God knows that."

Then men nodded and Herb started to cry and shudder as he leaned over Doug and put his face on his chest. "Jesus, Doug. Don't do this to me, don't do this."

As the three men crouched there together with their arms around each other's shoulders, Colonel Gibbs quietly walked away while Lieutenant Bionde walked up behind them. "At least they got the bastard, if that means anything."

Bob looked up at him and blinked, trying to understand what he was saying. He had not witnessed the battle. "What?" he asked.

"They killed the bastard that killed them," Bionde said solemnly. "Not that it helps any, but it's something."

"What happened?" Bob asked, as he pushed more tears off the side of his face and tried to keep from trembling.

"One of them came straight at the gun, Bob. Dutch put a round right down his throat, a round Doug loaded. They never flinched. It was the bravest damn thing I ever saw."

Bob nodded yes and then dropped his head and shook it no.

The men from the Graves Division had wrapped up the other three men and were now coming to get Doug. Herb jumped to his feet and grabbed one by the front of his coat and hurled him backwards.

"No!" he screamed at them. "You can't take him!"

The Lieutenant was about to step in but the Graves sergeant intercepted him and said, "Its ok, sir, we understand. We have time."

"Thank you, Sergeant. I appreciate it."

"We're soldiers, too, sir. He's one of ours, too. We'll take care of him."

"Thank you, Sergeant."

The men stayed huddled around Doug, and Bob brushed the snow off his face as it started to come down heavier now. "We have to take him to the truck now, fellas," he said softly.

"Can we take him to the truck?" Herb asked the sergeant who was standing close by. He had a blanket to wrap Doug in and he was patiently waiting for the men to let him go.

"Sure thing. You can wrap him up, too, if you'd like," he replied with a kindness in his voice and the blanket in his outstretched hand.

John took the blanket and spread it out on the ground next to him and Herby rolled him on his side. Bob and John pushed the edge of the blanket up under him before they rolled him on his back and crossed his arms in front of him.

They had all but his head wrapped when Herb leaned in and kissed Doug on the forehead, and at the sight of it, Bob started to weep and tremble. He leaned over and kissed Doug as his lips quivered and then moved aside as John did, too.

"I can't believe this is the last time we'll ever see him," said Herb, as he stared at his friend and shook his head.

"Goodbye, old friend."

"So long, movie star," said Bob, as he patted Doug's chest.

"See you on the other side," said John, almost in a whisper. "See you on the other side."

They covered his still handsome face, lifted him up and carried him to the waiting truck. The other men from Gun Six were already there, as well as all the Air Corp guys that were killed. The smell of burnt flesh and fuel wafted out of the back of the now full truck.

Doug was now just another body in a pile of bodies, dead among the dead — such sharp contrast to how alive he was among the living. Now he was gone, along with Miller, Pearson, and Dutch.

They stood there and watched as the tailgate went up on the truck. It slipped a little side to side before it got traction in the snow and headed away from the field. They looked on in silence until it disappeared from sight.

"I guess we should go back to the barracks and get dry and warmed up," said John, and Bob nodded, but Herby just stood there staring at the tracks in the new snow of the truck that took away his friend.

"C'mon Herb," said Bob, as he put his arm around Herb's shoulder.

"We'll be ok," John said to Herb as he got on his other side and put his arm over the other shoulder. "Let's get inside."

Herb looked at Bob and then at John and then dropped his head and looked at the ground. A few seconds later he nodded yes and the three of them started towards the barracks building, holding each other up as they went.

There was a fire going in a stove and many of the men were sitting around trying to get warm and dry, but it was silent except for the occasional rustling of someone trying to get comfortable.

Lieutenant Bionde walked in and nodded to the men. "You guys did a good job today," he said, and the men nodded and stared at their cold feet. Nothing he could say would make things any better, but he tried.

"The Colonel wants the men of Gun Six and Gun Five from "C" Battery at his office in thirty minutes, ok guys?"

The men nodded and some looked at their watches.

"Gun Five will be there, sir," said Wes.

"Gun Six will be there, sir," said John, answering for Dutch.

"See you there," said Bionde, as he turned and walked out.

There were twenty-four men left from the two guns and they started walking over to the headquarters building to meet with the Colonel. They packed into his makeshift office, and though they barely had room to move, they snapped to attention and saluted when he came in.

"At ease, men," said Colonel Gibbs, as he took off his hat and hung it on a hook next to his helmet. "We are going to keep this meeting informal."

Bob's eyes followed the Colonel and he glanced at the gold eagle painted on his helmet that Dutch had gotten him to paint. It made him think of Dutch, which made him think of Doug, and his head dropped down again to stare at the worn wooden floor beneath him.

" "A" Battery will be up here from Verdun this afternoon, and "D" Battery will roll in tomorrow morning," the Colonel began. "In other words, I am about to have plenty of guns to ring this field, so I'm taking Guns Five and Six out of service for a few days."

The men looked around at each other, and John shrugged when Bob caught his eye. *What now?*

"The men of Gun Six displayed a heroism that was nothing short of remarkable, but they paid a heavy price for it," Colonel Gibbs continued. "And Gun Five made two kills, and captured an enemy pilot."

No one else in the room responded, the only sound heard was the shuffling of feet and the crackling of the fire. Some of the men opened their coats as the room heated them up.

"I've decided to give all you men a three day pass," Gibbs continued. "Give a little time for "A" Battery to get here, and then I can cut you loose. Let's say midnight tonight, and be back in seventy-two hours."

The men nodded and looked around at each other, some of them even smiling as they thought about how they would use their time.

"Any questions, gentlemen?" asked the Colonel.

The men all shook their heads and looked around at each other again, and again not a word was said.

"Ok, Lieutenant Bionde will have your passes drawn up. Don't be late coming back. And thanks, boys, good job. Dismissed."

As the men shuffled outside, helmets went back on heads and zippers on coats went up as the cold wind bit into their faces and their warm breath puffed from them against the cold air like steam engines.

As they started back towards their barracks, Bob noticed the German pilot alongside the building, sitting on an upside down bucket with an armed guard on either side of him. Bob scowled at him, and so did Herb, and the German dropped his head between his knees and sobbed.

"He's just a damn kid," said John, when he looked at him. "What the hell kind of war is this that we are fighting kids? I don't get it."

Wes came over and stood with them. "We shot his young ass down, but then we had to save him from the fly boys. They were going to eat him for breakfast."

"I don't blame them," said Herb. "Bastard."

"Sorry about your crew," said Wes. "They were good men."

"Thanks, Sarge. Let's go fellas," said Bob. "I'm done looking at that Kraut, anyway."

Bionde came in and handed out the passes to all the men. The guys on Gun Five had already figured out where they were going, and it involved lots of drinking and lots of French girls.

"Paris," said Wes. "We are all going to Paris. If any of you Gun Six boys want to tag along we'd be proud to have you."

"I think I'm going back to Sainte Mère Église and see if I can find that little French girl," said Herb. "I don't want to go to Paris."

"I think I will go with you, Herb," said John. "Try to keep you out of trouble. How about you, Bob?"

Bob didn't answer right away. He was sitting on the edge of a cot pulling off his boots. *There is only one place in the world that I want to be right now, only one.*

"You guys go on," he said. "I have other plans."

"Are you sure, Bob? You shouldn't be alone now. You should stay with us."

"I won't be alone, I'll be fine. You guys go."

A few minutes after midnight, a truck rolled out full of men heading to Paris and then on, for some, to Sainte Mère Église. Bob packed a small bag and headed off in the other direction, hoping to catch a ride to another destination.

His plan was to make it to a nearby airfield and talk his way onto a transport plane. Come hell or high water, he was going to England.

He caught a flight from Verdun to Cherbourg, and then over to Poole. It took him a day and a half to get there, waiting on empty seats and talking his way into them. The pass signed by Colonel Gibbs certainly helped.

He got into Bournemouth about seven o'clock. *Ok, now all I have to do is find her.* He knew how hard it would be, but he shrugged off any doubts. *At least we're in the same city.*

Bournemouth seemed a little quieter than he remembered it. Most of the military forces were long gone. No more streets lined with tanks and clubs full of soldiers. There was a sleepy and peaceful feeling, as the threat of imminent invasion had passed and the war was farther away.

There's our bench. He smiled and then glanced over at the movie theatre. He got a warm feeling inside and his stomach fluttered a little as he thought how close he was to seeing Mickey.

301

Then he stopped in his tracks as an overwhelming feeling of pain and despair and even guilt came over him.

The scheme. I never would have met her if it wasn't for Doug's scheme.

He remembered how Doug winked at him and waved him on when he couldn't go that night. He remembered how Doug stumbled up the stairs with lipstick on his face and a girl under his arm in London, and how he talked their way out of being arrested.

I have to put this out of my head for now. I can't let Mickey see there is anything wrong. She doesn't need more to worry about. God, I hope I find her.

New Year's came and went for the girls and was rather uneventful. They shared a bottle of wine that Emily had been saving but the mood was more mundane than festive. Lillian's birthday was in a few days, and it was sure to be the same non-event as New Year's.

They were understaffed and therefore working too much, and she was just getting over a cold. The weather was miserable and cold, and she seemed to never be able to warm up, even shivering while under the covers in bed. It reminded her of the convent.

She hadn't been down to the seawall in a while, it was just too cold and windy. As a matter of fact, she hadn't been out very much at all, preferring instead to stay inside the almost warm Grand.

Now she had no choice but to go out into the cold. She'd been putting it off too long and she needed to go to the store and pick up a few things. She had just gotten some new ration coupons, and she needed to use them.

God, I dread going back out in that cold. She pulled on the heavy wool coat that always made her neck itch. As she was going out the door a young RAF lieutenant was coming in.

"Hello, love," he said, while taking off his hat politely. "Care to have dinner with a lonely lad from London?"

"Bugger off," she said, as she hurried past the now wide-eyed airman and out the door into the sleet.

I can't believe I said that to an officer. She shook her head. *But damn it felt good. God help the bastard who pesters me tonight.*

She put her head down and her hands in her pockets and bulldozed her way down the street, on a mission to get there and back in record time.

"Hey blondie," she heard the voice behind her.

Bloody bastard. Maybe if I ignore him he'll go away. But she knew they never did.

"Hey blondie, wait for me."

"Go away," she yelled over her shoulder and picked up the pace.

"Hey blondie, I have an extra ticket to the movies. Want to go with me?"

She stopped dead in her tracks and stood up straight. *It can't be.* She turned slowly, expecting to be disappointed, but still?

By the time she turned around, he had made up the two or three steps he was behind, so she now was face to face, and had to blink a few times to realize it really was him.

"You got the time, blondie?" he asked softly with a grin.

She finally smiled and replied, "For you, I have all the time in the world."

He leaned in and kissed her, and their cold noses touched.

She pulled back and looked at him and asked, "What are you doing here?"

"I came to ask you something," he said. He dropped down on his knees on the wet, slushy street, and said, "I came to ask you to marry me."

She smiled and shook her head, and then bent down and whispered in his ear, "I think you are supposed to take your hat off at times like this, love."

"Oh, yeah, sorry, you're right." He pulled off his hat and put it under his arm and looked back up at her, a little embarrassed, but he shook it off and grinned.

"Mickey, my darling, my sweet, I have nothing to give you. I don't know if I will ever have anything to give you. The only promise I can make is that I will love and adore you every day for the rest of my life."

She looked down at him and smiled. He looked so silly kneeling down in the mucky wet street, soaking his knees, turning the heads of passersby.

"Mickey, my love, will you marry me?"

She reached down and pulled him to his feet and giggled at the wet patches on his knees, but he didn't even seem to notice them. His eyes never left hers.

"How did you get here?" she asked.

"I got a three day pass. It took a day and a half to get here, so I have to leave in a few hours."

"How did you get a pass like that?" she asked, knowing how hard it was.

"We had the cleanest latrine in the Battalion," he said, grinning. "Now what about that question?"

"Well, I rather had my heart set on a ranch in Texas," she said, smiling.

Bob held his breath as his heart pounded almost out of his chest.

"Yes, you silly, bloody yank! Yes, I will marry you."

He picked her up and spun her around and they both laughed. "Can we go for a walk?" he asked. "Do you have time?"

"I have until curfew," she said. "A few hours, anyway."

"Well, better a few hours than nothing at all. I was worried I wouldn't be able to find you."

"I can't believe you came all the way here for just a few hours together. That's sweet," she said, and hooked her arm in his.

"I'd sail around the world for five minutes with you, doll."

"Let's not get carried away, alright, love?" she said.

"Ok, Mick," he laughed. "But it's the thought that counts."

"Most of you yanks have just one bloody thought, it seems."

"That's why there's so many yanks!" he said with a grin.

"Too many, some would say," and she elbowed him in the ribs making him chuckle.

"Have you been getting some nice goodie boxes from my mom?" he asked.

"Yes, lovely packages. The girls and I love the cookies. She makes such good cookies."

"Well," he said. "If the cookies are good then my mom didn't make them, but I'm glad you're getting some good stuff. I plan on getting you a ring, but this was kind of a last minute thing, you know?"

"I don't care about that. I'm just glad to see you."

They walked up to the Grand just a few minutes before curfew and he said to her, "I love you, Mick. You believe that, don't you?"

"I believe you. I wasn't sure at first, but I believe you, and I love you, too."

Bob smiled a big smile and reached down and pulled her tight against him. He gave her a big, long kiss, right in the middle of the street, and neither one cared who saw them.

At that moment, Sarah and Becky walked up to the Grand, and had to side step around the not-at-all bashful couple to get past them.

"She likes those bloody yanks, she does," said Sarah, making Becky giggle. "I hope this one's mum sends cookies, as well."

"Maybe we'll get packages from both of them," Sarah smiled and winked. "Now that would be a neat trick."

As the girls went inside laughing, the long kiss ended and they looked in each other's eyes, still in a warm embrace.

Bob noticed her lip quiver and a flash of sadness in her eyes, an almost imperceptible flash, before the smile reappeared, as did the warmth in her eyes.

"Don't worry, Mick," he said, and she dropped her head down.

He gently put his fingertips under her chin and lifted her head to once more look in her eyes. "I'll be back soon. I came back this time, I'll be back again."

"I know you will," she said, forcing a smile.

"Do you remember our promise?" She nodded and smiled.

"Tell me," he said.

"We promised there would be no goodbyes."

"That's my girl," he said with a big toothy grin. "We say so long. So long until we meet again, right?"

"So long," she said.

"Until we meet again," he said.

"So long, until we meet again," she said back, forcing a smile.

He leaned in and kissed her again. "You better go in now, it's curfew."

She nodded yes and put her hand on the side of his face and smiled, and turned away, and as soon as she did, he smacked her hard on the butt.

She turned quickly around with a shocked look on her face to see him standing there grinning, and she wagged her finger at him and said, "Bloody yank." Then in a heartbeat, she was gone.

He stared out the window as the plane lifted off, and he watched as it passed over the coast above the English Channel. As he looked through his reflection in the glass, the last few days played over and over in his mind like a movie.

This has been the best few weeks and the worst few weeks of my life. New Year's will never be the same, and neither will Christmas. Dammit, Doug. Why you? Why the hell did it have to be you?

This time the plane he hitched a ride on flew into Paris. He tried to scare up another flight over to Verdun, but he wasn't having much luck, so he climbed into a truck that was going in the general direction.

Three trucks later, zig-zagging across France, he finally rolled into Metz with a few hours to spare. He walked in to

306

find John and Herby playing cards with a bowl of pennies between them and said, "Did you high rollers have any fun?"

"As much as we could, under the circumstances," said John, and Herb nodded.

"Where did you go, Bob?" asked Herb.

"I went to England," he replied with a smile. "Mickey said she would marry me."

"No kidding?" asked John, getting to his feet. "Congratulations old buddy, that's great."

Herb gave Bob a big hug and then, holding him at arm's length, he said, "Way to go, brother. Way to go. I'm proud of you."

"Thanks, fellas, I appreciate it. I wish the movie star were here. He'd be proud of me, too."

"We all wish that, Bob," said John. "Now tell us all about your trip."

Chapter Twenty-Three

The Battle of the Bulge went on until about January 25, 1945. While it was nearly a successful strategy for the Germans, the Allies were able to hold the line, and it proved to be the last gasp of the Nazi war machine. What was left of their forces was now on the retreat.

Patton's army now slammed its way into Germany, destroying everything in its path, seemingly unstoppable on the way to Berlin. In mid-March word came that the Russians had pushed the Nazis out of Poland, and were now closing in on the German capital.

The 386th followed along behind Patton's Armored Division and infantry units, taking up anti-aircraft positions as needed along the way. The battalion moved into Germany, Wiesbaden first, then Frankfort, then on to Gottingen.

As the Battalion moved further into Germany, the living quarters and various "spoils of war" got better and better. The Nazis were in a hurry to get out of Dodge, so they left their barracks with all the comforts of home, including commercial kitchens, bath rooms and showers, and even motor pools.

Herby was sitting up on one of the guns, leaning back with his feet propped up and eating a sandwich. "This is my kind of war," he said.

"I haven't even seen a Kraut plane since New Year's," said Bob. "That must be because they're scared of Herby," John said with a grin.

"Nah," said Herb. "I think we got 'em all."

"I hope so," said Bob. "I've seen enough of them for one lifetime."

"Ten lifetimes is more like it."

"The girls here are not as friendly as the French gals, or the Brits," said Herb, shaking his head. "I've seen some pretty ones, too."

"What the hell did you expect?" asked Bob, astonished. "We've been bombing the shit out of them for four years."

"Herby is used to girls that don't like him," said John, making Bob laugh.

"You guys can just go to hell, is all I can say," said Herb. "You're just jealous and you know it."

"Jealous!" said Bob. "I've got my girl, why should I be jealous? And at least I know mine won't try to bayonet me when I go to kiss her."

"He's got a point, Herb," John chimed in.

"Hey, I did see one this morning that Herb would like," said Bob. "She had an uncanny resemblance to Babe Ruth."

"I said hit like Babe Ruth, remember?" asked Herb. "Hit, not look like. Besides they hate baseball over here, so what's the point?"

By early April the Battalion fell into an almost boring routine as the front got further and further away. The entire battalion was ordered to be screened for venereal disease, as well as a physical.

"They probably want to send us to Japan," said John. "They want to make sure we are fit enough to get shot."

"You have a completely blown out eardrum, soldier," said the doctor. "How the hell did you even get in?"

Oh shit, I forgot about that.

"Must have been a paperwork mix up, doc. You know how the army is."

"Well, we are going to take care of that right now," the doctor said as he pulled out a clipboard and shook his head frowning. "You're going home, Private."

"Wait doc, wait! You can't send me back now. I have a girl in England I promised to marry when the war ended."

"I'm sorry, soldier," the doctor said, looking up from his clipboard. "They will hang my ass out to dry if I pass you through. You're 4-F, but I'm sure you already knew that."

"C'mon doc, I earned this. I walked here all the way from Normandy. I lost friends, and I fell in love along the way."

The doctor just looked at him with a blank expression.

"Listen, doc. I never asked for or got any special treatment, and I pulled my weight the whole time. As a matter of fact, I've never even told anybody about the ear. You're the first to know."

"I don't know, Private. It's just, well, ah shit, I don't know."

"Just a few more months, that's all I ask. I'm sure it will be over by then, and I can go back and marry my girl."

The doctor looked at him with a scowl, and after a few moments said, "I need you to promise me something."

"Anything, sir, anything."

"For one thing, you were never here. You and I have never had this conversation, and I have never looked in that hole in your head that you call an ear."

"Ok, doc," Bob said smiling. "I can do that."

"And under no circumstances will you go to Japan, is that clear?" he asked, and Bob nodded. "If they try to send you, just complain of an ear ache and you will be on the next boat home, understand?"

"Got it, next boat home."

"Now get the hell out of my office, I never want to see you again."

"Yes, sir. So long, sir, and thanks."

"By the way, soldier," said the doctor as Bob was almost out the door. "What do you do for the battalion?"

"Well, you know the army, sir," Bob said grinning. "What else would they do with a half deaf soldier? They made me a radio operator."

"Did the pecker checker say you were ok, Bob?" Herb asked as Bob came in.

"Yeah, but he told me to stay the hell away from you."

Two days later, on April 12, 1945 came devastating news. President Franklin D. Roosevelt was dead. Harry Truman

311

stepped into his shoes, and ordered all the flags to Half Staff for thirty days in honor of their valiant leader.

Three weeks later, on May 1, 1945, Herby came running into the room where Bob and John were writing letters home. He was jumping up and down and waving his arms and yelling, "He's dead! He's dead! Ding dong the baseball hating son of a bitch, witch, is dead!"

"Calm down, Herb, for Christ's sake," said John as Bob looked up from his letter. "Who's dead?"

"Hitler, goddamn it! It's all over the radio. They think the Russians got him."

In fact, the Russians didn't get him. On April 30, 1945, at the age of 56, Hitler signed his last will, blaming the Jews for his failures, appointed his successor, and then blew his own brains out, too cowardly to face the world.

"Holy shit!" Bob yelled as he jumped up from the table, followed closely by John.

"About damn time," said John. "He lived about ten years too long if you ask me."

"Twenty," said Herby. "Shit, I wish Doug were here to see this."

"Let's go get lousy, rotten drunk, boys," said Bob on the way out the door.

Outside, the battalion was in full celebration. Men were jumping up and down, shooting guns in the air, and drinking everything that was in liquid form. One guy stripped naked and, grabbing the flag from the Colonel's office, ran all over the field in nothing but his boots. Even the Colonel laughed at that.

On May 8, 1945, it was Harry Truman's 61st birthday, and what a great birthday it was. It was the day that Germany unconditionally surrendered to the Allied forces. His only regret was that President Roosevelt died only weeks before seeing the victory he fought so hard to achieve.

In England, for the first time in six years, the church bells rang all across the country. They rang and they rang and they rang as people danced in the streets and everyone kissed everyone else.

The girls were having so much fun — it was a whirlwind celebration. Against all odds, the island nation had fought back the tyranny of the Nazis, fought back and won.

"Rip down those bloody blackout curtains," Emily yelled out. "No more living in the dark."

"Turn on every light in Bournemouth, I say," Lillian chimed in.

"I plan on eating so much cake," Sarah said, "that before long I won't be able to see my feet."

"I just can't believe it," Lillian shook her head in wonder and smiled. "He's really coming back. It's over and he's coming back."

King George VI with Queen Elizabeth appeared along with Winston Churchill on the balcony at Buckingham Palace to cheering crowds. The lights would once again shine, the bells would once again ring, and there will once again be blue birds over the white cliffs of Dover.

One down, one to go.

The 386th moved into a sports complex just outside Berlin, where they awaited their new orders that would either send them to Japan, or back home. All four batteries were there, as well as the headquarters battery, and while the danger had passed, there was an uneasy feeling that came with the state of limbo they were in.

Bob, John and Herby were walking to the big, modern mess hall that was part of the complex to enjoy another hot, sit down breakfast. They had eaten hot, real food, at every meal since they got here.

"Any word from the Colonel?" asked Herb. "He give you permission yet?"

"He's been kind of dragging his feet, it seems," said Bob. "I hope he decides soon or I will be shipped out before I can get back to England."

"Don't worry," said John. "He likes you, Bob. He'll let you marry that girl."

"I'm gonna stop by there on the way back to the barracks and see if Bionde has heard anything."

After a big breakfast, Bob headed off for the Colonel's office, stuffed full and gripping a toothpick in his mouth. He'd made this walk to check his request status at least a dozen times already. Standing in front of the gate to the stadium, was a soldier pulling guard duty.

"You know they got a big, hot breakfast going on at the mess?" Bob asked. "Hurry and you can still catch it."

"I know, I can smell it from here but I got two more hours to relief."

"I'll tell you what, give me the rifle and go grab a bite. I'll spell you," said Bob, reaching out for it. "Just don't be long, I got stuff to do."

"Thanks Mac," the guard said, and trotted off. "I owe you one."

Bob looked at the rifle and smiled. It was a pass around; most battalions had at least one like it. The rifle was a dirty, rusty, banged up thing that belonged to no one who would admit to owning it. *Never fired and only dropped once.*

He looked up as a truck approached the gate. *Shit. Holy shit.* He quickly scanned to his left and right. There was nothing to hide behind, and no one close by to shout at, so he looked back up at the truck. *Shit!*

The truck was a German truck, with iron cross markings painted on the sides, and two German soldiers up front, with over a dozen sitting in the back. *Shit, I hope these bastards know the war is over.*

Bob gulped hard, and stepped out in front of the gate with his broken down old rifle, put up his hand and said, "Halt!"

The two men in front sat stone-faced, staring at the lone American soldier in front of them. None of the men in the back moved or even turned their heads to look.

"Kommenzee yer ass over here," Bob said to the driver, who obeyed by stepping down out of the cab and walking around to the front to speak to Bob. Bob looked up at the biggest damn German he'd ever seen, almost a head taller with a chest like a Nebraska farm boy.

"Ok, Fritz, what's Los?" he managed to ask without stammering, but he could feel the sweat running down the back of his neck, and his hands getting clammy on the rifle.

"Futbol," said the German and nodded towards the stadium. Bob looked back over his shoulder and then back at the soldier. "Polizei."

"Polizei?" Bob asked. "You mean police?"

The big German smiled and nodded, almost as though he had enjoyed rattling this lone American. "Da, police."

Ok, security for the football game. Bastards scared the shit out of me.

"Go ahead," he said as he swung open the gate. "Schnell, schnell, let's go, let's go." They rolled through and as he closed it back, he could see the guard he spelled coming back from breakfast.

"Anything exciting happen?" he asked as he strolled up.

"Not a damn thing," Bob said, smiling and handing back the useless rifle. "Not a damn thing."

No word yet from the Colonel, but he kept mentioning it to the Lieutenant, knowing his time was running out. He had to have the Colonel's permission, and a pass to go back and marry his girl, or it may be years before he'd see her again.

Mickey was having a tough time on her end as well. In England at the time, a person had to be twenty-one to marry, or had to have permission. With no real family, she wrote to Aunt Margaret and asked her to help.

Dame Margaret Digby stepped in and put the wheels in motion for her. She had to be interviewed by U.S. military representatives to be sure she wasn't just using the soldier as a ticket to America. With it came a physical to check for venereal disease, pregnancy, and various maladies that would rule her out.

315

On August 5th, Bob was summoned to the Colonel's office. He was grilled for over an hour by his commanding officer, who held his fate in his hands. He didn't like these wartime weddings, saying they were impulsive. As a highly disciplined officer, he liked nothing impulsive, but agreed to give it some thought.

The next day, August 6, 1945, Bob got his permission to marry his girl. On the other side of the world, history was made on the same day, when a city called Hiroshima was all but destroyed by a single bomb that shocked everyone with its devastation.

Three days later, on August 9th, the same day Bob got his furlough papers, a second super bomb fell on Japan, destroying the city of Nagasaki.

On August 14, 1945, ten days before Bob's five-day furlough was set to begin, The Empire of Japan unconditionally surrendered. The last enemy had fallen. The war, the long war, was finally over.

Amid all the celebrations, Mickey went to Saint Augustine church and talked to the Vicar Peerless and his wife about their plans. She asked if they could have the wedding there, and schedule it for the 24th, the day Bob would arrive.

Bob wrote and told her that he planned to leave at midnight, and come hell or high water, he would make it there for a noon wedding. She forwarded him her new address, a modest little apartment, because they had just been moved out of the Grand.

"Have you heard from your Canadian, love?" she asked Sarah over lunch a few days before the wedding.

"Not yet," she said, while pushing the food around on her plate. "But I'm sure I will soon. I better be soon. Damn soldiers, I should know better."

"Yes, you should have," Lillian said with a grin.

"He better be here for your wedding or I may have to find another lad to take along," she said, grinning back. "I may just do that anyway."

316

"So how much longer, Bob?" John asked after walking back from chow.

"Two more days. Mick's got it all set up with the church and everything. I'm getting kinda nervous. I can't believe I'm getting married."

"Think of it this way: you still have two whole days of freedom left."

"Thanks, John, You're a big help."

Just then Herby came walking in with a wooden crate in his arms. "Am I interrupting anything, ladies?" he asked.

"What the hell you got there, Herb?" asked Bob.

"Well," he replied, "I'm not exactly sure. I think the writing on it is French, but the Krauts left it behind."

"If the Germans carried it here from France, it must be something important," said John.

"What I like about it," said Herby, grinning, "is the noise it makes when you do this . . . ." He rattled the crate a little and it made the unmistakable sound of bottles clinking against each other.

"Booze," said Bob with great delight. "Let's get the damn thing open."

As the top came off, a musty smell escaped the box, as well as a cloud of dust. The three of them peered down into the cobwebs but clearly saw the tops of twelve bottles poking up. Bob reached down and carefully pulled one out.

"Hey, let me see that," said John, and Bob handed it to him and pulled out two more. "This ain't booze, it's Champagne, and the label says 1883."

"Shit, 1883!" said Herb. "Do you think it's still good?"

Bob shrugged and looked at John and said, "What do you think, is it still good?"

"Well, I'm no expert, but I would say it's either really good, or really bad."

"Bob, you try it first," Herby said laughing.

"What the hell, you only live once," Bob said as he twisted the cork side to side until it blew out of his hand and half the

317

Champagne sprayed around the room as Bob tried to catch as much as he could in his mouth.

"How the hell does it stay fizzy for over fifty years?" asked Herb as he twisted on his bottle. "I'm gonna try not to lose as much out of this one."

They got their bottles open and quickly started knocking back Champagne. It wasn't long before they were all plastered. They started calling it "Bob's Bachelor Party."

They sat around in a circle on the floor when a very drunk Herb slurred, "Ok wait, wait, just wait a second, shush, wait, be quiet, goddamn it."

Bob and John stopped talking and looked at Herb, but he just sat there.

"Ok Herb, we're listening," Bob finally said.

"Oh yeah, sorry," said Herb. "Ok, I remember. A toast. A toast to the movie star, wish you were here."

"To Doug," Bob and John said while raising their bottles.

"And to Dutch!" said John, and they all took another gulp.

"To Miller, and to Pearson," each man getting a raised bottle and a swig.

"To Major Parker," said Bob. "He was a good guy."

The next morning found the guys very hung over. "Maybe that stuff was bad after all," said Herb. "Maybe the French wanted the Germans to take it."

"No, it was good," John said, rubbing his head. "Too damn good."

"What are you going to do after you get married, Bob?" asked John. "Got a honeymoon planned?"

"No, not really, we're broke, especially me. We'll probably just stay at her place, and that's just fine with me."

"Hey, Bob, why don't you take some of this fancy pants wine over there with you?" asked Herb. "It's like money over there."

"I can't exactly take it on the plane with me. If I get caught with it, they'll hang my ass for contraband."

"Leave that to me," Herb grinned.

318

A few hours before he was scheduled to depart, John and Herb used condoms to tie a bottle to each of Bob's arms and legs. His Army dress jacket covered his arms alright, but his pants were too tight, stretching over the bottle size bulges on his thighs, so they were anything but hidden.

That didn't stop Herby. He said, "My pants are two sizes bigger than yours and I have an extra pair, let's give it a try."

Bob slipped the pants over the bottles and John stepped back to look him over and said, "It just might work, Bob. As long as no one looks too close."

"Of course it will work," said Herb proudly. "Whose gonna look too close at his pants, for Christ's sake?"

At one minute after midnight, Bob, strapped with four bottles of Champagne, a pocket full of change the guys raised for him in a pool as a wedding present, a dozen candy bars, and Herby's pants, set off for England.

He stopped in Paris for a few hours before taking off for England. In Mickey's last letter she sent directions to her new address, so the plan was to go straight there once he landed. Neither one was sure about the time he would get in, so she left a note on the door anytime she left the apartment.

Sarah, Emily and Becky all pitched in and helped the bride every way they could. Sarah, of course, wanted a cake, but since they only had one egg and hardly any sugar, it was going to be hard to pull off.

They had plenty of flour, and some food coloring, and Becky came up with a can of condensed milk. "Mash some potatoes, we'll use them as frosting," said Becky.

They took two toy soldiers and painted one white, standing them side by side on the lovely new cake as bride and groom.

"That cake is really starting to look good, Sarah," said Becky.

"Yes it is, love," said Sarah. "Too bad it's going to taste awful."

Mickey was darting back and forth from her room to the church trying to coordinate everything, but not knowing exactly when Bob was getting in made it more difficult. She left a note on her door with the directions to the church in case he should show up when she was not there.

"You're not getting married in that, are you?" asked Mrs. Peerless, the Vicar's wife, as she looked Lillian up and down. Lillian looked down at herself and realized how dingy her old RAF uniform was looking, and shrugged.

"It's all I have, I'm afraid," she said.

"Go check on that man of yours, love. It will be hard to have this wedding without him. When you get back I will have something special for you," she said, with a twinkle in her eye.

Lillian took off towards her apartment as fast as she could, but was crushed when she didn't see Bob, and the note with the map to the church was still hanging there. *I'll wait here for him for just a bit, then I need to run back to the church and hope for the best.*

She scurried around the apartment, trying to keep her mind off the chaos that was closing in all around her, when she heard his trademark "shave and a haircut, two bits" knock on the door. She bolted across the room and flung open the door, and standing there, hat in one hand and duffel bag in the other, was Bob.

She stood in the doorway, put her hands on her hips, cocked her head and said, "Well, at least you took your hat off this time."

He dropped both his bag and his hat on the ground and, taking a step forward, scooped her up by the waist and spun her around, kissing her passionately.

Halfway through the first kiss in eight months, there was a loud pop and whoosh sound. Mickey took a half step back as Bob's pants instantly became drenched down the front, and a foamy liquid was pouring out from the cuff, making an ever growing puddle on the floor.

"Did you miss me, love?" she asked, and cracked a little grin.

"Very much," he chuckled, and kissed her again.

"Looks like you ruined your pants, Yank."

"That's ok," he said with a wink. "They're Herb's pants."

"Well, since we need to dash off to the church, you didn't happen to bring any pants of your own, now did you?"

"Sure, doll. Give me just a minute," he said as he pulled off his jacket. He told her the story of how they came across the champagne, and as the shirt came off next she saw how they were tied on with condoms.

"I can't believe you bloody yanks," she said with her arms crossed, shaking her head. She watched as Bob stripped off the wet pants and started to untie the last two bottles.

He glanced up and caught her looking and smiled. "Did you miss me, love?" he asked.

She turned red and turned away and said, "Hurry up you cheeky bastard, we don't have all day, unless you want to marry me with no pants on. That would make a lovely picture, now wouldn't it?"

"I couldn't get any film, you know," he said. "I couldn't find any anywhere."

"It's strictly rationed here," she replied, glancing back at his progress. "There is just none to be had. I guess we will just have to remember it."

"I'll never forget, Mick. You can count on that," he said as he packed the bottles in his bag and then pulled his jacket back on. "I'm ready, what are you waiting for?"

Bob looked great in his pressed, dress uniform when they got to the church, but Lillian was still in her ragged uniform. The obviously excited Vicar's wife popped out and immediately grabbed Lillian by the arm and led her away.

Once they were in a small ante room to the side of the church, Mrs. Peerless said, "Pull off that dingy uniform, my dear. We can't have you marrying in that, now can we?"

Lillian pulled off her hat and her coat as the Vicar's wife held up a white wedding dress, full of frills and lace. Lillian's moment of excitement faded quickly when she saw how big it was. Apparently Mrs. Peerless was as big when she married as she was now, and she was big.

"Now don't you fret, my dear. A few pins and a few tucks here and there and you will be the most beautiful bride, trust me."

In the next few minutes Mrs. Peerless had performed what could only be described as a miracle, at least it was to Lillian. She pulled all the slack out of the dress and bunched it up in the back, then after a few adjustments, Lillian was a beautiful bride in a beautiful dress.

Lillian just stared in the mirror and then back at the Vicar's wife and said, "I cannot thank you enough for helping me. It's lovely."

"It brought us good luck, child. Now just remember to face forward for your wedding picture."

"I'm afraid we have no film, Mrs. Peerless. There is none to be had, but this will be in my memory forever."

Mrs. Peerless gave her a little smile and said, "Don't worry, my dear, I'm sure it will all work out. Come now, we have a wedding to attend."

Lillian was intercepted as she exited the room by Becky and Emily. "Where did you get that?" asked Becky as Emily stood with her mouth agape.

"Long story, just don't get behind me or you might start laughing in the middle of my wedding. Oh my goodness! What did you do?"

"We got these for you, from the field across the road. They are only daisies, but we made the most out of them, don't you think?"

"They are so beautiful," Lillian said, and a tear of joy started to form as she took the huge bouquet in her arms. "Just lovely."

Sarah suddenly appeared and was speechless for a moment when she saw the transformed Lillian. She quickly shook it off and said, "Don't go getting all sentimental now, love. Your yank is already in there standing at the altar."

The girls walked Lillian down the aisle and then fanned out left and right as Lillian moved in next to Bob. The Vicar was already there with a big smile on his chubby face. Lillian was so nervous she could hardly breathe.

Bob had to blink a few times to convince himself it was her, she was so transformed from just twenty minutes ago. He smiled and gave her a little nudge and motioned for her to look down.

When she glanced down at her feet she saw about two dozen petals from the flowers, and more falling, because she was trembling so bad it was shaking them off. She looked back up at him and started to giggle, and so did he. She wasn't nervous anymore, she was ready.

The Vicar's wife had been playing a wonderful rendition of "Here Comes the Bride" on the church organ.

When the music stopped, the Vicar stood in front of the couple, and just before he said the first words of the ceremony, a crack of light came through the big church doors as they opened and closed behind them.

A figure slipped in, and took a seat in the back row. It was a soldier, an airman actually. A Canadian airman.

Chapter Twenty-Four

I must be crazy. I can't believe this is happening.

"I do," she heard. It sounded like he was shouting down a well at her because panic was drowning out all other sounds but the pounding of her heart.

Bob was looking at her with a soft smile, and so was the Vicar with his chubby red cheeks and a big yellow-toothed smile. She could smell the remnants of his last cigar wafting off of him.

"Well, Miss Bradley?" he asked, as Bob grinned broadly at her plight.

"Yes, I'm sorry. Pardon?" she asked.

"Do you take this man to be your lawfully wedded husband?" he asked her, apparently for the second time.

She blinked her eyes and looked at the Vicar, then over at Sarah who looked like she was about to cry, and then back to the grinning American soldier, took a deep breath and said, "Yes, yes I do."

With a sigh of relief the Vicar proclaimed, "I now pronounce you man and wife. You may kiss the bride."

Bob put his arms around her, almost crushing the big bouquet now between them, and he felt the big hump on her dress where it was all bunched up and pinned.

"The dress belongs to Mrs. Peerless," she whispered. "She insisted I get rid of that uniform."

"Thank God," Bob whispered back. "I thought you were pregnant."

She elbowed him and said, "I need to get this thing off."

"Now we're talking," Bob grinned.

"You two come with me now, we are not done yet," Mrs. Peerless said as she grabbed Lillian's arm and pulled her toward the front of the church.

Sarah was standing there grinning alongside her Airman, flanked by Becky and Emily.

As they got close, the big church doors swung open and the blinding light of the warm summer day burst in. Standing outside the door was a reporter and a photographer, smiling at the surprised couple.

The reporter was from the Bournemouth Echo. He addressed the couple with a huge smile and said, "Congratulations to you, the first Peacetime wedding in Bournemouth. Mrs. Peerless was kind enough to tip us off."

Bournemouth was a wedding town. People came from all over England to the romantic seaside village to marry and honeymoon, which is why the town is chocked full of churches and hotels. This was a big deal.

"May we take your photograph, for the newspaper?" he asked. The Vicar and Mrs. Peerless stood together with big smiles, and she slipped her hand in his while he smiled at her and gave it a little squeeze.

Sarah didn't even wait for them to answer before she arranged them in the doorway of the church until they struck a pose she approved of, like the director of a movie. She always was a take charge kind of girl.

"Looks like we will have that wedding picture after all," Lillian said smiling up at him, and he winked.

The reporter came over and asked the startled couple some questions about how they met and what led up to this wedding for his story, and then said, "The Echo would like to give you two a little wedding present. Consider this a gift from all of Bournemouth."

Behind him was a limo with a driver standing beside it, decorated with flowers and ribbons and even little flags. "He will take you to the train station, and here are two round trip tickets to London. Here in Bournemouth, we believe in happy ever after."

Lillian had to swipe at a tear trying to escape her eye, while the Vicar's wife was crying as though it were a funeral, not a wedding. "That's the most beautiful thing I have ever seen," she said, as she gave Lillian a big bear hug.

The smiling reporter told Bob that the limo would wait for them, to take their time, and with one last handshake and smile, he and the photographer left.

The newlyweds went back into the church, Lillian following the Vicar's wife to change out of the dress, and Bob with the Vicar to take care of the business of marriage.

Bob wanted to pay him, but his cash reserves were so low that he hoped he could barter instead.

"Would you consider taking this in trade, Father?" Bob asked as he pulled a bottle out of his bag.

"Oh my," he said, as he took it in his hands and looked it up and down. "My, my. I would indeed. Yes, indeed." His spectacles were perched on the end of his nose as he read the French writing on the bottle, translating it in his head. "Oh my."

"Well then, it's a deal," Bob said, as he stood up and put his hand out.

"Not just yet, not just yet," the Vicar said, never looking up from the rare bottle. "The Mrs. would not approve, not for a moment. There is only one thing to do."

"What's that?" Bob asked, fearing his plan was about to fall through.

"Well," said the Vicar as he looked up at Bob and smiled. "We will just have to drink it now."

"Well, ain't this turning out to be the perfect wedding?" Bob smiled broadly and sat back down. "I'm with you, Father."

Bob twisted the cork out slowly while the Vicar pulled some glasses out of a cabinet. "To the happy couple," he said with a clink and a gulp. He wasted no time pouring himself a second one, and halfway through it, Lillian poked her head in the office.

"My wife?" the wide-eyed Vicar asked as he craned his neck to see around Lillian.

"Outside," Lillian answered, looking at Bob suspiciously, who could only shrug his shoulders.

"A toast then!" he proclaimed, and set another glass in front of Lillian.

"Just a sip," she reluctantly agreed. "A small sip."

He splashed a tiny gulp into her glass, once again filled his own, and the three held up their glasses and clinked to long life and happiness. Then Vicar Peerless poured the rest of the bottle into his glass and gulped it down, drinking at least three quarters of the bottle in under five minutes.

"The registry!" he proclaimed. "You must sign the registry. This happy day will be recorded forever in our humble little church," he slurred.

The couple went back outside to see the girls and the Canadian standing there with the decorated Limo behind them. The Vicar's wife seemed to be looking around for her husband.

"One more thing," declared Sarah proudly while Emily and Becky flanked her with big grins. "We all pitched in our coupons for these, love. You can't walk around London like that. There'll be enough bloody soldiers there as it is."

As Lillian opened the little box and peered into it, she saw two pretty little sundresses, one bright yellow, and one white with a flower print on it. The tears she had managed to hold back all day started running down her face and dripping off her chin as she hugged her friends.

The limo driver opened the door and stood there with an inviting smile, ready to whisk the happy couple away to their dream honeymoon when Bob chuckled and elbowed her gently, nodding for her to look down the road past the limo.

Mrs. Peerless had gone back into the church to look for her husband, but there he was making his escape on a bicycle, wobbling down the road and drifting side to side, somehow managing to keep it tires down and seat up.

"See what you did?" Lillian said, shaking her head. "You're nothing but trouble, Yank."

"Yeah, but you love me anyway," he laughed, as he took her hand and led her to the limo. "Now let's go have some fun."

Once they got to the train station, Bob tipped the driver with a pack of gum, leaving Mickey shaking her head. "I can't believe you," she said.

Bob kept trying to kiss her even though there were people all around them. She would giggle and push him away, and he would make an exaggerated pucker and say, "Kiss me, kiss me."

"Stop, you silly bugger," she said. "People are watching."

Two elderly British men were standing nearby watching the show and frowning. "Only three things wrong with those bloody Americans," one said.

"Only three?" the other replied.

"Overfed, oversexed, and over here."

The couple slid into their seats and Mickey, frowning, nodded up at the window and said, "Close that bloody thing, will you, love?"

Without taking his eyes off her, and smiling that silly grin, he reached up and closed the window. He didn't care why.

"I can't believe you tipped that driver a pack of gum," she said, shaking her head.

"Well, I wasn't going to give him a bottle of Champagne!"

"Maybe you are worried that's the only thing in your pants that will impress me," she teased, as the train lurched forward.

"Well, we'll just have to see about that, now won't we?" he replied. "Besides, they were Herby's pants."

Having no idea what they would do when they got there, or where they would stay with their meager few dollars and two bottles of Champagne, they rumbled on towards London, kissing and giggling without a care in the world.

A bus took them to downtown London, and the place was full of soldiers and revelers. The celebrations were still going on in full force, so the only problem they were now faced with was finding a place to stay, as the whole city seemed to be packed.

"C'mon my love, I have an idea," he said, and took her by the hand through the crowded streets, asking directions a few times along the way.

They found themselves standing in front of the American Servicemen's Club, and Bob told her, "They won't let you in here, my darling. I'll go see what they say. You wait right here, I'll be back in a minute."

She wasn't standing there more than two minutes when a woman in spiked heels swinging her purse said, "Move along, love. This is my spot."

Mickey was caught off guard and just stood there blinking at the hooker. "On with you now," the woman urged again.

She backed into the shuffling crowd feeling that crushing feeling again, smelling cigars and beer and an assortment of unpleasant odors. Beginning to panic and feeling a bit claustrophobic, she looked around for a place to escape when Bob suddenly stepped in front of her, grabbing her arm and rescuing her out of the sea of people.

"Tell me you found something," she said. "My feet are killing me."

"Sorry Mick, no luck. Don't worry, we'll find something."

"I'm almost ready to go back to the train station. At least we have a bloody place to stay in Bournemouth."

He smiled at her, and she gave a small grin back. Then he started to laugh, and she couldn't help but laugh along with him.

"Worst damn honeymoon ever," he laughed.

"Worst," she agreed, and they leaned against a wall, just feet away from the passing throngs, and kissed and giggled.

"Well, we survived Hitler," he said. "This should be a piece of cake."

"What about the Red Cross," she asked. "Can't they help?"

"I asked the guy in the club and he said they were overwhelmed over there, too. Probably not worth going all the way over there."

"So what now?" she asked.

Bob shrugged and said, "Train station, I guess. I hear Bournemouth is a nice place for a honeymoon."

Lillian laughed. "Half the people here probably wish they were there."

"C'mon Mickey, my darling," he said, as he pulled her to her feet. "Let's try to find a cheap cab."

Because gas rationing was still in effect, cabs were allowed to be shared, which was just fine with the newlyweds. When they got to the corner taxi stand, there were people lined up ahead of them, talking amongst themselves about which way they were going and who might share a cab with whom.

"Where are you two lovebirds going?" The heavy cockney accent almost yelled in Mickey's ear, making her flinch and look up.

"Sorry if I made you jump, love," the woman laughed. "Where are you going?"

Bob and Mickey looked up and down the unlikely couple standing next to them. The man was a Canadian soldier, a private. He was an average looking guy in an average looking uniform in a sea of young soldiers, so it was not like he stood out.

She, however, was quite the sight. She wore a gaudy purple hat on her blonde head, with a white feather on it, and a purple feather boa wrapped around her neck.

She wore a light purple dress with dark accents, a plunging neckline, and a slit up the side. Her breasts were bulging out as though trying to escape, and her garter belt and lined silk stockings were visible when she moved. While perched on a pair of spiked heel shoes, she topped it off with an assortment of bracelets, pins and pearls so she jingled when she moved.

Mickey and Bob, speechless, stood there looking at the couple, well, looking at her actually. Mickey looked back to see Bob looking at the tall blonde with a little too much interest, and she gave him a scowl, making Bob grin and shrug his shoulders.

"So where are you going, love?" the woman asked again. "Bill here says you can share our cab if you like."

"Well," Mickey managed to stammer out. "Back to Bournemouth, I suppose. Back to the train station."

"You don't look very happy about that, love. I've heard it's a lovely place by the sea. Maybe Bill and I will go there sometime, isn't that right Bill?"

Bill stood there stone-faced, never responding or even blinking his eyes.

Mickey told her the whole story, of the wedding and the trip to London, and about how they couldn't find a place to stay so it seemed returning to Bournemouth was their only choice.

The hip swinging woman in the purple feather boa then showed her soft side as she fought back tears welling up in her eyes. "What a lovely story, just lovely. Isn't that a lovely story, Bill?"

Bill never changed his expression and never said a word.

"My name is Amy," she said, and put her arm around Mickey's shoulder. "And that one there is Bill."

"My name is Lillian," said Mickey. "And this is my husband, Bob."

Amy turned and looked at Bill and then back at Mickey and said, "Bill says you should stay with us, at least for tonight."

Bob and Mickey looked at each other and both thought the same thing, that Bill never said a word, not even a nod or a wink.

"Are you sure it's alright?" asked Mickey. "It would really mean so much to us. We really didn't want to spend our first night as man and wife sitting on a train all night."

"Bill insists," she said, again with no reaction from Bill. "It's only about ten minutes away, in the taxi with you."

Soon they were standing in front of a beautiful, and very expensive apartment building near downtown London. "Bill says we have to be very quiet going upstairs, alright, love? Don't want to wake the bloody neighbors, now do we?"

They crept up one flight, and then another, and the four of them stood silently in front of a door made of English oak. Bill reached down and pulled a key out from under the mat as Amy smiled at the nervous couple behind her. The lock turned with a clunk and the door to the dark but sweet smelling apartment opened long enough for the four of them to slip in.

Bill made a right turn and disappeared, while Amy grabbed Mickey's elbow and led her to the left with Bob close behind, glancing over his shoulder and wondering where Bill went. They walked through an immaculate living room full of lovely antiques and artwork, and down a short hallway to a small bedroom facing the street with its own bathroom off to the side.

This room was also furnished with lovely antiques, such as the Queen Anne bed, the paintings that covered the walls, the Persian rugs and velvet curtains. It was a room that could rival even the nicest hotels.

"You lovebirds have a good night," said Amy with a wink as she stood in the door about to pull it closed. "I plan to, love."

"Wait," said Bob, and he grabbed his bag and pulled out one of the bottles. "May I offer up one of these? It's pretty good."

Amy took the bottle and with a smile said, "I'm sure Bill will like it, thank you. Now you two get on with your bloody honeymoon."

With some tears and hugs, Amy pulled the door closed behind her and Mickey turned to see her husband standing there, the first time they were alone together as man and wife. They nervously darted their eyes around the room and then at each other.

"Do you think it's alright to stay here?" Lillian asked.

"Well, Bill doesn't seem too worried, does he?"

Mickey laughed. "How could you tell if he was?"

Bob looked at some of the pictures lined up on the nightstand and mantle. Some were family photos, some were wedding pictures, and most prominent was a picture of a British officer in full regalia.

"I wonder who that peacock is," Bob chuckled.

"Well, we could ask Bill," she said, and they both laughed.

"Not much of a talker, is he?"

"I think she talked enough for the both of them," Mickey said. "But she is sweet. I like her."

"Me, too," said Bob, pulling the last bottle out of his bag and starting to work on the cork. "She's a gas."

Using two water glasses he picked up off the dresser, he handed her one and lifted the other and said, "To us, my darling, my Mickey."

"To us, my love, my Yank," she replied.

They both set their half full glasses down on the nightstand, and sitting on the bed, they started to kiss. From the next room they heard the pop of a Champagne bottle, and Amy's loud cackle of a laugh, and they giggled at the thought of the odd couple having fun.

Bob grabbed her and they fell back on the feather pillows, kissing as he pulled her close. He reached over her to the antique lamp on the nightstand, and pulling down on the string, turned off the only light in the room.

A few hours later, Bob was blinking himself awake and trying to figure out where he was when he realized she was no longer next to him. He pulled himself up on his elbows and smiled when he saw the light coming from under the bathroom door.

Climbing out of bed, he grabbed the half bottle of flat Champagne and stood naked in front of the big picture window. Even though there was a blanket of fog outside, he could still see the outline of Big Ben jutting above the buildings in the foreground.

The few streetlights that were lit shined a spooky halo through the haze, casting no shadow. The moon was a mere glow above the overcast sky. An occasional crack in the fast moving clouds gave him a glimpse of it and some of the black sky around it.

He stared up at the sky and thought about nothing in particular. The last few days had been a whirlwind and it was just soaking in as he gazed at a star twinkling in the space between the clouds.

He smiled and tilted the bottle up towards it. "I finally got laid, movie star — are you proud of me?"

It was the only star in the sky and it seemed to wink at him. "So long, my friend, so long until we meet again." He took a swig just as the clouds moved back over the sky and the little star disappeared

Mickey came out of the bathroom and put her arms around his waist. "Do you know what day it is?" he asked her.

"What day is it, my husband?"

"Today is our one day anniversary, my wife."

They giggled and climbed back into bed.

A few hours later Bob felt Mickey shaking him out of his groggy sleep. "Did you hear that?" she asked.

He perked up as another gentle tap-tap-tap came from the bedroom door. "Shit, it's still dark out," he moaned.

Mickey, wrapped in a blanket, cracked open the door to see Amy there with a big smile, barely any clothes, and reeking of perfume. "Time to go, love," she said. "Be as quiet as a mouse when you leave, we will meet you at the little café around the corner in half a mo, alright?"

The newlyweds quickly dressed and crept down the squeaky stairs and out the front door, where Bob dropped his bag and grabbed her, spinning her around as they both laughed. "That was the craziest night ever," he said.

"I feel like a bad girl, but I don't know why," she giggled.

"Well then, kiss me you bad girl. Kiss me, kiss me and kiss me some more!"

"Ahem," they both heard and turned to see two London Bobbies standing there under the street light staring at them. They stood there holding their Billy clubs behind their backs and rocking on their heels.

"Shit," said Bob as he lowered her to her feet. "Did you bring the marriage license? You look like a sixteen-year old in that little dress."

"Maybe," she said with a grin.

"I don't think they like me," he said, and she started giggling. "C'mon, let's go."

He took her hand and walked towards the corner. He had to walk her right past them to get to the café, and both of them stared at Bob the entire way. Hand and hand they walked, rounding the corner, and a block later they walked into the café.

They were just sitting down when Bill and Amy strolled in, her feather bouncing along on its purple hat, with her loud cockney cackle that could be heard a mile away.

"Did you see those bloody Bobbies?" Amy laughed as she sat down with Bill in tow. "What they must have been thinking."

"I thought they were going to say something but they didn't," said Bob.

"Not a word, not a bloody word," she laughed. "You have to wonder what they were thinking seeing first you two creeping out of there before dawn, and us right behind you."

"I have to ask," said Bob. "How did you get such a nice apartment? I can't believe our luck considering our honeymoon almost turned into a big flop."

"Well, love," she said. "Bill said it was alright if I tell you."

Bob and Mickey gave each other a quick glance, each thinking that once again, Bill never said a word.

"You see, Bill here is having a bloody affair with a Colonel's wife, and that is their apartment, isn't that right Bill?" she asked, never looking at him, and he never blinked.

"His wife leaves the key for him so he can let himself in, nice and quiet. She went out of town to be with her husband for a few days, so Bill called his old friend Amy, and here we are!"

"That is the most amazing story I've ever heard," Bob said, and looked over at Bill. Bill made the smallest grin and there was a little twinkle in his eye before he went stone-faced again. "What a pair you got there, fella."

After breakfast and a few hugs and kisses, the two couples separated, Amy swishing and laughing past the two Bobbies who said nothing with her soldier who said even less, and they were gone.

They managed to secure a modest room with the help of the Red Cross for a couple nights, and made the most of seeing the sights of London. There was so much ruin from the bombing, yet it was still such an amazing city with amazing people. They had spent part of their honeymoon living like royalty, and part of it like paupers.

"Best damn honeymoon ever," Bob whispered to her on the train ride back.

"Best," she whispered back and fell asleep on his shoulder.

The plan was for him to stay the last night at her apartment in Bournemouth before catching a flight to Berlin. When they got there they found two packages on the doorstep. Bob carried the bags in and Mickey got the parcels and bought them inside.

The first one she opened as they sat on the bed together. It was a framed picture of their wedding, the picture they almost never had. Inside was a short note. "Congratulations and Good Luck! The Bournemouth Echo."

"This is wonderful," she said with a sniffle. "It's just wonderful."

Bob handed her the second package and she tore it open. "It's from Aunt Margaret," she said, and read the card out loud. "Congratulations my little one, I am so proud of you. Aunt Margaret."

In the box was a carefully packaged bottle of French Champagne. She looked up at him and they both started to laugh.

"I like this Aunt Margaret of yours," he said.

"This is just what we needed," she replied, shaking her head. "Something else for you to shove down your pants."

"You mean Herby's pants," he grinned. "I don't have enough room in my pants."

"Well, aren't you the funny yank. Does that explain why his pants are so much bigger than yours?"

"Now who's the funny one?" he asked, grinning.

A thunderstorm rolled in that night. As the rain beat against the roof, the flashes of lightning illuminated the streets outside and the house rumbled with every distant boom, but the newlyweds never heard a thing.

"Mickey, my darling," he said the next morning, standing in her doorway with his bag in one hand and hat in the other. "I'll come get you as soon as I can. With the war over now, it shouldn't be long."

"I had such a lovely time, my husband, I want you to stay. I'm not ready to say goodbye yet."

"I want to stay, too, doll, but I can't. I would if I could. Besides it's not goodbye, it's only so long."

"So long until we meet again," she smiled. "I remember. Now you'd better hurry along or you'll be late."

Bob gave her a kiss, and then another, and then put on his hat and was gone. She sat on the bed and looked at the wedding picture and smiled. *The only reason I am this sad is because he makes me so happy.*

She touched his face on the picture and set it on the nightstand, then unpacked and lay down to take a nap after the long week.

Was that a knock? She tried to shake her groggy head awake.

Tap-tap-tap she heard again, this time swinging her legs out of bed and peeking out the gap she had pulled in the curtain. "Well, that was quick," she said aloud.

He was standing there grinning when she opened the door, with hat in hand. "I missed my flight," he said and shrugged his shoulders.

338

"I told you to hurry, you silly, bloody yank. Now you are sure to be in trouble," she said, shaking her head.

"Mind if I stay the night with you?" he asked sheepishly.

"You think you are the only American that has asked me that question?"

"Probably not," he grinned. "But I'm the most handsome."

"Maybe so, but not the best singer."

"You got me there."

"Well, inside with you then," she said, swinging the door open. "I'll have to put you up for another night, I suppose."

The next morning he left earlier to be sure to catch the one flight a day that would take him to Berlin. She worried about him getting in trouble but he assured her he could handle anything they doled out. *What was one day late when the war is over?*

A few hours after landing he was able to make it out to the sports complex, and what he saw, or rather didn't see, unnerved him. The guns were gone, and so were the trucks. The battalion had moved out, and he had no idea where.

He walked hurriedly around the crowded complex and saw many soldiers occupying the area, but none from the 386th. He went in and out of buildings asking about his missing battalion, but nobody knew, and nobody seemed to care.

"Pulled out yesterday afternoon," the guy with the clipboard said. Bob stopped him and figured him to be a clerk or aide of some kind. "There might be some officers left. They'd be in that building over there."

Shit. Bob looked in the direction the guy was pointing, and after mumbling a thank you he started walking that way. The battalion headquarters sign he had made was hanging over the doorway, so with a gulp and a prayer, he rapped on the door.

"Come in" said the unmistakable drawl of his commanding officer, Colonel Robert Gibbs. Bob pushed the door open to find the Colonel standing in front of a mirror shaving, his back to him.

Bob snapped to attention and saluted and said, "Private Anstey reporting, sir."

"You are late, Private."

"Yes sir, I am late, sir," he said deciding to just admit it without making excuses.

"Did you get married, Private?"

"Yes sir, I did, sir."

"Did it go well?" asked the Colonel as he rinsed off his razor and reached for a towel.

"Yes sir, it did, sir. Best honeymoon ever, sir," Bob said trying to hide his grin.

"So then it was worth getting in trouble for, eh, Private?"

"Yes sir, I suppose it was, sir."

The Colonel turned to face him and started pulling on his shirt. "At ease, soldier," he said, and Bob relaxed a little bit. The Colonel said nothing for the next few minutes, and as he tied his tie he never took his eyes off Bob.

"Well, Private, today is your lucky day," Colonel Gibbs finally said. "I need someone to take my jeep down to meet the battalion. I am flying to London this afternoon. They are about twenty miles from here, and will be shipping out the day after tomorrow."

"Yes, sir," Bob said, not believing his good luck. "May I ask where, sir?"

The Colonel was pulling on his coat when he looked back up at Bob and said, "Home, Private, we are going home. In a week we will be back on the Queen Mary."

"Yes, sir. Home, sir," Bob said, amazed that this day had finally come.

"Here, Private," the Colonel said, and tossed the keys to Bob. "Dismissed."

"Thank you, sir," Bob said with a salute. "Thank you for everything, sir."

Bob was halfway out the door when the Colonel said, "Private, one more thing."

"Yes, sir?"

"There is another soldier that ran off and got married and he is late getting back as well. Wait around a few more hours to see if he shows up, and then the both of you get down there and join the rest of the battalion."

"Yes sir, I will, sir."

Bob went out and sat in the jeep, deciding to bang out a quick letter to his mom to let her know he would be home soon when a truck pulled up. A duffel bag was pitched out the back and a soldier jumped out.

"Herby!" Bob said, blinking his eyes in disbelief. "What the hell did you do?"

"Well," Herb said. "Remember that brunette that I would flirt with back at Sainte Mère Église?"

"Don't tell me," Bob said smiling.

"Well, she is now Mrs. Herbert Weinstein."

"When did you decide to do this?" asked Bob, now laughing.

"Been thinking about it for a long time," said Herb. "After you left I still had four more bottles of champagne, so I figured what the hell, might as well take a shot at it."

Bob laughed again, "Does she love you?"

"I think so, but you know I don't speak French."

"So you finally got laid, eh, Herb?"

"Finally got laid, Bob. Finally got laid."

Herby threw his bag up into the jeep next to Bob's and climbed in next to him. Still laughing, Bob pushed the shifter into gear and they headed off to join the battalion.

Chapter Twenty-Five

The Queen Mary made yet another safe crossing carrying over sixteen thousand soldiers home, including the 386th. Bob and Herb stood at the railing looking out over the endless ocean.

"Hell of a ride, eh, Bob?"

"Hell of a ride, Herb."

"Would you do it again if you could?"

"Not for a million bucks, Herb, but I'm glad I did it the first time for free. I don't know about you, but I'm tired of being a soldier."

"Me, too," said Herb. "I'm ready for baseball, apple pie, and my little French wife to move to the Bronx."

"God help her," Bob smiled.

"You, me and John need to catch a ballgame together sometime," said Herb. "We need to stay in touch."

The 386th was officially disbanded, and the three friends found themselves stationed at Fort Dix. On December 7, 1945, four years to the day the Japanese bombed Pearl Harbor, Bob was honorably discharged from the army and went back to Brooklyn.

In England, the 60,000 girls who married Americans were stonewalled with red tape, and the couple watched as their hope of spending Christmas together faded away. Then, just before Christmas, the United States Congress passed the "War Brides Act."

This eased immigration laws for the brides and expedited processing and transport for them and their children, paid for by the United States Army. It was a mission they took seriously, and the families of the veterans were considered the families of us all.

Lillian sat with Aunt Margaret at an open air café drinking tea and watching as the seabirds made their inland loop before once again circling the beach. The now lively town was full of bustle and noises as rebuilding went on and people shuffled by.

"It seems the older boys have stayed close to your mother," Margaret said softly. "She has a strong influence on them. You should stay away from her."

Lillian hung her head for a moment and looked up asking, "And my sisters? Anything of my sisters?"

"I'm sorry, my child. It seems they are lost to history."

"Will you keep looking, Aunt Margaret?"

"Go to your new life, Lillian. Your future is with your husband. There is nothing for you here."

"Will you keep looking?"

"Of course, my dear," Margaret smiled. "Mrs. Sharpe has never stopped looking, and probably never shall."

Lillian sat there silently for a few moments, blinking her eyes and trying to absorb what Margaret just said. Clearly, Margaret had just let something slip.

"Mrs. Sharpe?" she asked loudly. "The same Mrs. Sharpe that ripped me away from my sister? The Mrs. Sharpe that lied to me and abandoned me at that awful place for all those years, that Mrs. Sharpe?"

"Lillian, you don't understand."

"What don't I understand?" Lillian said, and banged her hand on the table.

"You don't know the whole story, Lillian."

"Tell me the story then, Margaret. I have a right to know, don't you think?"

"Her job was to place unwanted and orphaned children," Margaret started speaking softly while shaking her head. "But there were fewer and fewer places, and there seemed to be so many children. So many cold and hungry children with no place to go. She came to me out of desperation because she knew your mother was trying to sell you to the work houses."

"And you found a place for me at Saint John's?"

"They would only take you, I'm afraid, your sister was too young. As a matter of fact, you were the youngest girl to ever be accepted by the nuns there. We had hopes that your sister could join you in a year, but then she disappeared."

"But she lied to me, Aunt Margaret," Lillian said with tears of sorrow and of anger welling up in her eyes. "She lied to me and left me there all alone. I hate her."

Margaret looked down and then back up and said, "Please don't hate her, my child. It was the hardest thing she ever did. She never stopped caring about you and she never stopped looking for Molly, and for Alice, and even for Mary."

"She ruined my life, Margaret. I have no family because of her."

"She was trying to save you."

"Did she tell you I was sick? Is that why you came to the convent?"

"That is why, Lillian. You asked me to help find your sisters, but what you didn't know was that we had already been searching, and we have never stopped. I fear that with the passage of time and the destruction from the war, we may never find them."

Lillian went over the facts in her mind. Perhaps Mrs. Sharpe had made some effort to help her, but what she did was unforgivable. Lillian needed someone to blame, and that someone would always be Mrs. Sharpe.

"Did you help me because you felt guilty, Margaret? Another favor for Mrs. Sharpe?"

"She asked me to check on you," Margaret said, looking Lillian in the eyes. "But once I met you, I fell in love with this amazing little girl. A little girl a lot like me. I have no family my dear. You are the closest thing to family I have ever had, and I don't regret for a minute helping you. I will always love you."

"I love you, too, Aunt Margaret, but I never want to talk about her again," she said. "Never."

"I understand, my dear," said Margaret. "Your life is ahead of you now, go live it and don't look back."

Back in the states, Bob was competing with the millions of other returning soldiers struggling to find work. He was drawing a $30.00 per month benefit check from the army, but that would run out soon. He took classes in welding, TV repair, and refrigeration, some of the up and coming industries, but still had no luck.

He worked a few odd jobs, always temporary, and was always met with a scowl from his father when he got home. "Still useless," Archie would say aloud, shaking his head.

Bob started refrigeration repair school on April 1, 1946, the same day that Mickey got the letter. The day had finally arrived — the United States Army wanted to take her to her new home, and take her in style. These were her travel papers.

She was to leave Bournemouth on April 10th, and a first class train ticket to Camp Tidworth was enclosed. Tidworth was a base near Southampton that the Americans had taken over and were now using for "Operation War Brides."

She was instructed to travel light, as she would only be allowed one suitcase. She packed her most precious belongings, and left behind the rest of her things with her friends.

The first class ticket did not end with the train ride. The camp was set up with every comfort the girls could imagine, and the royal treatment was nonstop. There were even German POW's working as waiters and cooks, and Mickey was surprised to see how much fun they were and how much the girls enjoyed their antics and flirting.

Over the next few days, the war brides would take some classes about America, and have all their passports and documents processed. The final plan of the War Brides Act would be to deliver the girls to the U.S. mainland, with but a stamp of the passport. Red tape had been cut away.

On April 19, 1946, the USS John Ericsson, a luxury liner that was commandeered by the United States during the war, pulled away from the piers at Southampton with over eight hundred brides, and scores of their children.

Mickey watched her first sunset at sea on the first night of the voyage, and was fascinated at the glistening light cast on the water from the sinking sun that seemed to draw a golden line right to her.

Follow me west. That is my yellow brick road.

She met many other girls like her but yet so different among the ship of nervous girls. A ship of girls taking a giant leap of faith that the man they fell in love with would be there, and everything they dreamed of was true.

The crew pampered the ladies, and great buffets of fresh fruits and meats and everything else was laid out before them every day, no more rationing for them. The crew was under captain's orders to make the ladies feel special, and they did a great job.

On April 29th the USS John Ericsson steamed into New York Harbor and a flotilla of ships and boats came alongside, including a U.S. Navy Cruiser with all hands in white dress at the rail in salute.

"Now don't all you ladies rush over to that side at once or you will tip my ship," the captain chided them over the loudspeaker. A New York City fireboat also pulled alongside the ship of brides, and shot streams of red, white and blue water into the air.

The flotilla escorted them past the statue of Liberty, and in sight of the New York skyline, with the Empire State building in the distance reaching towards the heavens. Then the engines powered back on the Ericsson as the tugs came alongside to take her in.

The great pier that jutted out into the blue green white-capped water of the harbor seemed strangely deserted. It was the longest pier she had ever seen. *But where are the husbands?*

As the ship was being maneuvered into place, she heard the loudspeaker blare out her name. "Mrs. Lillian Rose Anstey, please come to the bursar's office and see Mr. Bradley. Mrs. Anstey, please see Mr. Bradley at the bursar's office."

Mickey heard the announcement, and then heard it again as her blood started to boil. She picked up her suitcase and marched that way. *See Mr. Bradley, eh? It must be one of my brothers. If he thinks he can keep me from my husband, then he will be surprised when I punch him square in the nose.*

Furious, she stormed into the office to find two crewmembers and a young man in a nice suit with a big smile. "Mrs. Anstey?" he asked.

"What do you want?" she barked at him.

"My name is Harry Bradley," he said, still smiling. "I'm a friend of Bob's. As a matter of fact, we grew up together. I'm here as a favor to him. You see, I work for the Immigration Department and you are going to be the first bride off this ship."

She stared at him in disbelief, and when he stamped her passport and visa and handed it to her with a smile, he said, "Welcome to America, Mrs. Anstey. These gentlemen will escort you down. Say hello to Bob for me."

Mere moments later she was deposited on the top of the gangway where another crewmember was waving at her from the bottom to come down. Glancing over her shoulder, she could see the hundreds of other brides lined up along the rail looking down at her.

I feel like the bloody queen. She giggled to herself.

Barricades and police officers were holding back the crowd, mostly men, at the shore end of the pier. They were all straining to see the great ship of white and the precious cargo it carried.

Mickey started walking toward the crowd, but glancing back she realized she was still alone. None of the other ladies were disembarking yet. She was all by herself on that huge dock. She thought about turning and running back to the ship.

"Who is that? Where are all the girls?" the impatient crowd started to murmur, as they became increasingly restless. Bob tried to see what they were talking about, but from three rows back trying to look over hats and under umbrellas, it took a few minutes before he realized.

"Mickey!" he shouted, and plowed into the crowd in front of him before bursting out but still behind the barricade. "Mickey!" he shouted again.

Bob ducked under the barricade and started running towards her. "Hey," a young police officer shouted.

"Let him go, Mike, it's ok," his sergeant said, putting his hand on the younger man's shoulder. "Hell, let all of them go."

Mickey almost had a heart attack when she saw this strange man in a suit running towards her, with hundreds more right behind. More girls were now starting to trickle down the gangplank and on to the pier.

Running as fast as he could, Bob's hat flew off, and for the first time she realized it was him. She dropped her bag and started running to him until they met and he spun her in the air, kissing her and spinning her again.

The crowd cheered when the two came together, and moments later a sea of American men flooded the newly arrived brides, looking for the loves of their lives. Men were charging up the pier, and women were running from the ship, and in the middle of it all, stood Bob and Mickey, kissing.

Somewhere a signal was given and the U.S. Army Band started to play the Star Spangled Banner, though few noticed as they found their loved ones and, like Bob and Mickey, were oblivious to the world.

Hats and bags and even some shoes were scattered all over the pier, abandoned temporarily in the thrill of the moment, the moment that took so long to get here. Babies cried as strangers now held them, strangers named Daddy. The USS John Ericsson would leave for England the next day, and bring back more American brides.

Bob finally lowered her to the ground, looked into her blue eyes and said, "Welcome to New York."

She smiled back and said, "Harry says hello."

Bob chuckled. "Let's go home. You have to meet all the people I've been bragging to about you."

349

He took her by the hand and, picking up her bag and his now crumpled hat, they made their way through the crowd and off the pier. As they walked to the train station Mickey asked, "Where did you get that tie?"

"Do you like it?"

"It's quite possibly the ugliest tie I've ever seen," she said, shaking her head.

"Hmmm," he said looking down at it. "Maybe that's why I can't get a job."

They laughed and walked a few more steps hand in hand when she stopped dead in her tracks and said, "Wait, what?"

"Don't worry, Mickey, my love," he said, as they rocked along on the subway ride to Brooklyn. "Something will come along soon, I'm sure of it."

They moved in with Bob's parents for a while, who predictably, didn't like her. "Take me back to the boat," she said, more than once. "I'd rather live with the Mother Superior again than spend another night under that old goat's roof."

He worked odd jobs here and there and they soon moved into a boarding house as managers for free rent, and Mickey made a few extra dollars a week cooking for the men who lived there.

Over the next few years, Bob landed a good job at NBC studios in the air conditioning department. They were able to scrimp and save and buy their first house. It was modest, but it was a place of their own.

In a four foot by four foot opening in the concrete at the sidewalk, a tree grew tall and proud. Though it was the target of every male dog in the neighborhood, and every kid and cat on the block had been stuck in it at one time or another, it was their tree. The tree in Brooklyn.

It wasn't long before Mickey became pregnant, and their first child was born in 1947 — a girl. Two years later, along came a son.

On July 4, 1950, Mickey stood nervously in front of the judge who would either grant her citizenship or not. She studied for months so she could answer any question he might throw at her. She looked over her shoulder to see Bob smiling and a few of her friends there for support. Margaret was there, as well.

She stood there as the judge went through her file and then slipped off his glasses and looked down at her and asked, "Mrs. Anstey, do you know what today is?"

"Yes, your honor," she said proudly. "Today is Independence Day."

"Independence from whom?" he asked.

Mickey's smile dropped from her face and her mouth went dry. All her girlfriends sitting behind her were British born, and they all sat forward in their seats. Margaret sat back and crossed her arms.

"Well, Mrs. Anstey, independence from whom?"

Mickey blinked her eyes and glanced back at Bob, who was grinning and enjoying the show. *No help there, you cheeky bastard.*

"You are going to have to say it, Mrs. Anstey," the judge said, now leaning forward in his chair to hear the quiet admission she was sure to make soon, and he grinned. "Well, Mrs. Anstey?"

"England," she blared out. "Bloody England, are you bloody happy now?" She couldn't believe she talked to him like that.

"You tell that bloody wanker, Lilly," one of her girlfriends whispered from behind, earning a scowl from Margaret.

The clearly surprised judge leaned back in his chair, slipping his glasses back on as he looked back at her file. After what seemed like forever, he finally looked over the top of his glasses at her, as she braced herself for the next question.

"Happy Independence Day, Mrs. Anstey, and congratulations, you are now a citizen of the United States of America. Is there anything you would like to say before I dismiss you?"

Mickey looked around at Bob and her friends. Bob was shaking his head no while the girls all nodded yes with big smiles. Margaret was stone-faced.

"Yes, your honor, just one thing."

"Go ahead, Mrs. Anstey," said the judge.

"God save the King, your honor," she said smugly. Her girlfriends all laughed and even Margaret smiled and shook her head.

In 1957 a third child came along — another boy — the same year the Dodgers left Brooklyn. Bob never watched another game of baseball for the rest of his life. He would get taunting postcards from Yankee stadium, and though there was no return address, it didn't take a genius to figure out who was sending them.

In 1959 they welcomed another girl. They named her Margaret. The family often went on camping trips together, first in tents, then a VW bus, then after crashing it up it was back to tents. A few vacations later and the tents were traded in for a pop-up trailer, and then eventually, an actual camper.

John started a reunion group for the 386th and they had annual meetings in Fulton County, New York. During one of the early meetings, Colonel Gibbs was there and was pleased to see Bob and Mickey still together, as well as Herb and his wife.

The group always took time to remember comrades no longer there, and that list grew longer with every passing year.

Crisscrossing the country on summer adventures found them in the Ozark Mountains one year, and they discovered a remote piece of property for sale, six miles down a dirt road in the middle of nowhere, so they bought it.

"This is where we will retire someday, Mick," said Bob, as the two of them stood in the middle of their forty acres and decided where the house would go. And a few years later, that's right where it went.

Bob spent thirty years at NBC before retiring. He met many celebrities along the way, but the most memorable had to be J. Fred Muggs, or Mr. Muggs. Mr. Muggs was a chimp, the sidekick of Dave Garroway, the founding host of the Today Show.

One morning as Bob stood alone in an empty elevator waiting for the door to close, Mr. Muggs on roller skates came ripping around the corner followed close behind by four or five panic stricken handlers at full speed.

The monkey charged into the elevator through the closing doors and spun around so he was standing next to Bob. He looked up at Bob and Bob looked down at him and Mr. Muggs unceremoniously stuck out his tongue, so Bob stuck his out, too.

The door opened on another floor. Bob just stood there, and so did the monkey. Bob reached over and hit the button for the floor it all started on and returned the hairy skater to his much-relieved handlers. J. Fred Muggs liked to keep people on their toes.

Mickey went to work as an office manager for a doctor whom the family met when he did a house call for her while she was sick in bed with her third child. Dr. Carl became a family friend and inspiration. He had lost his entire family in the Holocaust because of his Jewish background, and survived by hiding in the woods for over two years.

Aunt Margaret visited the family whenever she was in New York, bringing gifts from faraway lands, and stories of her adventures. She died in 1985 as Dame Margaret Digby, Knighted with the "Order of the British Empire." She would be remembered as an advocate for Israel and a tireless worker in the fight against hunger.

"Let's retire, Bob," Mickey said, sitting next to him on the couch. "You heard the doctor."

"Just a few more years, Mick," he replied. "I'll get that pacemaker thing he wants to stick in me. That should give me a little boost."

He soon got his pacemaker. During the surgery he was put under a local anesthesia that numbed him from the neck down and a drape was set up under his chin so he couldn't see. At one point the phone rang in the operating room and he said, "If that's for me tell them I'm busy."

At Mickey's urging, because of his heart issues, they decided to go ahead and retire early and move to that home in the Ozarks they had built on their land. Sometimes dreams do come true.

A few years later, Bob went up to New York to visit friends and decided to wear his cowboy hat, boots, jeans and big belt buckle. As he stood on the corner of 47th street and Broadway, he looked down to see a little buzzed head kid looking up at him in awe.

"Hey mista, are you really a cowboy?" the kid asked.

Bob smiled and with his best Curly imitation he replied, "Soitenly."

Over the years came grandkids and great grandkids, turning that chance meeting in front of an English movie theatre into generations of new lives. New lives to keep the tradition of never saying goodbye alive.

They didn't say goodbye when their oldest son went to Vietnam, or when their oldest grandson went to Afghanistan, twice.

One afternoon Mickey answered the phone and a nice young lady with a British accent asked for Lillian Anstey, and if her maiden name was Bradley. Mickey almost dropped the phone and had to sit down before she fainted.

"Aunt Lillian, I found you!" the girl proclaimed. "My mother is your sister Alice."

Bob came in to find Mickey sitting in the chair with tears dripping off her chin. "You found Molly, too?" she said into the phone, astonished. "I'm going to get a ticket right away and let you know when I will be there, and thank you."

After almost sixty-five years, Lillian had finally found her sisters. Poor Mary would never be found, and her fate with the salesman would never be known.

"I'll hold down the fort, love," said Bob. "You get your butt over to England."

The three sisters and extended family members spent three weeks together and shared their life stories. There wasn't much contact with the older brothers because, well, some things never change.

Molly was sent to a work house and escaped at age nine, but was then sent to a notorious home for girls that ended up getting shut down by the government after the war for the horrid abuses they had inflicted, making even the convent seem good.

Alice was sent to a work farm after the younger girls were gone and was pretty much enslaved there. Both Alice and Molly married nice men after the war and, like Lillian, raised their children and lived good lives.

"Our mother managed to have fifteen children, eight of which lived," Alice said, as they sat around talking.

"Wait, eight?" Lillian asked, doing the math in her head.

Molly looked at Alice and then back at Lillian. "Of course, you didn't know?"

"Didn't know what?" asked Lillian.

"Henry," said Alice. "Henry was born after we were all gone. He's the youngest."

Lillian was shocked, and in a moment they all started laughing.

"Like a bloody rabbit, she was," Molly laughed.

"Milkman or mailman, I'd say," said Alice, and they all laughed again.

"How did you find me?" Lillian asked. "After all these years, how did you finally find me?"

"Well," said Alice, "after our mother died we were going through some of her old papers, and there were some letters a woman wrote to her, and she was looking for us. One of the letters mentioned that she wanted to place Molly in the same place you were sent."

"The Convent," said Molly. "The Convent of Saint John. We managed to track you down from there, although it wasn't easy. Thank God the RAF kept good records."

"Who wrote the letters?" Lillian asked, holding her breath.

"I don't know much about her," said Molly. "Only that the letter was signed, "Mrs. Sharpe.""

"Good Lord, then it was true," said Lillian, and she proceeded to tell them the rest of the story.

Bob met Mickey at the airport and he could see the peace in her eyes and the joy in her heart. All of her questions, all the mysteries of her life had been answered. She found them, and she would never lose them again.

The couple settled into a nice retirement, and became active in the community. Both Bob and Mickey did volunteer work for the local church, the hospital auxiliary, and the Special Olympics.

Mickey took up painting, and Bob started wood carving; after that all the Christmas presents were priceless homemade treasures.

They also loved going to the local fares and roadside arts and crafts stops that are so popular in the Ozarks. On one such shopping trip, Mickey bought a little homemade knick-knack that was less than ten bucks.

It was a plaque shaped like the front of a farmhouse and it had two doors on it. One door had a farmer in it, the other the farmer's wife. They were on a pivot so when one was out, the other went in. The idea was that when the farmer came out it would rain, and on sunny days, his wife would be there, with him inside.

Of course, it was just a silly decoration, and couldn't possibly work. Then one rainy morning as she sat in the kitchen sipping her tea, she looked up to see the farmer standing on his front porch.

That's funny. I thought she was out. Silly thing must have gotten bumped.

She would have never given it another thought until two days later when the sun was baking the front lawn, there she was, the farmer's wife. And for months, at every change in the weather, the little barometer was dead on in its predictions.

When she told Bob about it, he shrugged his shoulders and told her she was nuts, which earned him an elbow in the ribs, so she didn't tell him about it again, but she loved waking up in the morning to see what the farmer had to say.

As their 50th wedding anniversary drew near, they made plans to visit England, to visit the church in Bournemouth, and even make the trip to Normandy, but alas, Bob's health took a turn for the worse and they had to cancel.

As a gift to him, Mickey made a donation to the church's building fund, and had her sister go by and take a picture of their names, still listed in the registry. He smiled, thanked her, and signed the card they sent with the check.

Within days Bob had to be rushed to the hospital, suffering from congestive heart failure. He spent a few days in the ICU before being moved to a private room, with tubes and wires and things that beeped all over him, while people poked and prodded and stuck him constantly.

A family meeting with the doctors revealed that he could be kept alive for a little while like that, but he would be very uncomfortable and his chest would fill with fluids, making him feel like he was drowning.

Or, he could be taken off all treatments, unplugged from all the beeping things, and tubes and pokes and hospital food, and go home to pass in a few days in a peaceful way, as though drifting off to sleep.

While explaining what the doctors said, before the last sentence was said, he grinned and said, "Take me home."

While we waited for the ambulance to transport him back home, Mickey said, "You know, it's funny, my little barometer stopped working. The bloody farmer won't go back in his bloody house. I should take it back."

Bob started to chuckle, and then started to laugh. He laughed harder than a guy as sick as he was should be able to. He laughed so hard he almost pulled off some of the wires they had yet to disconnect from him.

"What the hell are you laughing at, you silly bastard?" asked Mick.

"I have a confession to make," he said, and Mickey looked at him with a scowl. "I get up every morning at five and put

357

my good ear against the radio and get the weather, and I set it before sneaking back to bed."

"You've been doing that all these months?"

"Every day."

"And you never told anyone?" she asked.

"Nope, not a soul," he said. "Sorry Mick, I just got a kick out of you checking that thing every day. You're still so cute after all these years."

She leaned over and kissed his head and whispered, "Thank you, you silly Yank. I love you very much."

"Been a great ride, eh, Mick?"

"Been a great ride, Bob."

Bob was propped up in his bed at home living like a king, eating some of Mickey's famous spaghetti, and even a glass of wine. He was happy, and he was at peace. "No regrets," he would say. "I wouldn't change a thing."

When he was in the hospital, he befriended a nurse there named James. James was a Vietnam veteran and served in the medical corp. The two of them would talk sometimes on quiet evenings, about service and friends and about things only fellow soldiers could understand. They also talked about God.

Bob called James one night a few days after going home and said, "I wanted you to know that I understand what you said, and I'm not afraid. Thank you, James."

"Thank you for telling me, Bob," said James. "It means a lot to me."

"I'll see you again, James."

"I'll see you again, Bob."

Soon Bob's breath grew shallow, and his skin began to ashen. He slipped into a deep sleep while holding his beloved Mickey's hand.

Suddenly Bob startled awake, pulling his head off the pillow and blinking his eyes.

"Are you ok?" Mickey whispered in his ear.

He looked around the room for a few seconds, then at Mickey and said, "Crap, am I still here?"

She chuckled a little at his silly antics — some things never change. With a smile he gave her hand a little squeeze, and drifted off to sleep.

Bob slipped away quietly a few hours later, Mickey never leaving his side, or letting go of his hand.

At his request we played "My Way" at his funeral, and "As the Roll is Called Up Yonder."

The pastor asked us if we would like a chance to say our goodbyes, but we declined. We knew better.

We said, 'I miss you, Pop.' We said, 'I love you, Dad.' We said, 'So long, so long before we meet again.'

But we never, never ever, said goodbye.

Epilogue

As of this writing, Lillian Rose, "Mickey," Anstey, is 91 years old, and is still as amazing as ever. She is the sole surviving sister. She lives with her daughter, Peggy, and her blind pug, Magoo.

Bob and Mickey were married for over 50 years.

Herb and his French wife were married over 60 years.

John and his high school sweetheart were married over 60 years.

Mr. Muggs, the monkey, retired and moved to Florida with his girlfriend.

Over eighty million people died in World War II, or about 2.5% of the world's population. May we never forget.

Photographs

and

Letters

Bob in Brooklyn, 1935

The 40mm Bofors Gun

Bob on the Queen Mary

Mickey at the Passing Out Parade, 1941
(first row, lower far left, seated on ground)

Mickey on the Seawall

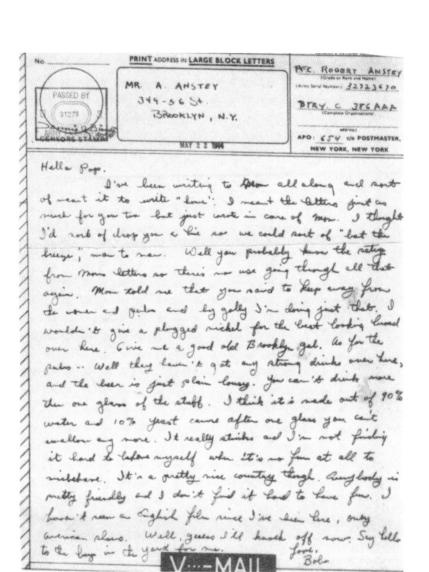

Letter to Pop

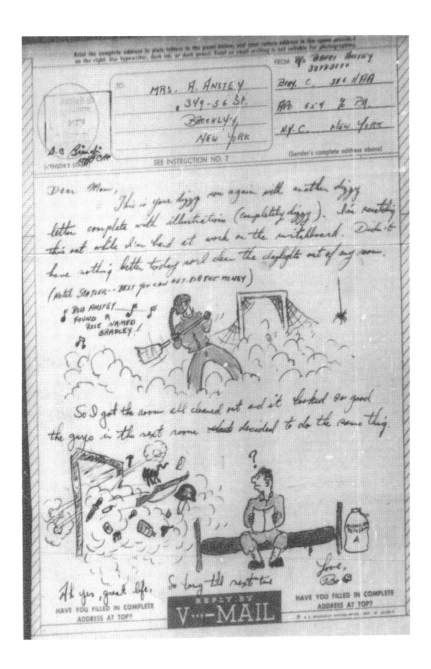

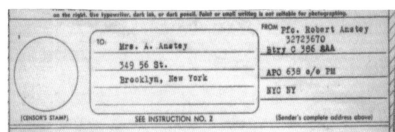

TO:
Mrs. A. Anstey

349 56 St.

Brooklyn, New York

FROM Pfc. Robert Anstey
32723670
Btry C 386 AAA

APO 638 c/o PM

NYC NY

[CENSOR'S STAMP]   SEE INSTRUCTION NO. 2   (Sender's complete address above)

Dear Mom,

Well there's nothing to write about but I didn't write in the last day or two so I'd better get on the ball. I started to write yesterday but I never got around to getting finished. I don't seem to be able to concentrate on writing lately because there's little or no mail coming in because of this new A.P.O. I guess when it does come in it will all come at once and then I'll never be able to catch up with it all.

Nothing new has happened lately. I said that before hah? I've declared war on a certain Staff Sergeant in the battery. He's a platoon Sergeant and I'm in headquarters so technically I'm not under his command. He told me to paint a sign yesterday and I didn't like the way he told me so we are now having a feud. I could louse him up a lot more than he could me so I think I'm going to come out on top. After all what could he do to me? Take my dessert away at chow time? I painted the sign by the way. On one side I painted the letters all backwards so it looked like letters seen in a mirror. On the other side I painted it the right way. I'll hang it up with the loused up side showing. When he starts raising cain about it I'll just turn it around and say that he was looking at the wrong side. I'll let you know how the joke comes out.

Naturally he'll look for a way to get back at me and I already got a new gag cooked up. I have a Belgium automatic which is supposed to be turned in. I'm going to turn it in and get the reciept for it from the Captain. Then I'm going to wear the holster so it's sticking out under my shirt. When he sees the holster he's bound to tell me to take it off because he won't see that there's no gun in the holster. I'll get fresh with him so that he'll take me to the Captain so the gun will be confiscated and then I'll take the reciept out of the empty holster. I'll also let you know how this gag works out.

He can't put me on any details like digging garbage pits because I'm already marked "Extra Duty" because of the switchboard shift. Well I can't think of any thing else to say so I guess I'll bring this to a close.

So long for now and don't worry about me.

Love

Bob

18

372

FROM Pfc. Robert Anstey
32773574

TO
MRS. H. ANSTEY
349-56 St.
Brooklyn,
New York

Btry. C. 3rd AAA
H.P.C. 654 % P.M.
N.Y.C. N.Y.

(CENSOR'S STAMP) SEE INSTRUCTION NO. 2 (Sender's complete address above)

Dear Mom,
Mar. 21, 1945
France

Seems like I can never find enough to write about so I'm going to try this idea for awhile. It might give you an idea what kind of life I am leading.

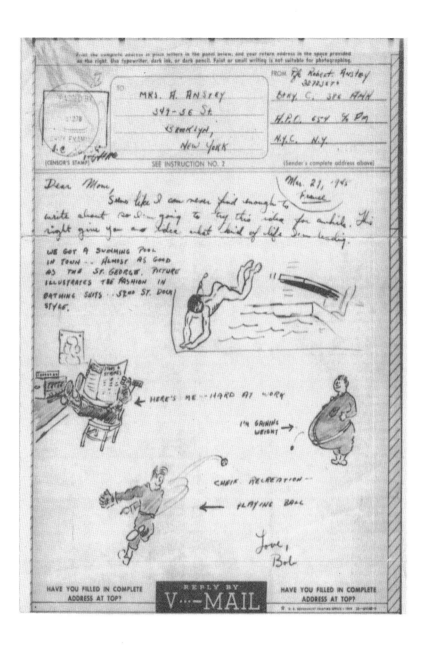

WE GOT A SWIMMING POOL IN TOWN -- ALMOST AS GOOD AS THE ST. GEORGE. PICTURE ILLUSTRATES THE FASHION IN BATHING SUITS -- 52nd ST. DOCK STYLE.

← HERE'S ME -- HARD AT WORK

I'M GAINING WEIGHT →

CHIEF RECREATION -- PLAYING BALL

Love,
Bob

373

From: Pfc. Robert Hastey
32 72 36 70

To: Mrs. A Hastey
349-56 St.
Brooklyn.
New York

Bldg. C Ste 9AA

APO 51 C Pm.

N. y. C N. y.

Dear Mom,

Got another package from you today. This makes the second one of the bunch you sent recently. This one was the cake, chicken, peanuts, handkerchiefs, and the pictures. It was swell and the gang also liked it.

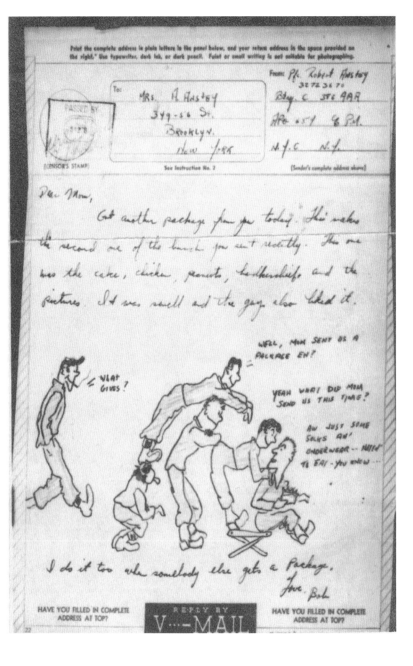

WELL, MOM SENT US A
PACKAGE EH?

WHAT GIVES?

YEAH WHAT DID MOM
SEND US THIS TIME?

AW JUST SOME
SOCKS AN'
UNDERWEAR -- STUFF
TO EAT -- YOU KNOW ...

I do it too when somebody else gets a Package.

Love. Bob

Bob in Bournemouth

The Friends

Herb and Bob

Dec 10, 1944

Hello Mickey Darling,

I've been neglecting you something awful lately but please believe me I couldn't help it. I can't explain due to military regulations but I'm sure you would understand if you knew the circumstances.

Say you sweet wonderful creature, it looks like you're getting worried because I didn't write. It seems you're afraid that I don't love you anymore. Well get that foolish idea out of your cute little blonde head. Ever hear that saying about absence makes the heart grow fonder. Well if it's at all possible I not only love you but I'm falling harder in love with you every day. In fact I not only hope to go to England after the war but I'm going to see to it that I get there if I have to swim the channel. The reason I want to get to England so bad is to see you and ask you to marry me. With all the inconveniences that a war offers I'll be damned if I'm going to propose by mail. I want to be right there looking straight at you and say "Mickey, my sweet, my love let's haul off and get married." And I want you right there to tell me either yes or to go to hell whichever you wish. Thanks to your landlady I had to tell you that I loved you on the street corner. I hope that this time I can come in the house to propose.

Of course there's a few drawbacks to this whole deal. I've only been with you for a week but hell that's long enough. A guy doesn't really love a girl if he has to have more time to think things over before he marries her. Another thing I don't know how you'd compare Brooklyn with Bournemouth for the rest of your life if you did marry me. By the way just how would you like to live in the states? Write me a nice long letter and let me know how you feel about this whole thing.

378

Before you do write however I want you to take plenty of time out to think things over. Marrying me would mean that you might never see England again. That's really a pretty drastic step in itself. Then too is the character that you would attach yourself too. But of course you have your own opinion of me and the answer you give would be entirely up to just how much you do love me.

Well it's now five o'clock in the morning and I've been on and off this letter since twelve last night. I think I said what I really intended to say. That is I love you so much that I want to marry you. I'm not kidding about this honestly I'm not. It's no laughing matter. Don't forget now we have a date after the war so that I can propose to you.

all my love,
Bob;

Letter from Bob to Mickey, 1944

Truly didn't your card - Wishy!

Dear Rose, it was kind of you
to send the V Mail. Looks like
Art definitely runs in the family!
The picture Bob drew sure tells
it all about the Bulge - windy, snowy.
Cold and no Christmas dinner. At
the airport I was at the French rail
would say Belgium people came up and
gave us a rabbit they caught and cooked
for us - covered with its own skin to keep
it warm, "Ears and all"! They sang
their Christmas songs as they came in.
They really spooked us and we thought
they were Germans at first - Couldn't
see them in the snow and fog. Your V Mail
sure brought back memories of 1944!

Wishing you peace and love
during this beautiful holiday season
and throughout the new year.

Lots of Love
John Lennon -

- I am OK now I had a pacemaker
installed with a Defibrilator in it,

John's Christmas Card describing the
Belgian Christmas of 1944

Bob with Shot Down Plane

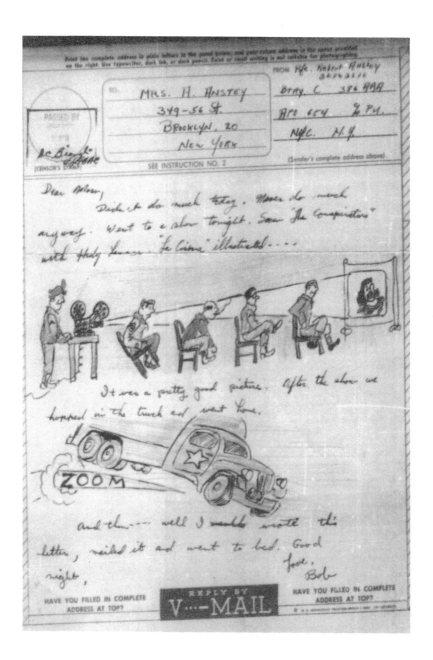

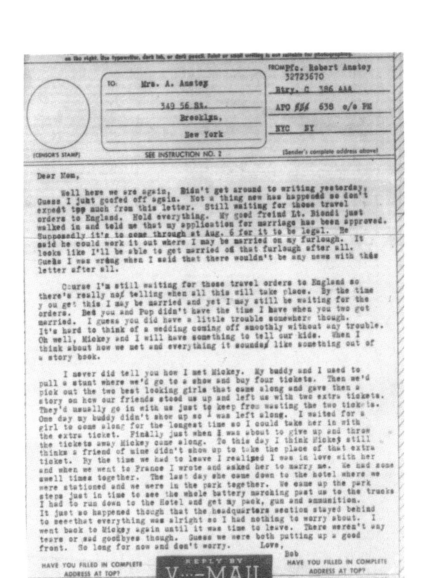

TO: Mrs. A. Anstey

349 56 St.

Brooklyn,

New York

FROM Pfc. Robert Anstey
32723670

Btry. C 386 AAA

APO ~~646~~ 638 c/o PM

NYC BY

[CENSOR'S STAMP]   SEE INSTRUCTION NO. 2   [Sender's complete address above]

Dear Mom,

Well here we are again. Didn't get around to writing yesterday. Guess I just goofed off again. Not a thing new has happened so don't expect too much from this letter. Still waiting for those travel orders to England. Hold everything. My good freind Lt. Biondi just walked in and told me that my application for marriage has been approved. Supposedly it's to come through at Aug. 6 for it to be legal. He said he could work it out where I may be married on my furlough. It looks like I'll be able to get married on that furlough after all. Guess I was wrong when I said that there wouldn't be any news with this letter after all.

Course I'm still waiting for those travel orders to England so there's really not telling when all this will take place. By the time you get this I may be married and yet I may still be waiting for the orders. Bet you and Pop didn't have the time I have when you two got married. I guess you did have a little trouble somewhere though. It's hard to think of a wedding coming off smoothly without any trouble. Oh well, Mickey and I will have something to tell our kids. When I think about how we met and everything it sounds like something out of a story book.

I never did tell you how I met Mickey. My buddy and I used to pull a stunt where we'd go to a show and buy four tickets. Then we'd pick out the two best looking girls that came along and gave them a story on how our friends stood us up and left us with two extra tickets. They'd usually go in with us just to keep from wasting the two tickets. One day my buddy didn't show up so I was left alone. I waited for a girl to come along for the longest time so I could take her in with the extra ticket. Finally just when I was about to give up and throw the tickets away Mickey came along. To this day I think Mickey still thinks a friend of mine didn't show up to take the place of that extra ticket. By the time we had to leave I realized I was in love with her and when we went to France I wrote and asked her to marry me. We had some swell times together. The last day she came down to the hotel where we were stationed and we were in the park together. We came up the park steps just in time to see the whole battery marching past us to the trucks I had to run down to the Hotel and get my pack, gun and ammunition. It just so happened though that the headquarters section stayed behind to see that everything was alright so I had nothing to worry about. I went back to Mickey again until it was time to leave. There weren't any tears or sad goodbyes though. Guess we were both putting up a good front. So long for now and don't worry.   Love,

Bob

HAVE YOU FILLED IN COMPLETE
ADDRESS AT TOP?

REPLY BY
V····MAIL

HAVE YOU FILLED IN COMPLETE
ADDRESS AT TOP?

18

"How I Met Mickey"

385

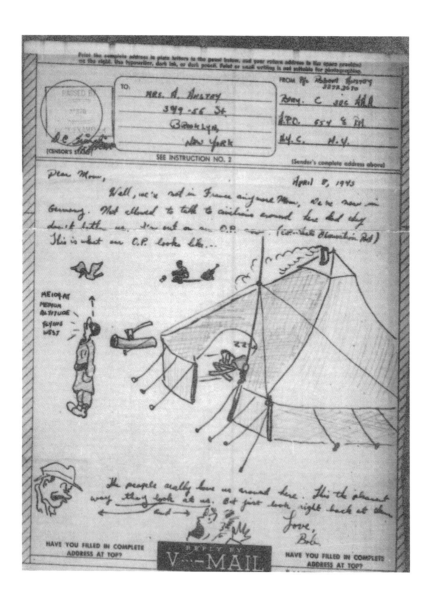

on the right. Use typewriter, dark ink, or dark pencil. Faint or small writing is not suitable for photographing.

TO:	FROM: Pfc. Robert Anstey
	32723670
Mrs. A. Anstey	Btry. C 386 AAA
349 56 St.	APO 638 c/o PM
Brooklyn, 20, New York	NYC NY 16 June, 45

(CENSOR'S STAMP)   SEE INSTRUCTION NO. 2   (Sender's complete address above)

Dear Mom,

    Not a thing has happened as usal since yesterday but I know how you worry if I don't write. Of course I'm still waiting for the travel orders to go to England. It sort of looks like there won't be too much news in this letter because I can't think of a thing to say. I guess I'll fill it up with some sort of baloney though.

    Did you ever get the air mail letter I sent you telling you about nearly everything that happened since I went overseas? I got an air mail from you today. How is Lois Jean making out? Seems funny to talk about her. I think the last time I saw her she didn't even have any teeth. Guess we'll get along good together when I get back. She's almost three years old now isn't she? A year and a half anyway.

    My buddy took my carbine and helmet liner to the rest camp with him. Case you didn't know a helmet liner is a plastic hat that fits inside the steel helmet. I just got a brand new one and he took it with him. Guess the reason he didn't take his own was because I shot it full of holes with my carbine. He took my carbine because it was easier to carry. He shot my old helmet full of holes with his German lueger so I went to work on his. It was all in fun anyway. The main thing wrong with it was that it was an awful waste of the taxpayers money.

    My pinky finger gets awful tired on this typewriter. It's a Kraut machine and it has the z where the y should be and vice versa. It means that I have to use my pinky every time I have to strike y and it's much more often used than z.

    Which brings us to the fact that you can see I'm just marking time trying to fill up this page with nonsense instead of really having anything important to say.

    As far as the ear drum is concerned, the medical officer already knows all about it. It was entered in a report about a month ago when we had a physical examination. What the exam was for I don't know but we haven't heard anything further on it so far.

    Guess I'll sign off now and knock out another letter tomorrow. So long for now and don't worry about me. Everything is going fine as could be expected. Hope I'll see you soon. Love,

        Bob.

HAVE YOU FILLED IN COMPLETE ADDRESS AT TOP?  HAVE YOU FILLED IN COMPLETE ADDRESS AT TOP?

REPLY BY V...-MAIL

Herb and his French Wife

Wedding Photo
(Restoration by Carmel Brown)

Army of the United States

SEPARATION QUALIFICATION RECORD

SAVE THIS FORM. IT WILL NOT BE REPLACED IF LOST

WTS 7-11

This record of job assignments and special training received in the Army is furnished to the soldier when he leaves the service. In its preparation, information is taken from available Army records and supplemented by personal interview. The information about civilian education and work experience is based on the individual's own statements. The veteran may present this document to former employers, prospective employers, representatives of schools or colleges, or use it in any other way that may prove beneficial to him.

1. LAST NAME—FIRST NAME—MIDDLE INITIAL				MILITARY OCCUPATIONAL ASSIGNMENTS		
ANSTEY ROBERT F				10. MONTHS	11. GRADE	12. MILITARY OCCUPATIONAL SPECIALTY
2. ARMY SERIAL NO.	3. GRADE	4. SOCIAL SECURITY NO.		3	Pvt	Basic Training C A (521)
32 723 670	PFC	082-18-2434		14	Pvt	Machine Gunner Heavy (605)
5. PERMANENT MAILING ADDRESS (Street, City, County, State)				18	PFC	Switchboard Operator (650)
349-56 Brooklyn N Y Kings Co. N Y N Y						
6. DATE OF ENTRY INTO ACTIVE SERVICE	7. DATE OF SEPARATION	8. DATE OF BIRTH				
26 Jan 43	7 Dec 45	30 May 24				
9. PLACE OF SEPARATION						
FORT DIX NEW JERSEY						

SUMMARY OF MILITARY OCCUPATIONS

13. TITLE—DESCRIPTION—RELATED CIVILIAN OCCUPATION

SWITCHBOARD OPERATOR

Installed, operated, and performed minor maintenance on portable magneto type switch boards. Answered calls and completed necessary connections to make circuit. Kepted switchboard 709

WD AGO FORM 100
1 JUL 1945

This form supersedes WD AGO Form 100, 15 July 1944, which will not be used.

390

Since it is impossible to address you as a group, I will use our battalion paper as a means of conveying to you a short message of appreciation for the loyalty and cooperation you have given me. It has been my good fortune to be in command of what I sincerely believe is the finest AAA AW battalion on the continent.

Throughout my lifetime I will continue to remember with pride the 386th, and its outstanding record through Louisiana maneuvers, England, France and Germany. Our battalion has received the highest praise and numerous commendations from all of our higher commands. A commendation from General Patton, the Commanding General of the Third U. S. Army, is included among these. At no time during our career has there been a single incident by an individual, section, or battery that would bring discredit upon the battalion or the service.

In the redeployment of units we are losing a large number of our personnel, to what extent it is impossible to learn at present. Wherever you go as individuals or groups, we know that you will carry with you the same spirit that has continually prevailed throughout the 386th. The organization that you are joining will be richly benefittd by your knowledge, enthusiasm and patriotism. We still have a war to win against Japan, and the responsibility rests upon us as American citizens and soldiers to put forth our best efforts toward that goal. A country worth living in is worth fighting for.

As for those of us who are left behind, we will strive to continue to put forth every effort possible to carry on the tradition of the 386th. If reinforcements are sent in to us, they will not be able to fill your places. That can never be done, but we will help them to make a place for themselves. I know that I will meet many of you somewhere in the army, and I hope that it will be possible to meet all of you as civilians.

To those of you who are scheduled to be discharged soon, and to the large majority who will be, sometime in the future, I hope that if the occasion ever arises when I can be of assistance, that you will not hesitate to get in touch with me. I sincerely assure you that I will always be interested in your welfare both in the army and in civilian life, and will be very happy to see you at any time.

In closing, I wish to salute you as the finest group of officers and enlisted men in the United States Army.

Lt. COL. ROBERT F. GIBBS

Civilian Address: Luray, Virginia

Letter from Colonel Gibbs, 1945

1909 W139ST
Leawood, KS 66224

Dear Mr. Anstey,

It is always nice to receive a
letter such as yours from someone interested in the
386th. I may not be of much assistance but will do
my best to fill you in on some events. I was the
TECH/SGT in charge of S-2 (intelligence) at Hq. Btry.
My job was essentially to plot gun positions, draw
maps for the Btry. Commanders, and keep track of the
advance of the war in general.

I knew of Bob but was never a close
friend. He was sent to radio school according to my notes
and was in Btry C. I did read some of his "Poop from
the Snoop" articles and wrote a few myself. Evidently he
was an "articulate" and had a great sense of humor.

Now about the "HANGOVER RAID." I have
more knowledge of this as I was sent to Metz in
advance to plot some gun positions and prepare some
information for Headquarters. The guns were in position
between Xmas and New Years. The field was in a flat
area between 2 quite high hills and we were assigned
to protect the field. It was our understanding that
the German pilots were told we would not be alert
and the raid would be easy, hence the title above.

They came down the valley, very low between
the hills, and attacked the field longitudinally and
destroyed many planes in the process as the planes on
the ground (ours) were lined up on the tarmac. We

396

really surprised them and were able to destroy 18-19 of the German fighters. I was told none were able to get away. By the way, the German pilots were only 16-17 years old. They were pretty desperate in Jan 1945. I do not have any knowledge of the part Bob played in all of this as my records do not contain names of individuals.

Some general info!

We lost a couple guys on the beach at Omaha. Stepped on mines set by the German Army. I lost my immediate superior (Lt. John Hamill) as we were bombed in an apple orchard at the top of the hill. He was killed about 50' from me. Also wounded was Major John Parker, head of S-2 intelligence. He was (at the time) Supt. of Schools in California someplace and encouraged me to go into teaching, which I did after the war.

We were also "back up" at the Battle of the Bulge. Our guns were all changed to enable them to fire at ground level in case of a German break through. It didn't happen, thank God.

Good luck with the book. I would like to get a copy when published. Please forward any info you can. At age 84 reading has become a very pleasant way to spend my time.

Sincerely,
William H (Bill) Smith

P.S. Send your Mom's address. I'm near Arkansas and go to Hot Springs occasionally

Dame Margaret Digby

Sept. 10, 1996

Dear Rose,

I am very sorry to hear that Bob passed away on May 3rd. I remember when you and he were at one of the earlier reunions. I will pass on the bad news to the fellows on Oct. 5th.

The reason for these reunions is to remember our comrades of the 1940's who have passed on.

We will remember our old friends for as long as we are here, and then history will remember their contributions to our country during World War II.

With sympathy, from
The Members of the 386th AAA Btn.
For the Btn.

John P. Lennon
"D" Btry.

386th AAA A.W. S.P. BTN. Assoc.
John P. Lennon, Treasurer
123 Mamaroneck Avenue, Apt. 111
Mamaroneck, New York 10543
(914) 698-9035

October 23, 2002

Finance Commissioner
Frontage Road, City Hall
Gloversville, New York 12078

Dear Sir:

The 386th Anti Aircraft Artillery Automatic Weapons Special Battalion Association was founded in Gloversville and Fulton County by men who served in that battalion in World War II. For over fifty years, during our time in service, and afterwards, reunions were held to honor our comrades who died in the war and those who passed on after returning home.

It is now sixty years since the battalion was formed in 1942. The number of members still attending formal reunions has fallen to about 12. We have decided to discontinue the association and the formal meetings in favor of yearly informal social meetings. They will be held in Johnstown until we, like all old soldiers, quietly fade away.

We voted to contribute the remainder of our treasury to "The Monument for Fulton County's Heroes" as our last formal action. Many members of the 386th Association are not from Fulton County or New York State but we all revere our Fulton County and Gloversville members. They originally formed the 386th Association to remember and honor their buddies of World War II.

It is only fitting that we close our Association by contributing to Fulton County's World War II Memorial.

Sincerely yours,

For the 386th AAA – A.W. SP. BTN. Association

George Holland – President   Raymond Smith – Vice President
Little Falls, New York   Gloversville, New York

Ben T. Anadio -- Secretary   John P. Lennon – Treasurer
Gloversville, New York   Mamaroneck, New York

Andrew T. Campbell – Sgt. At Arms
Ponce Inlet, Florida

encl.: Check # 789, for $400.00.

401